RUSSIA AND THE CHOLERA, 1823–1832

RUSSIA
AND THE CHOLERA
1823–1832

Roderick E. McGrew

Madison and Milwaukee, 1965
The University of Wisconsin Press

Published by
The University of Wisconsin Press

Madison and Milwaukee
P.O. Box 1379, Madison, Wisconsin 53701

Printed in the United States of America by
Kingsport Press, Inc., Kingsport, Tennessee

Library of Congress Catalog Card Number 65–20638

TO MY MOTHER AND FATHER,

WITH HEARTFELT APPRECIATION,

THIS BOOK IS DEDICATED.

PREFACE

The first cholera epidemic is only a means for opening to analysis certain historical questions. The project began as an inaugural lecture for the University of Missouri Society for Medical History, and developed from that beginning as it became apparent that important aspects of Russian social, intellectual, and political life were revealed during the cholera's first visits to the empire of the Tsars. The major studies of the reign of Nicholas I (1825–1855), especially those of N. K. Shil'der and Theodor Schiemann, present the cholera as a striking crisis, but neither these works, nor Nicholas Riasanovsky's splendid recent study, attempt to go beyond the crisis itself. It is the purpose of this book to tell the story of the cholera's visit in 1830–1832, and of the years leading up to it, in such a way as to highlight some fundamental characteristics of Russian life and at the same time suggest the way those characteristics affected the mechanics of Russian historical development.

The inspiration for this study came from three widely separated sources. First, Professor William L. Langer's address to the American Historical Association, December, 1957, entitled "History's Next Assignment," provided an historiographical milieu, and though some of Langer's theses are qualified if not contradicted in what follows, the idea that traumatic shock on a societal level is an historical phenomenon offered a central theme. Second, Professor Louis Chevalier's brilliant studies of the cholera in Paris suggested associations and projections which have been used consistently throughout the study. The published data on the cholera in Russia is much too incomplete to reproduce the detailed and meticulous analysis which Chevalier did on Paris, but his theses are the foundation on which large segments of the general interpretation of the cholera's social significance rest, while the chapter on Moscow draws heavily on his methodology. Third, my colleague and close friend, Professor Charles F. Mullett, whose major work on the bubonic plague in England showed precisely and empirically what Langer discussed synoptically and theoretically, has been a constant source of aid, comfort, and encouragement. Mullett's firm belief in medical history as an essential part of cultural history, and his insistence on the relevance of medical development as an historical phenomenon, played a major part in my expanding the study from a narrow description of the epidemic, and was particularly important in leading me to stress the growth of Russian medicine and Russian medical education as significant cultural phenomena.

The sources for this study were widely scattered, and I am deeply indebted to many people for their collection. I owe a special debt to the staff of the University of Missouri Library, and particularly to Mrs. Anne Todd Rubey, who is in charge of inter-library loan. Thanks to her indefatigable efforts, rare and unusual publications were brought into the library from every corner of the country for my use, and it is no exaggeration to say that without her assistance, the study could never have been completed. I am also indebted to Mr. Sam Hitt, Director of Acquisitions, who greatly facilitated the purchase of rare source data, both in book form and on microfilm, and who has contributed significantly to the development of a Russian research collection. Mr. William K. Beatty, former head of the Medical School Library at the University of Missouri, took an early interest in this study and placed his invaluable knowledge of medical bibliography at my disposal. A similar debt of gratitude is owed to the staffs of the Harvard Law Library, the Widener Library, the Slavic Room of the Library of Congress, and the National Library of Medicine. Mr. Peter Fisher and Mr. Thomas Morton, formerly of the Germanic and Slavic Languages Department, gave their time freely on problems of transliteration, and Mr. Fisher read portions of the manuscript. Mr. Guenther Jacob, my research assistant for this project, worked faithfully and well, and Mr. Robert Frost, a graduate student in geography, prepared two of the maps which appear in the text. The originals from which the maps of St. Petersburg and Moscow were prepared came from the British Museum, and I am grateful to Dr. Helen Wallis for helping me find and reproduce them. Finally, the Alumni Achievement Fund and the Graduate Research Council of the University of Missouri have provided financial support for research and preparation of the manuscript.

Columbia, Missouri   RODERICK E. McGREW
January 5, 1965

TABLE OF CONTENTS

LIST OF MAPS

RUSSIA
AND THE
CHOLERA,
1823—1832

Chapter 1

THE CHOLERA AND HISTORY

Since its advent in 1817, Asiatic cholera has attacked nearly every
civilized nation on the globe, and even today it remains a major
threat, especially in the Orient.[1] Within the European circle, however, cholera's most important effects appeared during the nineteenth century, and in its first pandemic period it emerged as a
powerful force which highlighted and accelerated basic social and
political developments. Even so, historians have been slow to study
cholera's historical role, and as late as 1934 the *Cambridge Modern
History* included a chronological table of leading events which made
no mention of the disease. Nor was it different in the text: the section
discussing the Polish war of 1830–1831, the Fast Day Riots, the
battle over the Great Reform Bill, and popular unrest in Paris in
1832 left out the cholera, although in each instance it played an
important role, and to ignore it meant ignoring an important aspect
of the times.[2]

It is precisely omissions of this sort which, in William L. Langer's
phrase, define "history's next assignment."[3] Today's historian may
seek new interpretations and understanding by exploring established
historical problems with the innovating techniques provided by the
newer social sciences. Social psychology offers such tools, and Langer
used bubonic plague to exemplify a massive social trauma which
affected European culture, and which, if properly understood, could
deepen historical perception. The same argument, with different
emphases, applies to cholera. Though less deadly than its late
medieval predecessor, cholera scored the European social consciousness, exacerbated contemporary tensions, intensified the impact
of current social problems, and as it did so, revealed fundamental
characteristics of European life and outlook.[4]

The first European nation to suffer cholera's ravages was Tsarist
Russia, and the epidemic's visitation provides a new opportunity to
analyze Russian historical development and to open portions of

Russian life which have not had intensive study.[5] This opportunity is important historiographically, for the remarkable expansion of Russian historical studies during the past two decades has produced only a modest interest in the non-Revolutionary aspects of the Russian past, and has left immense areas of Russian history relatively untouched. The recent period has had the heaviest emphasis, and a very broadly conceived intellectual history has dominated the subjects studied. The intelligentsia has been a major focal point, and a great part of the work on pre-Revolutionary Russia has been semibiographical, portraying those rebellious individuals who denied the autocracy, added a leaven of protest to the golden literary age, and participated in the opposition parties of the late nineteenth and early twentieth centuries. To the extent that modern historians have studied the autocracy and its social system, they have done so in terms of its failures and in the shadow of the impending Revolution.

This pattern, as, indeed, the expansion of Russian studies itself, reflects the striking importance of Soviet Russia in contemporary affairs, but it also underlines an outlook that has traditionally conditioned Western attitudes toward Russia. During the nineteenth century the autocracy meant stagnation and repression, and in some minds, especially English, represented a continuing threat to liberal constitutional governments.[6] In turn, those who had hopes of Russia's future looked to a reform movement which would sweep away antiquated despotism and introduce enlightenment and progress. When the Revolution came, it did not create the anticipated utopia, but the old hopes have not been forgotten, and Russian history has been written without undue attention to the decaying artifices of the Romanovs. This approach has produced a skewed historical perspective, and though studies by Marc Raeff, Nicholas Riasanovsky, and Richard Pipes have partially redressed the balance, broad areas of social and insititutional history remain to be considered.[7]

To return to Professor Langer's theme, the first cholera epidemic was a major disaster, and its study should reveal basic elements in Russian cultural development. The first pandemic began in Russia in 1823 and reached its greatest intensity in 1830 and 1831. When the peak of the epidemic passed, more than a quarter of a million of the Tsar's subjects had died, and the overall mortality among those striken stood just below 50 per cent. The cholera's influence, if not its immediate effect, permeated the Russian system: recruiting for the army stopped, interior commerce came to a standstill, and quarantine regulations strait-jacketed the nation. The people became restive; riots and rebellions broke out; and the international crises of 1830–1831 found the Russian economy and military so hampered in their effectiveness that Chernyshev, then Minister of War, wrote General Dibich that the cholera "places us in such a situation as never before existed."[8]

The first pandemic was by no means the worst that Russia suffered, and in the period 1847–1851, medical officials reported more than two and one-half million cases, with over a million deaths. The first epidemic, however, came when the disease was generally unknown, and it wrote its effects on an unmarked slate. Ignorance sharpened social reactions; the administration, working without experience's guide, hastily devised expedients which clearly showed the weaknesses in its own organization, while the medical profession exhibited its resources and resourcefulness under the most difficult circumstances. Unprepared as Russia was for the cholera, her reaction had the special truthfulness of unconscious reflex, and if the epidemic provided, in Charles Rosenberg's phrase, an opportunity "to discuss some of the ways in which one community [New York] attempted to fabricate a consistent conceptual apparatus with which to explain the inexplicable [and] provide security where there was only uncertainty....,"[9] it also revealed a dimension of social response which reached beyond reason to the emotional substructure of social attitudes.

The state of medical knowledge greatly enhanced the cholera's social significance, and the then persistent belief that "the life of the organic world is the expression of a process called forth and sustained, in organisms that are capable of life, by the sum of all the influences which act upon them from without," directed attention to issues which were social and political rather than medical.[10] Medical ignorance concerning cholera's origin, propagation, contagiousness, and treatment reinforced an environmentalist approach, and early writers on cholera used historical, geographical, meteorological, and demographic sources as well as medical classics and straightforward medical reports.[11] Although modern medical technology, particularly micro-biological analysis, has enabled epidemiologists to ra-

tionalize their methods, demography, social planning, and public
health remain intimately associated as well as politically sensitive,
and we are continually reminded that epidemic disease is a social
phenomenon which cannot be divorced from organized society and
its problems.[12]

Although major discoveries concerning cholera's epidemiology
were made during the nineteenth century, the disease is still a serious
threat, especially in undeveloped nations. The cholera was first
found in dense concentrations of population along the rivers of
India and in their delta regions. From the beginning, cholera has
been a disease of massed humanity whose ravages have been most
terrible where conditions of human habitation have been worst,
where sanitation has been least developed, and where the debilitation of the population has undermined the capacity for resistance. It
was this fact which made cholera a significant social force when it
reached Europe, for the disease made its heaviest inroads where
people lived jammed together in urban slums or packed tightly in
noisome country villages, while the poorest, the weakest among the
population suffered its most deadly effects. During the nineteenth
century, statistical studies in urban centers showed a direct correlation
between cholera incidence and those areas where general mortality
was highest, where crime was most abundant, and where living
conditions were positively the worst. That the wealthy could also die
was well attested, but this seemed only to underline the danger of
living near the poor who always suffered. The class character which
the cholera exhibited was prefigured in urban death statistics; even
before the cholera epidemics, there had been a dangerous rise in
mortality figures, which suggested worsening social conditions. In
Paris, for example, between 1817 and 1835, annual mortality per
1000 of the population increased steadily from 31 to 34, and,
significantly, the age group 20 to 39 showed an even sharper
increase—from 42 to 56. Louis Chevalier summarized the importance of these figures when he wrote: "Death in all its forms is the
measure of a wretchedness which, in certain periods, surpasses the
individual's capacity for physical resistance. It is also the measure of
[social] violences whose ideological and political descriptions do
not reveal that they express in terms of life and death a problem
which is itself life and death."[13]

The cholera epidemics clearly outlined the social imbalances which Chevalier's statistics indicated, but they did something more. As the disease swept the indigent away by the thousands, the lessons of inequality were driven home, resentment burgeoned, and the disease produced a confused belief that in some way the wealthy had discovered a new instrument of oppression. As a consequence, violent upheavals marked the entire cholera period. Local conditions gave the particular form which the explosions took, but one universal fact emerged: the population could not understand the selective way the cholera killed and thus identified the disease with the fears and tensions inherent in their way of life.[14]

The identification between poverty and cholera was suggested very early in the epidemic's European phase, but the reasons for its spread among and effect upon the lower classes were not understood. We know today that cholera is a contagious disease which may be transmitted directly through contact, or indirectly by an intermediary substance. The causative organism for cholera is the *vibrio cholerae,* which lives in the intestines and is exposed through the dejecta of cholera patients. The disease is considered less contagious than small pox or measles, since it is necessary to ingest the *vibrio,* and the most common means of communicating cholera has been through polluted water. Any contact with a cholera patient, however, which involves the possibility of touching material soiled by the patient's feces is potentially dangerous, and one most important method of protecting both a person and a community against the disease is rigorously maintained cleanliness. Cleanliness in the personal or the general sense was precisely what was lacking in nineteenth-century urban slums and among the technically undeveloped and culturally backward sections of Eastern Europe and Asia. In Europe, the lowest classes were most dangerously exposed thanks to their way of life and the character of the disease, and by the same token, the nations which were most advanced in social thought and public health planning were those which were able first to protect themselves effectively against the cholera.

None of this was understood during the first pandemic period, and it was only in the middle of the nineteenth century that substantial evidence was found on which specific sanitary policies could be based. During the 1830's the cholera was a central issue between "localists" and "contagionists," with the former maintaining that a combination of circumstances in a given area—temperature, soil conditions, humidity, etc.—caused cholera, and that therefore there was no effective means of controlling the disease.[15] This point of view, which was defended stoutly until Koch produced final evidence of a bacterial cause for cholera, directed attention specifically to environment, and was undoubtedly influential in fostering efforts at slum clearance and urban redevelopment, but it also prevented early acceptance of a germ theory for cholera. Non-contagion, or "localism," won wide support, for it eliminated the need for quarantine regulations, but it helped as well to create a more dangerous situation. Knowing today that cholera is contagious, we can appreciate the remark made by Dr. Jeremias Lichtenstaedt in 1831:

> The subject of contagion has been much debated. The non-contagionists have found many adherents among the medical men and gained the support of the public, which sees in quarantine work only what is irksome and disadvantageous. Though one must unhesitatingly admit that the system of cleansing measures led to exaggerations, an unbiased observer cannot consider this as great an evil as the possibility of a spread of this disease. . . . May there be finally an end to the often reiterated postulation of the non-infectivity of cholera! It belongs in the category of the most dangerous errors of our time.[16]

In one sense, of course, Lichtenstaedt was only partially right, for quarantine regulations without an understanding of the mechanism of cholera's extension, and particularly of the need to control and purify water sources, were bound to fail. This understanding in turn demanded specific knowledge of the character of the causative organism, or at the very least, a substantial theory. As early as 1819 it was suggested to the Bengal Medical Board that cholera was caused by a "pestilential virus, which acted primarily upon the stomach and the small intestines," but the Board rejected this view. In 1831 several writers argued that a *contagium vivum* caused cholera, and in 1838 Boehm actually claimed to have seen the causative organisms in the dejecta of cholera patients. His claim has been rejected by modern authorities, though the theory is interesting. Finally, in 1840, F. G. J. Henle wrote that "with the exception of malaria, the infectious diseases were due to a living contagion, being perhaps caused by vegetable organisms." And nine years later, the now famous John Snow wrote in a pamphlet entitled, "On the Mode of Communication of Cholera":

Diseases which are communicated from person to person are caused by some material which passes from the sick to the healthy, and which has the property of increasing and multiplying in the systems of the persons it attacks ... the morbid matter of cholera having the property of reproducing its own kind, must necessarily have some sort of structure, most likely that of a cell. It is no objection to this view that the structure of the cholera poison cannot be recognized by the microscope, for the matter of small pox and of chancre can only be recognized by their effects and not by their physical properties.[17]

Snow was not alone in developing this idea, and in a letter to the *Times,* September 5, 1849, one of England's foremost pioneers in germ theory, William Budd, pointed out that the cholera was caused by organisms, "a distinct species of fungus which, being swallowed, becomes infinitely mltiplied in the intestinal canal, and the action thus excited causes the flux of cholera...," and Budd also believed, as did Snow, that "water is the principal means of the dissemination of the disease"; he argued that "too much care could not be exercised in procuring pure drinking water." [18] These formulations were given practical application in 1854, when John Snow made his researches on the cholera in Broad Street, and did his equally important work on the Southwark, Vauxhall, and Lambeth Water Companies. In both instances Snow proved that the cholera could be traced to contaminated water supplies, and his work has become classic. Snow's proofs, however, were not accepted at once, and the papers which he submitted to the French Academy went unpublished. Nevertheless, John Snow's work carried the study of cholera into a new phase, and it only remained to the German bacteriologist Koch to isolate in 1883 the *vibrio cholerae,* or as it was originally called, the *comma bacillus.*[19]

Once cholera's cause was established, the contagion issue could be settled, innoculation procedures developed, and the epidemiological character of the disease thoroughly explored. Even so, the nature of cholera requires the services of a highly developed society for control. Dr. Pollitzer lists five necessary elements for effective cholera controls: 1) adequate intelligence services, including laboratories for rapid diagnosis; 2) sufficient facilities for isolating patients; 3) a sanitary engineering service to deal with contaminated water supplies, and if necessary, to replace those supplies; 4) implementation of measures to control, or prohibit, sale of potentially dangerous cold drinks and food, and to control flies; 5) large-scale public health propaganda to ensure that people take all necessary precautions.[20] Of course, the most important preventive measure in the long term has been the elimination of polluted water sources and the maintenance of strict sanitary controls. It was advances in these areas, often made without specific knowledge or thought of cholera, which enabled Western Europe to free itself from the cholera by the end of the nineteenth century in all but its most backward areas, while cholera continued unchecked in Eastern Europe and in Asia. Russia suffered horrible outbreaks in the 1890's, and the ultimate control of cholera in Russia was only accomplished after 1926. Today the pattern is similar, for the cholera remains a major danger in underdeveloped, overcrowded, and backward nations. In the Orient it continues to kill its tens of thousands, and the means to arrest or control the disease in those areas still do not exist. Cholera has finally supplanted bubonic plague as the disease which has claimed the largest total number of victims, and, as Dr. Pollitzer has pointed out, "In the case of cholera . . . methods of treatment and control combining easy application with full efficiency must still be sought," and though bubonic plague may be considered under control, "the many still-unsolved problems of cholera continue to call for urgent attention." [21]

The conundrums of cholera's cause and contagiousness worsened its social effects during the first pandemic period, and cholera's class character gave it an unpleasant significance in nineteenth-century Europe. Cholera's social impact, however, went beyond its class character and resulted from other attributes of the disease, for it spread as insidiously as rumor, marking and striking down its victims without warning, and carrying them off in transports of agony. The cholera created a nameless dread, a paralyzing fear, which neither public proclamations nor learned articles could dissipate, and fear in turn dissolved normal reticence, eroded behavioral standards and ethical norms, and left human beings stripped of their dignity as men. In this respect the cholera's effect was universal. The *London Medico-Chirurgical Review* introduced a long article on cholera by noting, "In Asia, the fiend was contemplated by us with curiosity—in the wilds of Russia with suspicion—in Germany with alarm—but on English soil, with TERROR!" Count P. D. Kiselev, who administered the Divans of Moldavia and Wallachia during the cholera period, commented that "What is remarkable is the terror which the cholera inspires among people who count the plague as nothing. From the first noble to the last slave . . . all flee the sick and abandon them to their own devices. All natural bonds disappear, and as honor no longer exists, egoism appears in all its nakedness, in all its horror." [22]

Ignorance bred fear, for nothing in the people's experience prepared them for the cholera, and neither governments nor professional medical men were able to comfort them. Quarantines and administrative regulations proved all but useless in preventing the cholera's spread, and from the popular viewpoint, doctors seemed unable to work a cure, while the methods which were used were violent enough to frighten anyone. An objective observer would probably have agreed with Imperial Physician in Ordinary, Dr. Rauch, that "the cholera will not be cured by nature's powers alone without the help of [medical] art. . . . ," and statistics indicated that mortality was lower among those who received medical attention than it was among those who did not. [23] Objective observers among the people were few, however, and statistical reports offered little encouragement to those who lived with death. The physicians' failures and the governments' inadequacies were far more important immediately than the positive contributions which each made. The turbulence attending the cholera came from fear, and it found its outlet in already established antagonisms.

On this point, a qualification is needed which, when taken in conjunction with what we have already said, adds a further dimension to the cholera's significance. The Chevalier thesis emphasizes that epidemics do not create abnormal situations, but intensify the normal aspects of abnormal situations. Thus an epidemic sharpens behavior patterns, but those patterns, instead of being aberrations, betray deeply rooted and continuing social imbalances. Granting that this proposition is valid, disease in history illumines latent or developing social characteristics. However, if the proposition is valid, its converse should also be true. Areas that were able to absorb the epidemic's impact and contain the fear and desperation which disease can breed, suggest a stable society. Mr. Rosenberg, for instance, notes that New York did not succumb to complete anarchy, and he points out that respectable people of regular habits felt they had little to fear from the cholera. Even more striking is a comment made by the Rev. Henry Whitehead in *The Cholera in Berwick Street* (London, 1854), that even though the population was literally decimated, no panic occurred, a fact which the author found surprising, as he had "always heard and read that great pestilences were invariably attended by wholesale demoralisation of the population." [24] A comparison between this description and the reactions which followed the cholera in Russia in 1832 suggests a social change of major importance and re-emphasizes the necessity for treating the cholera first in terms of the particular environment in which it occurred.

In Europe, the cholera's effect was felt most strongly in urban centers in which sociological and demographic structure were similar enough to produce comparable reactions. The cholera in Russia presents a different problem, for it affected an infinitely greater geographical area which exhibited a wide range of ethnic, social, and cultural characteristics. Soviet historians, however, who have written on cholera have overlooked variety and emphasized common reactions, generally violent, which expressed popular resentment against the regime. The very distinguished Mme. Nechkina, who contributed to Chevalier's collection, pointed to "the crisis in feudal society ... [which] constituted the social foundation for the events described...." and argued that, "The people's discontent caused by serfdom, discontent hidden for a long time, exploded when the epidemic battered the population." [25] Yet the fact is that the Russian population did not react uniformly. Some accepted the cholera as God's will; others fled infected cities, and took refuge in the churches or in quackery; still others revolted, and when revolts did occur, the reasons for their outbreak were as various as the regions affected. Certainly there is a large degree of truth in the assertion that the autocracy was unable to help the people, and there is no question that the brutal and repressive means used to maintain the quarantine lines fostered resistance. The fact remains, however, that in many areas the people withstood both the cholera's attack and the government's effort to protect them. The "crisis in the feudal order," if such it actually was, was so diverse in its individual aspects as to cast doubt on the meaning of the phrase.

As the cholera made its most serious inroads in those sectors of the population where conditions of life were worst, it also acted as a catalyst in bringing about social reform. As we suggested above, it was unnecessary to have exact knowledge of cholera's epidemiology to take steps which could reduce the cholera's effects. A combination of enlightened governments and a more sophisticated population brought Western Europe to the verge of controlling cholera before scientific proofs of cholera's epidemiology were final, while in Eastern Europe, cholera remained a serious threat long after its biologial cause was known. In Europe generally, the period after 1815, and particularly after 1830, was a time of growing concern with social reform, and this reforming movement differed sharply from that which preceded it. The eighteenth century conceived reform in moral terms, and the men who preached liberty, equality, and fraternity paid relatively little attention to sewers. Precedents, of course, did exist, and as early as the fourteenth century England took hesitant steps on what Charles F. Mullett has called "the highway to health," while during the eighteenth century quarantine regulations, vaccination, and the development of professional training in medicine all received attention. These steps, however, were obscured by the larger concern with legal equality, constitutional safeguards, and economic freedom. It remained to the nineteenth century to spell out social justice through specific social reforms, and the revolutionary explosions of the 1830's and 1840's underlined conditions which required immediate attention. By the middle decades of the nineteenth century there was a broadening recognition that governments' responsibilities extended to housing conditions, sanitary facilities, factory conditions, and indeed all the details of human life in an increasingly complex society.[26] As reforms progressed, especially in the areas of sanitation, housing, and controls over living conditions, the cholera was affected incidentally, and those nations which were furthest advanced in social controls and reform policies were those soonest freed of cholera's effects.

While the control of epidemic disease in general, and cholera in particular, benefitted from social progress, the cholera itself advanced social reform and public health measures. Everywhere that cholera struck, it jarred some minds to an awareness of social problems. That awareness often began by identifying cholera with the lower classes, and the myth arose that cholera was divine retribution for those who were debauched, dissipated, and, above all, poor. There were others, however, who saw the cholera in a different light. These men rejected the idea that the disease was a just punishment for evil, and they looked to a better day when both cholera and crime could be controlled. Those detailed statistical studies which identified the cholera with the conditions of poverty and reinforced the disease's class character also hastened the demand to level the slums, purify water supplies, and open the dark and crowded tenements to light and air. In this respect the cholera gave impetus to the reform movement, emphasized government's responsibility for social problems, and fostered new reform concepts. As David Eversley wrote concerning the cholera in England: "The great figures of the '30's and '40's were neither Malthus nor Lauderdale, but Chadwick, Kay Shuttleworth and Southwood Smith, Shaftesbury and Sadler, Owens and Engels. From the medical point of view the history of the cholera of 1831–1832 is perhaps without great interest; from the point of view of politics and the social sciences it marks the opening of a new era." [27]

The social reforms the cholera produced were only a beginning, and the reform movement had far to go. Beyond industrial Europe the people suffered almost without relief, and, as we shall see, Imperial Russia was better at devising restrictions than at offering positive reforms. Even in ostensibly civilized nations, the central government was not always quick to act. France, for example, was cultured and wealthy, and though civil disturbance was never far off in the hectic thirties, the government retained control. Yet Louis Philippe and his administrators did little directly to ameliorate the people's suffering, and in one instance, at Bordeaux, frankly disclaimed all responsibility for aiding the municipality in its effort to control the cholera. Municipal and provincial authorities were given a free hand, and it might be added an impossible burden, while the government followed a policy of *laissez faire,* if not *laissez passer.*[28] On the other hand, local commissions collected a vast quantity of data concerning cholera, while official deputations were sent abroad to observe the sanitary methods and medical treatment which were used elsewhere. This data was used to advantage later and aided the reforms instituted in succeeding years.

England went much farther than did France in developing administrative methods for dealing with the cholera, and the speed with which the English government reacted to its responsibilities was praiseworthy, even though its best efforts were bitterly attacked. The administrative centralization implicit in generally applied public health measures was identified in the public mind with abrogation of the basic rights of Englishmen, and the same groups which protested the "Peelers" rioted against the government's cholera measures. It was a misfortune that the cholera appeared concomitantly with the great debates over the Reform Bill of 1832, for the proponents of electoral reform saw an anti-reform conspiracy in the government's sanitary policies. So violent did this opposition become that the cholera itself was declared to be a humbug perpetrated on the people to serve the ruling class' interest. Despite all this, the British government made important strides in sanitary policy, and it laid the foundations for the later development of health boards and planning commissions.[29]

Russian social reform movements lagged by comparison with Western Europe, and though the autocracy possessed the political power necessary to enact the most complete social program imaginable, neither the government nor the people thought in those terms. The Imperial family took the lead in philanthropic activity; the great aristocratic families, the Sheremetevs or Golitsyns, maintained their private charities, while the merchants and their guilds supported hospitals and benevolent societies and contributed largely during crises. On paper, the Imperial administration appeared very advanced in public health and regulatory matters, but the reality was far different from the appearance, and though powers existed to do a great deal, those powers were seldom effectively exercised.

The cholera revealed both the inadequacy of public health administration and the essential weakness of Russian administrative procedures, and to that degree it added to a continuing demand for governmental reform. It failed, however, to produce anything comparable to the demands for social reform which followed the cholera in the West, and even the social protests which were made failed to connect with any substantial reform theme except that which specified certain limited administrative objectives. The cholera riots in 1831 struck no responsive note among the free intelligentsia, created no tradition of protesting martyrs, and though the horrible repression which followed made some men grind their teeth, it brought no positive response and added little or nothing to the literature of protest. These omissions themselves are important, for the cholera struck hard, and the nation reacted to it without calling into question the autocratic system as a whole. The people were concerned with other matters; their horizons were limited, and their outlook narrow. Their reactions reflected immediate, local issues, and they lacked any generalized revolutionary orientation.

In the following pages we will develop the ideas introduced here through an intensive analysis of the cholera in Imperial Russia. The time period covered, 1823 to 1832, is fairly short as historical reckoning goes, and it by no means exhausts the cholera's influence in Russia. Russia's last major cholera epidemic occurred in 1925, and the Soviet regime deserves the credit for the cholera's ultimate control. Our concern, then, is not to write the history of cholera in Russia, but to study one epidemic within a particular historical context. Within the chronological framework, three major themes provide the elements for a composite picture of Russian cultural development. The first theme, following Alexander Brückner's thesis that medical history is an index to cultural growth, develops both a quantitative and a qualitative appraisal of Russian medical facilities, training, and methods as they were revealed in the struggle against cholera. The second theme offers a detailed analysis of the administrative techniques which the autocracy used to control the cholera and maintain the country's normal functions during a crisis period, while the third and final theme traces the social reactions which the cholera produced. Taken together, these themes outline a particular social crisis, but they also should provide a clearer understanding and better appreciation of Russia in the age of Nicholas I.

Chapter 2

RUSSIAN MEDICINE AND THE COMING OF THE CHOLERA

The decades following the Napoleonic Wars were uneasy years for the European world. The struggle which had absorbed Europe's energies since 1789 was finished, but in its wake came economic dislocation, political agitation, and social unrest. Statesmen feared the outbreak of another international struggle; the Revolution remained a haunting spectre, and society's restlessness served to flesh that ghost. Between 1815 and 1830, violence flared from Greece to Spain, from Peterloo to Petersburg, and the order established at Vienna was challenged again and again.

The early assaults on the established order projected ideas which had been current during the Revolutionary epoch, and the slogans of national determination, equality, and constitutional government were enthusiastically mustered and carried forward by intellectuals, student societies, and secret revolutionary organizations. But deeper currents were gathering as well, and what might be called the proletarianization of the protest movement was taking form. Urban centers expanded rapidly, and as they did so, social issues became more pressing. Economic adjustment to the Wars produced unemployment, while population growth accelerated, carrying forward the demographic revolution which radically changed Europe during the nineteenth century. This population growth was reflected in soaring crime rates, higher mortality, especially in metropolitan areas, and sheer misery among the lower classes. The age of material progress began in a setting of unparalleled, and unrestrained squalor, filth, and helplessness.

The prevalent social restlessness extended even to those regions which seemed most tranquil and most powerfully controlled. Contemporaries saw Russia as an ordered despotism whose massive armies were a latent threat to Europe's order. Yet behind that façade, anxiety and unrest gathered. The Wars had all but bankrupted an already overstrained and antiquated government economy. The condition of the peasantry had not improved since Alexander took the throne in 1801, and reintroducing the military colonies in the post-war period sharply intensified local peasant resentment. Both reformers and conservatives found much to criticize, yet the Tsar seemed oblivious to the crises plaguing his domain. During Alexander's last years the tempo of public protest increased sharply as peasant uprisings and secret revolutionary societies reflected disturbed conditions throughout the empire. A crisis was reached with Alexander's death in 1825, and the Decembrist revolt exposed major social problems. Although the revolt failed, the issues which produced it remained to provide explosive material for the next crisis, which came when the cholera set off a new round of protests, disturbances, and rebellions.[1]

The first widely reported cholera outbreak in the nineteenth century occurred in British India in the spring of 1817, though this was by no means the cholera's initial appearance in India. It is now thought that cholera has existed in India since earliest times, and there is positive proof of its presence for the last three centuries. Portuguese records of the sixteenth century describe a deadly disease "which struck with pain in the belly, so that a man did not last out eight hours time..." and Macpherson's *Annals of Cholera* quotes sixty-four authoritative accounts between 1503 and 1817, which describe or refer to cholera; ten of those accounts make it plain that epidemic conditions existed.[2] It is equally clear, however, that epidemic cholera did not reach Europe until the nineteenth century, though medical writers from Hippocrates to Sydenham described a disease which bore many external similarities to true Asiatic cholera. The distinguishing feature was that the Eruopean disease never attained an epidemic extent, though it was apt to become prevalent. The disease which Sydenham described in London in 1679–1682 was restricted to the city, and one authority pointed out that "Sydenham makes no mention of a widely disseminated outbreak ... and Wells expressly states that the country was quite free from the malady, and in fact one of its characteristic features was that its ravages were confined to the city of London."[3]

The later eighteenth century was a period of intense cholera activity in India, and the disease attacked neighboring Ceylon and Burma as well. The evidence of greatest activity is for the period

1770–1790, when major outbreaks occurred in the Arcot region, inland from Madras; on the Coromandel coast; in Uttar Pradesh, where, in April, 1793, 20,000 pilgrims died in eight days; and in Vellore. Between 1790 and 1817 only scanty evidences appear, although in 1814 a violent outbreak occurred in Bengal. From this it would seem that the cholera pandemic which began in 1817 was part of major cholera activity stemming from the preceding four decades, and it was in 1816–1817 that the pandemics began which rendered the cholera a major world health problem.[4]

Between 1817 and 1823, the cholera attacked the Asiatic world, moved into the Middle East, touched Africa, and stood at the gates of Europe. During 1817 and 1818 it spread rapidly across India, reached Ceylon and in early 1819 moved from Bengal to Nepal and Arracan, Burma, Siam, the Malaccan Peninsula, and ultimately Singapore.[5] In May, 1819, the cholera struck Sumatra, and early in 1820 broke out in Java and Borneo, where it raged for almost three years. During these same years, the disease moved westward from Ceylon to Mauritius and the Isle of Bourbon, finally touching the Zanzibar coast of Africa. Also in 1820 the cholera broke out in the Moluccas and the Philippines, and between 1820 and 1822 laid waste the Chinese Empire. Its eastward extent was reached in the latter year when it appeared in Japan. The cholera came to the Middle East in the spring of 1821 attacking Muscat on the east Arabian shore, and from there spread into Persia. After a brief check in the winter of 1821–1822, it followed the Tigris toward Kurdistan and also moved westward into Syria, reaching Aleppo in December, 1822. Subsiding during the winter of 1822–1823, it broke out with new fury in the spring, spreading south along the coast of Syria to Palestine, and north toward Russian territory, touching the Transcaucasian frontier, penetrating to Tiflis and Baku, and, in September, 1823, reaching Astrakhan, the gateway to Russia and the West.

When the cholera first reached Russian territory the most reliable intelligence concerning it came from English sources. Between 1819 and 1824 a series of reports appeared which described the cholera in India and adjacent territories and presented the first detailed recommendations for treatment.[6] These reports became extraordinarily influential, and the first authoritative accounts published in Russia relied heavily on them. Other sources of information existed, notably French cholera reports and data collected by Russian frontier officials and representatives in Persia, but these were neither so full nor so circumstantial as the English materials, which were especially valuable for a description of cholera's symptoms and for recommending treatments.[7]

The initial Russian cholera publications contained no first-hand data, for they were written before the disease reached Astrakhan. Their primary purpose was to inform medical and customs personnel concerning a potential threat and to provide some standard means for dealing with it. The cholera's history indicated that Russia could not hope to remain immune; the pattern of its spread suggested insuperable difficulties in controlling it, and the heavy death toll which the cholera left in its wake pointed to a striking danger.[8] Despite all this, an optimistic tone pervaded the early cholera literature and persisted until 1830. Although English medical literature provided no definitive answers to the complex questions of cholera's contagiousness and cause, English physicians saw no reason to doubt that they could treat the disease successfully. The *Edinburgh Medical and Surgical Journal* introduced it discussion of the Bombay report asserting that, "it would make our readers thoroughly acquainted with the history of the epidemic, and, what rarely occurs in our professional pursuits, of the means by which it may be almost stripped of its terror . . ." while in a later review the same journal reported that, "The treatment of epidemic cholera forms one of the greatest and most undoubted triumphs of modern physic. . . ." [9] This belief emerged in the Russian surveys, and even following the Astrakhan epidemic, the chairman of the Medical Council of the Ministry of the Interior regarded the English treatment as established and pointed to cause and contagion as the issues requiring immediate solution. Finally, when the influential and for all practical purposes official gazette, the *Journal de St. Pétersbourg,* published its first popular cholera survey in 1830, it echoed the sentiment that medicine had penetrated the cholera's secrets and could cure the disease effectively.[10]

Medical optimism rested on peculiarly insubstantial grounds, for the English treatment was little more than an effort to alleviate particular symptoms. Furthermore, the unusual point in the English treatment was early recognition of the cholera's presence, because experience in India proved that methods which would work at the cholera's onset had little effect once the patient was fully in its grasp.[11] Consequently the widest possible publicity needed to be given to precursory symptoms, a factor which was very important in fostering a policy of open information during the later and more violent epidemics in Russia.

The cholera's symptoms seemed to follow a regular pattern, and though later divergences were noted, the diagnostic image of the disease was fixed in the first publications. At the cholera's onset, a person felt oppression and anxiety coupled with intestinal upset and dizziness. These gave way to a violent diarrhea and vomiting, intense muscular seizures in the extremities which became catatonic, a burning sensation in the pit of the stomach, and an insatiable craving for water. The period of violence, which often varied in its particulars, was followed by a "sinking stage" during which the pulse faded away, body temperature plummeted downward, and the patient sank into lethargy. It was this stage which almost always foretold the approach of death as the face changed, becoming sunken and cadaverous, a liverish color appeared around the eyes, the lips became drawn and blue, a bluish tinge marked the fingernails, the tongue turned cold and sometimes coated, the voice sank to a husky whisper, and even the breath seemed chill.[12] These very clearly marked symptoms were paralleled by equally distinctive post-mortem appearances. The stomach and intestines were often distended with air, and sometimes a viscous fluid; no bile was present in the small intestine or the stomach; the veins of the liver, and sometimes of the bowels, were filled with blood, while the gall bladder was often filled with dark bile. The lungs were shrunken and collapsed, while the muscles were soft, as in a person struck by lightening.[13] Later dissections added still more information, but even at the epidemic's beginning there was substantial anatomical data to aid diagnosis.

With such distinctive, even horrible, manifestations, there was little excuse for not recognizing the disease. The misfortune was that when the most distinctive symptoms appeared, and the disease could infallibly be recognized, death was not far away. Nevertheless the symptomology produced the treatment, and Russian physicians were told to administer large doses of calomel and opium to control the spasmodic condition, to bleed extensively if the case were caught in the early stages, and to use warm baths and clothing together with frictions and counter-irritants on the skin to counteract the circulation's failure and the deadly decline of vital powers. Where improvement could be seen, carbonate of magnesia or cold-drawn castor oil were recommended to provide a gentle laxative action. Above all, patients were to be kept warm, quiet, and segregated, for though contagion was not proved, it seemed a clear and present danger.[14]

Diagnosis and treatment were the issues which the English handled best, but when Russian physicians looked for material on the cholera's cause and mode of propagation, they found themselves faced with a mass of contradictory evidence. In the first Russian cholera publication, contagion was flatly denied, a position which followed the available English reports.[15] Further experience, however, modified that view, and when Dr. Reman summarized the position in 1824 for the Russian medical profession, he expressed a contagionist view, though he admitted that the mechanics of contagion were still unknown. The official instructions published for the Astrakhan epidemic accepted contagion and emphasized quarantine and sequestration for the sick. Government policy, however, was most uncertain concerning the mechanics of contagion, and this produced vacillation throughout the entire epidemic period.[16]

Evidence concerning cholera's cause gave the impression of being more substantial, but the impression was misleading. The first cholera outbreaks in India were laid to eating rank fish and spoiled rice, but the very extent of the epidemic soon eliminated that explanation. Nevertheless, diet continued to be regarded as significant. A more general thesis which continued through the epidemic period was that certain conditions pre-disposed persons to the onset of cholera, and bad diet, inadequate clothing, exposure to inclement weather, and dissipation were singled out for blame. The initial recommendations for preventing cholera in Russia included attention to such matters, and Dr. Reman explicitly accepted the mode of life as a significant consideration.[17] To say this much, however, was not really to say anything at all, for, as one early writer noted, the poor were by far the most numerous of the population, and he concluded that "we are, and we ought to acknowledge it, quite ignorant of the cause of cholera morbus."[18] It was in implicit recognition of this fact that the Russian physicians sent to Tiflis in 1823 were particularly charged to collect information concerning cause and propagation, for sufficient data existed in neither area, yet both were of first importance for public health decisions.[19]

The views we have described represented available contemporary data concerning cholera. Later studies changed many details and offered more elaborate descriptions, and it was inevitable that more sophisticated and complex theories concerning cholera's nature would be developed. But all that was in the future, and in 1823, and again in 1829–1830, Russian medicine and the Russian government based their efforts on the views we have outlined. Russia was the first European state to have cholera in her home territories, and the only effective precedent she had for dealing with it was the English experience in India, and even the English were of little help in the areas which affected administrative policy. Nevertheless, the Russian government was alive to its responsibilities, and, through the Medical Council, moved in 1823 to meet them.

Although the Central Medical Council recognized the cholera's potential danger, its information lagged far behind events, and the materials it published to aid physicians and officials lagged even behind the intelligence available to the Council. When it was supposed that the epidemic was still near the Euphrates, or even farther away, in the desert region between Africa and Asia, it was actually entering Russia. On August 17, 1823, a report dated July 17 was received from Tiflis, which indicated that in May the cholera had appeared in the Talishchinskii canal district, that four men had died of it at the Lenkoran fortress on the Caspian, that it had spread into Shirvan Province, and that it had committed extensive ravages in Salian on the Kur River. Every indication was that the disease was spreading.[20] The Russian Empire was vast and unwieldy; controls even in the heart of European Russia were difficult to maintain, while the frontier areas were beyond effective centralized control. Nonetheless, some minimal steps were taken, and when the Tiflis report was received, several newly graduated physicians were ordered to Georgia to join the personal staff of the Governor-General and to supplement the work of experienced physicians already on the scene. General-Staff Doctor Reman was personally responsible for this decision, and he, more than anyone else, realized the potential danger of the cholera. Indeed, it is likely that nothing would have been done had Reman not insisted. The first incursions on the frontier did not in themselves trouble Reman; it was rather what they promised for the future. Consequently, the personnel shifts that were made were only a stop-gap, and Reman urged the government to begin planning against the possibility of a major epidemic. His most important recommendation was to establish a special agency whose sole purpose was to deal with cholera. Such an agency was necessary because the Central Medical Council of the Ministry of Interior had such broad responsibilities that it was unable to devote full attention to any particular problem. What Reman ultimately envisioned was a special "cholera council" which could act as a clearing house for information, and, should epidemic conditions develop, serve as a focal point for administration.[21] Dr. Reman's recommendations were acted on in October, 1823, when a Central Cholera Council was called into being, and it was this Council which was the prototype for Zakrevskii's Cholera Commission, formed in 1830. The Council's work in 1823–1824 was minimal, comprising only the collection and dissemination of data, and the Council disappeared in 1824, leaving only a precedent behind. That precedent, however, was important, and in 1829–1831 it became the nucleus of the government's anti-cholera campaign.[22]

Russian medicine first saw the cholera through English eyes, but as the cholera encroached on Russia itself, European medicine began to take an active interest in Russian cholera publications. In 1823, and more particularly in 1829–1831, the West followed Russian medical reports closely for new data, new ideas, and new procedures. The first official cholera survey issued by the Medical Council on August 24, 1823, was widely circulated despite the fact that it contained information readily available from other sources, while Russian surveys of the Astrakhan outbreak together with data from the main epidemic period became part of the general cholera literature.[23] Oddly enough, earlier cholera outbreaks contributed relatively little, even to the British materials, and as a consequence Britain's Indian reports offered the most complete information available before 1830. Since the early materials could not be definitive, any subsequent information was eagerly sought, and Russian data and theories were regularly scanned in the West. Russian publications offered little, however, before 1831, and even then, though Russian studies and reports were widely republished, they produced no striking results and reached no definitive solutions. Russian medical thought was framed in the assumptions and methods which were current in the rest of Europe, and the early cholera publications contained very little that was new.[24] The startling fact is not that Russian medical thought presented little that was new, but rather that for the first time in modern history European science looked to Russia, and Russian ideas were given wide distribution. Striking as this may be, a more important fact lies behind it. Prior to the third decade of the nineteenth century, Russian medical science produced almost nothing which would have been of value to Europe, for the nineteenth century and the Russian medical profession appeared together. Modern medicine in Russia dated from the beginning of the eighteenth century, but in 1830 an indigenous medical profession was scarcely three decades old, and Russian medical facilities were scarcely developed at all. The cholera thus arrived at a crucial point in Russia's cultural development, and its impact on Russia should be seen in the context of an emergent rather than an established medical system. Thus the story of the growth of medicine in Russia has a direct bearing on the history of the cholera, for the medical profession's nature, size, and training materially affected scientific, social, and administrative aspects of the epidemic period. Since relatively little has been written on the history of the Russian medical profession, we may digress here to follow its development to the second decade of the nineteenth century, and in the process we shall be able to see the foundations of the regulatory, administrative, and institutional system which was used against the cholera, and come to appreciate further the significance of Russian medical publication in the period 1823–1832.

The history of medicine in Russia before the Tatar invasions need not detain us, for it was only with the establishment of Moscow's primacy that Russian medicine took the first hesitating steps on the road to modernity. Though the evidence is fragmentary, apparently close contact with both the Byzantine and Islamic worlds brought learned physicians to Kiev, and though first civil war and then the Tatar invasions destroyed Kievan culture, and medical science with it, monastary libraries retained exemplars of foreign medical classics which showed how far Kiev had come before she fell. During the Tatar period, the Greco-Arab tradition was lost, and only the books remained, but Russian religious orders kept practical medicine alive. The monastaries were all but useless for academic medical training, however, and when Ivan III wished to educate medical students, he sent them to the West. Ivan's reign (1462–1505) found Russia awakening, and cultural relations were established between Russia and Europe which became the foundations for the westernizing process which culminated in the eighteenth century. Medical students played their part in these beginnings, and one such, Georgii Drogobychskii, was declared Doctor of Medicine at Bologne, while his dissertation, *Judicum prognosticon Magistri Georgii Drohobicz de Russia* was published in Rome in 1483.[25] In the fifteenth century, only a handful of future physicians studied in the West, but in the sixteenth, and especially the seventeenth century, the number grew markedly, and Russian students appeared at Padua, Halle, Leiden, Frankfurt, and Bremen.[26]

Although the monastaries had played an important role during the Tatar period and after, the monastary tradition was essentially a passive one, and contributed next to nothing to scientific advance. It remained to the state to create the bases for scientific medicine and public health in Russia. The seventeenth century was the turning point. In the period following the Time of Troubles, Tsars Mikhail (1613–1645) and Alexis (1645–1676) forged a new political instrument in Russia, a centralized state system, which Peter the Great completed and extended. Medical affairs early came within the state's purview as plague outbreaks in the reign of Alexis Mikhailovich produced the first generalized quarantine regulations and the means to enforce them, while the demands of constant warfare produced institutional and educational developments in the field of military medicine. In 1654 a military-medical training school was founded at Moscow, and in 1682 two military hospitals were built in the capital, one of which was to be a training center.[27]

Peter the Great consolidated the advances made earlier and gave new impetus to medical development. Peter's medical reforms, like his reforms in general, stemmed from practical military considerations and the necessity for competing on equal terms with the European states. In 1706–1707 Peter founded a chirurgical academy at the Moscow military hospital to train medical men for the Russian armies, and this academy became the first Russian center for scientific medical training. In succeeding years an anatomical theatre was set up at the academy, a botanical garden was established, and scientific personnel, including Bidloo, Kellermann and Köhler were brought to Russia to staff the new enterprise. The Moscow center was only the beginning, and in 1715, following the idea that

Petersburg was to be the center of new Russia, naval and military hospitals were founded in the capital. Another academy was established at which anatomy and "practical" surgery were taught, and by 1730 Peter's system had produced seven physicians and eleven underphysicians.[28]

The personnel which Peter's academies graduated were not medical doctors, but physicians, technicians, attendants, and aides. Their training was pre-eminently practical and emphasized specific functions rather than scientific knowledge. Even so, the lack of secondary school training made recruiting for the academies extremely difficult, and the low social standing of medical practitioners further hampered development. Peter was forced to rely on imported physicians, and even those he hoped to train in Russia required education abroad to prepare them for their work. With these hindrances, the graduation of even eighteen physicians and underphysicians was an accomplishment, though in numerical terms the accomplishment could not compare with the need. Peter's immediate successors were even less successful, and made little effort to expand the medical system. The number of foreign medical men diminished after Peter's death, and by 1740 there were only forty-six fully trained medical men in the entire empire. Peter had gathered one hundred twenty-five doctors during his reign, and both Elizabeth and Catherine II acted to increase the medical establishments, so that by 1796 the number had risen to two hundred twenty-nine, but a significant hiatus in the 1730's, which was only partially redressed in the forties and fifties, greatly weakened the original impact of Peter's medical planning.[29]

The combined problems of social status and secondary education seriously restricted the development of native Russian talent. Elizabeth Petrovna took an important step toward solving this problem when she opened the academies and university to the children of clergy who could graduate from the seminary schools.[30] Even so, the number of native Russian physicians remained very small throughout the eighteenth century, increasing only from twenty-one in 1760 to thirty-eight in 1800.[31] This situation changed radically, however, in the first two decades of the nineteenth century, for not only did the number of medical personnel expand, but a larger and larger percentage were Russian subjects and many received part or even all their education in Russia. The University of Moscow, the

Medico-Chirurgical Academies at Petersburg and Moscow, and ultimately the universities at Kharkov, Kazan, and Dorpat produced graduates for leading administrative positions. This changed the character of the Russian medical profession, and by the middle of the nineteenth century Russia's medical leaders no longer were drawn from foreign sources.[32]

The changing national character of Russian medical personnel indicated the gradual development of Russia's human resources, the expansion and consolidation of the Russian educational system, and the growth of a professional class. Each of these points are indices of Russian cultural growth and the strides Russia was making toward social and cultural maturity. At the opening of the century Baron Storch had warned against the stagnation and sterility which followed on the failure to develop the nation's resources, and he regarded foreign domination of Russian academic life as an evil which was necessary to draw out and train national talent, but he stressed that Russia's progress would at best be halting until she could produce her own scientists and intellectuals.[33] Russia reached that stage in the first half of the nineteenth century, and thus prepared herself for substantial contributions to science as well as the arts.[34]

Though Russian medicine developed a national base by the early nineteenth century, that base was far too narrow to support the social necessities built upon it. The development of a native Russian medical profession indicated progress, but the continued numerical and institutional deficiencies under which the profession labored pointed up the profound social and economic imbalances which characterized Russian life. Although Russian medicine expanded remarkably, so also did the population which it had to serve, and the Imperial system, both before and after serf emancipation, failed to develop the fiscal and recruitment policies which could have bridged the gap between need and performance. This condition affected all aspects of Russian life through the entire century and demonstrated fundamental failures in the Tsarist system. Military medicine was a field which received early and persistent attention, yet Rossiiskii noted that in 1812 there were scarcely five hundred medical men of all types to serve an army of more than a million. Despite the work done in the seventeenth and eighteenth centuries, training in military medicine was still elementary, and Uden at Petersburg and

Mudrov at Moscow had just begun their work in military hygiene.[35] A medical directory published in 1809 provides another view. The medical profession in all its branches numbered a mere 2,596, which, when set against Russia's contemporary population of some 35,000,000, provided a ratio of only 1 : 3,730, and, of course, the number fitted to do general work was actually much smaller.[36]

This problem was cause for continuing concern. Dr. A. B. Granville, to whom we shall refer again, noted in 1828 that Russian medical education was primarily organized to meet military needs, and though the Imperial family and the capital's aristocracy were well served by foreign physicians, there was little medical help available for the population at large.[37] One Russian physician, writing in 1882, observed that in epidemic periods the police played the primary role, and he pointed to the great imbalance in the distribution of Russia's admittedly inadequate medical personnel despite the establishment of the *zemstvo* (i.e., roughly "county") medical councils.[38] Alexander Brückner, writing at approximately the same time, compared Russia with the West and noted that in Italy there was one physician for each 2,280 of population, while in Russia the ratio was 1 : 18,000. In England there was one military surgeon for each 3,118 population; in Russia the ratio was 1 : 12,-400. In Prussia there was one hospital for every 22,000 population; in Russia the ratio was 1 : 176,000. Even though Russia had advanced significantly since the opening of the nineteenth century, she continued to lack personnel and facilities.[39]

Despite the numerical deficiencies which vitiated the general effectiveness of Russian medicine throughout the nineteenth century, there was equally substantial evidence of growing scientific sophistication. Granville complained of fragmentation and obsolescence when he observed Russian medical practice in St. Petersburg, and he argued that the dominance of foreign physicians prevented the development of a "national" Russian medicine, while a shortage of current resource materials rendered Russian practices out of date by European standards. Granville did affirm, however, the competence of the medical staff, and though he found no "*marquant* or *tranchant* characters," he indicated that many were of "acknowledged merit," and there were others "who to that united the advantage of long personal experience."[40]

The polarity which Granville implied between theoretical advances and practical medicine in Russia was generally accurate, for Russian medicine as a scientific discipline was only just emerging in the early decades of the nineteenth century, and the demands on the medical profession were such as to absorb its energies in developing training and basic services. At the same time, there was greater vitality and a higher standard of knowledge than Granville reported. His experience with Russian medicine was limited to St. Petersburg, and since he knew no Russian his contacts were with the foreign physicians who occupied leading posts at court and in the administration. This had obvious advantages, for the men Granville knew bore immediate responsibility, but it also meant that he was cut off from the rising generation of native Russian physicians. Sir James Wylie, who headed the Petersburg Medico-Chirurgical Academy, or Reman could provide information and opportunities for observing medical establishments, but these were men who were advanced in years, who carried heavy administrative responsibilities, and who represented an earlier era in Russian medicine. The same could be said of Stoffregen, Ruhl, Harder, Crichton, and Leighton, all of whom held important posts either in the administration or at court. These were the men whom Granville knew, and consequently many of his comments were more important for what had been rather than what was coming to be.

Contacts between Russian and European medicine were much closer than Granville thought, and the speed with which English materials on the cholera were introduced and disseminated through Russia suggests a substantial familiarity with Western medical literature. Russian physicians continued to study abroad, and the younger generation showed a lively appreciation of the successes and failures of Western techniques. Even more important, however, was the growing volume of medical publications in Russia during the late eighteenth and early nineteenth centuries which provided an increasingly large sample of European medical literature as well as reflecting scholarly efforts by Russian medical men themselves. According to contemporary book lists, a wide variety of materials were available in all fields of medical science in the Russian language. One such list, published in 1828, catalogued four hundred and thirty-eight items including fifty-one in the field of veterinary medicine. The fields covered included the history of medicine, anatomy, physiology, pathology, pharmacology, therapy, legal medicine, midwifery, surgery, hygiene, dietetics, cosmetics, and practical medicine. The last, with one hundred forty-seven titles, was the largest single classification, and nearly half the titles in the entire list were translations. Though some of the publication dates were from the eighteenth century, the bulk of the list was published between 1800 and 1827. Handbooks, surveys, and reference materials were most common, and the heavy emphasis on practical medicine reflected accurately Russian medicine's primary interest as well as the general orientation of medical publication.[41]

While the book lists evidence the availability of Western works in Russian translation, they offer even more striking proof that Russian medical scientists themselves were beginning to publish in substantial quantity, and the period from 1830 to 1860 saw a positive flood of Russian medical publications.[42] Sheer numbers, of course, should not be taken as evidence of quality, but they do suggest a medical profession which was becoming increasingly confident and which was developing a scholarly tradition. Early-nineteenth-century Russia lacked the bibliographical resources as well as the clinical and laboratory facilities available in European centers, and publications consequently were syntheses and applications of established principles rather than original contributions, but this was precisely what was needed to build the foundations for later research.

Another aspect of medical publication was the development of a periodical literature. The *Acta,* later *Mémoires,* of the Imperial Academy of Sciences at St. Petersburg published general scientific treatises, and in the later eighteenth century, statistical data which were important for the public health field. During the eighteenth century, however, a number of publications appeared which carried medical data as such, beginning with the "Mesiatseslovy" or "Calendars" and coming to include several journals in which medical data predominated. The first true medical gazette appeared in 1792 under the title, *Sankt-Peterburgskiia vrachebniia vedemosti,* and continued publication for two years—fifty-two issues. In 1808 another medical gazette was founded, the *Mediko-fizicheskii zhurnal,* and this was paralleled by the *Commentationes Societas Physico-Medicae.* Both journals were published under the auspices of the Moscow Medico-physical Society. Ultimately the *Mediko-fizicheskii zhurnal* was attached to the University of Moscow, and after 1821 it was published by the Moscow University press, continuing publication until 1830 when it was superceded by the *Zapiski obshchestva vrachebnykh i fizicheskikh nauk.* This series, beginning with the *Zhurnal* and the *Commentationes,* marks the start of substantial scientific medical publication in Russia.[43]

The Imperial Academy of Science of St. Petersburg maintained contacts with Western science, and there were also several medical societies which recorded advances in European medicine. The most important of these was formed at Moscow University in 1804 under the name, Obshchestvo Sorevnovaniia Vrachebnye i Fizicheskii Nauk. This organization was devoted to the collection and dissemination of medical literature and medical research, and it maintained correspondence with physicians in England, France, the Germanies and Italy. As such, it offered another avenue for the collection of data on non-Russian medical developments. Similar societies were formed at Vilna in 1805, at St. Petersburg in 1819, and at Warsaw in 1820. Finally, the Obshchestvo Russkikh Vrachei was founded at St. Petersburg in 1833.[44]

The publication of medical journals and the growth of medical societies reflected the development of Russian medicine during the eighteenth and early nineteenth centuries, and the increasing number of native Russian medical works during the later phases of that period was further evidence that Russian medicine was developing a tradition. Even so, the problems which had to be overcome were overwhelming, and nowhere were they more clearly indicated than in medical education. Soviet writers have emphasized that a Russian empirical-clinical tradition countered and contradicted the Schellingist formulas current in German scientific thought, but the fact was that Russia's needs were for practical fundamentals, and there was an understandable impatience with idealistic formulae and theoretical constructions.[45] Russian medical education needed basic equipment for anatomy demonstrations, laboratories for experimental work, clinics for observation and treatment, and above all a corps of teachers familiar with Russian needs who could develop Russian talents. Zubelin made a major contribution when he began lecturing in Russian at Moscow University in 1768, and an even more significant advance was made when F. T. Barsuk-Moiseev received the first Russian doctorate at Moscow in 1794.[46] But these advances only heightened the contrast with what remained to be done.

Mudrov, who must be accounted one of the leading figures among the younger generation before 1830, studied both in Moscow and abroad, and though he criticized his foreign mentors for their theoretical approaches, he painted a dismal picture of Russian medical education. Reflecting on his experiences, he wrote:

> Professor Kereszturi . . . [was] a man of profound intelligence, but he was never able to finish a course; [and] there was no practice upon cadavers. The dissector interrupted our work with worn out stories, or supplied putrid cadavers. The anatomical museum was unheated, and the surgical instruments were wretched. Professor Richter lectured excellently in surgery, but he demonstrated operations on neither the living nor the dead. Concerning the legal section we knew as much as it was possible to learn on two or three accidental cases. In anatomical pathology, we were told only the names.[47]

The deficiencies which Mudrov described were fundamental, for without laboratory materials and clinical work effective medical training was almost impossible. Furthermore, the intellectual orientation of the early Moscow staff, an orientation which emphasized the abstract and the definitional, did not square with Russian needs. Mudrov himself contributed to an empirical-clinical tradition, and Pirogov's description of his student days in the 1820's indicates that medical education had improved markedly.[48] When A. B. Granville visited the Petersburg Medico-Chirurgical Academy in 1826, he was impressed favorably by the breadth of the curriculum and the quality of the teaching. Deficiencies continued to exist, and one of the most notable was the lack of clinical training in midwifery, but on the whole the Academy seemed to be on a substantial footing.[49]

Petersburg and Moscow were the primary centers for medical training on the eve of the cholera outbreaks, and the medical work which was being done in the two capitals represented the best that Russian medicine had to offer. From the time of Peter the Great medical education had been a state function, and in 1763 Catherine II created a special state commission to integrate all medical activities and to direct the development of medical training facilities. This commission was given collegiate status and from 1763 to 1803 the Imperial Medical College functioned autonomously and on terms of equality with the other administrative colleges. When Alexander I formally organized the ministries, the Imperial Medical

College lost status and reappeared as the Third Section of the Ministry of the Interior. In 1804, the Medical Section of the Ministry of Interior was divided into three separate offices, the Medical Section of the Ministry of War, the Medical Section of the Ministry of Naval Affairs, and the Civil-Medical Council of the Ministry of the Interior. Though there was some duplication of function, the Civil-Medical Council was the most important medical-administrative organ and possessed the widest jurisdiction. In the field of medical education this body was the main directive influence in curriculum and institutional organization, though the Ministry of Public Enlightenment retained control over personnel following the abolition of University autonomy in 1823.[50]

The Imperial Medical College was responsible for establishing the Imperial Medico-Chirurgical Academy in 1799–1800. The Academy grew out of a series of hospital schools or academies which were founded during the eighteenth century. In addition to the schools set up by Peter the Great, a medical-chirurgical institute was established on November 8, 1783, in conjunction with the Secret Hospital for Syphlitics which had been founded the previous year. This school was to train young men for the Baltic provinces, and in the beginning the language of instruction was German. The course lasted three years, and a fourth year of "internship" at the naval or military hospitals completed the sequence. In 1786 a surgical institute was formed at the main Petersburg military hospital. This institute offered a practical course oriented to military needs, and was of little use for general practice. Altogether, including Kronstadt, there were four medical training centers in the Petersburg region at the end of the eighteenth century, and on February 12, 1799, the Imperial Medical College presented Tsar Paul with a project for consolidating those schools into a single Imperial Medico-Chirurgical Academy. The recommendation was accepted and approved on September 16, 1800, and the new academy held its first conference on October 20 of that year.[51]

The first Medico-Chirurgical Academy, it will be remembered, was established at Moscow, and that institution also continued through the eighteenth century. Following the foundation of the University of Moscow in 1755, however, and the creation of a diversified course of scientific medical training, the Moscow Academy became superfluous. In 1804, during the general reorganization of the Russian system, the Moscow Medico-Chirurgical Academy was merged with the Imperial Academy at Petersburg, and some forty-five students transferred from the old capital to the new. A further reorganization occurred in 1808, when the Academy was again divided between Petersburg and Moscow, with the Moscow institution becoming a branch of the Petersburg Academy. Tsar Alexander then removed the Academy from the control of the Civil-Medical Council under the Ministry of the Interior and took it under his personal direction. This arrangment changed again in 1823, and the Academy returned to the authority of the Ministry of the Interior where it remained until 1839.[52]

The hospital schools had offered specialized, practical training, and even after the establishment of the new Academy the title granted was that of *Subchirurgus* (*podlekar*). In 1764 the Imperial Medical College had been given the right to authorize the degree Doctor of Medicine, but it was not until 1791 that the degree was formally approved for the University of Moscow, which offered the only substantial curriculum. When Johann Peter Frank took over the direction of the Imperial Academy at St. Petersburg, he immediately set about broadening the curriculum, a process which had actually begun with recommendations of the Imperial Medical College in 1793. It was Frank, however, who made the Academy into a general medical school with the development of courses in Latin and German, the establishment of chairs of physiology, pathology, and hygiene, the foundation of clinics for therapeutics and surgery, and the development of disciplinary compartmentalization within the Academy.[53]

Between 1808 and 1822, the reorganized Academy graduated 654 physicians and 108 veterinarians, and between 1824 and 1838, 677 medical trainees of all types.[54] By 1829, the Academy offered a well diversified curriculum spread over a four-year period. In the first year, or class, the students studied principles of medicine and veterinary surgery, natural history, mineralogy, zoology, anatomy, mathematics, and natural philosophy. The second class included physiology, pathology, anatomy demonstrations and dissection, botany, and chemistry. During the third year, pharmacy, the art of writing formulae, general therapeutics, clinical medicine respecting acute disease, and surgery were offered. And in the final year, the curriculum included the continuation of theoretical and practical surgery, therapeutics, midwifery, *materia medica,* the medical police, and opthalmic surgery.[55] In 1824, Sir James Wylie had succeeded Johann Peter Frank as President of the Academy, and he continued the emphasis on general scientific training as a part of medical education which Frank had initiated.[56] Both in numbers of graduates and the quality of education offered, the Medico-Chirurgical Academy contributed significantly to the growth of Russian medicine.

The University of Moscow was an equally important center of medical education and though it was founded long after Peter's hospital schools, it actually led the move toward general scientific training for doctors. Indeed the purpose of the University, according to M. V. Lomonosov, was to provide general as well as technical training, a point which he made in his correspondence with I. I. Shuvalov, the newly appointed director of the University.[57] Lomonosov thought that in the beginning the University could maintain only a faculty of twelve, and he recommended that those twelve be divided among Jurisprudence, Medicine, and Philosophy. Jurisprudence and Medicine would each have three men, and Philosophy six. He suggested that the medical faculty include Professors of Chemistry, Natural History, and Anatomy, while a Professor of Physics would be attached to the Philosophical faculty. Lomonosov's recommendations paralleled the final form which the University took, and recent authorities have insisted that, although he was not officially recognized in the opening ceremonies, Lomonosov's influence was paramount in the University's original organization.[58]

Lomonosov considered medical education as a synthesis of descriptive science and practical techniques. The study of medicine had to be more than a recital of recommended cures and needed the rigor and discipline which scientific analysis provided. Furthermore, he sensed that treatment would be most successful when the practitioner built his knowledge of disease on a substantial scientific foundation which provided knowledge of the basic relationships underlying organic life. Thus he held, for example, that a professor of anatomy should begin by analyzing anatomical structure and prove his theoretical propositions by concrete demonstrations, and then he should relate his demonstrations to particular medical practices. In this way general scientific procedures and knowledge would provide the explanation for particular curative techniques.[59]

Unfortunately, Lomonosov's pedagogical ideal was not realized, although sixty years later it was this approach which underlay Frank's reforms of the Medico-Chirurgical Academy, but Lomonosov did define a methodology which gradually came into being with later Russian scientific medicine.

Nine students entered the University's medical program in May, 1755, and they were met by a single instructor, for even the modest plans which had been proposed proved too difficult to realize. The person who held the single post was Johann Christian Kerstens, who was Master of General Science and Philosophy and Doctor of Medicine, a man peculiarly well suited to being a one-man medical faculty. Shuvalov brought Kerstens from Leipzig, and during the fifteen years he remained in Russia, he lectured and wrote on a wide range of subjects including chemistry, mineralogy, mathematics, physics, *materia medica,* and sanitary regulations. He was soon joined by Professor I. F. Erasmus from Strasbourg, and two talented Russians, S. G. Zubelin, whom we mentioned earlier, and P. D. Venianinov; when Kerstens returned to Leipzig in 1770, the medical school was well started.[60]

Between 1770 and 1830, the Moscow medical faculty developed and expanded, and at the same time the quality of instruction improved as disciplinary specialization brought more rigorous methods into both research and teaching. Foreign training continued to be sought, but an increasing number of Russian-trained medical scientists were appearing, and as early as 1806 the Moscow medical faculty was predominantly Russian.[61] As Granville noted, Russia produced no medical giants during these years, but on the eve of the cholera epidemic every evidence pointed to the existence of a competent, though small, medical profession. Russian medicine was not an indigenous growth, nor can the advances which it made be considered evidence of any peculiar Russian national genius. But it would be equally indefensible to regard Russia as innately inferior. The first cholera publications reflected a fundamental debt to English observations and ideas, but they showed as well a developing scientific spirit, an emphasis on empirical verification, and an ability to use the methods and techniques which were part of medical science's contemporary methodology. In these terms, though it lacked a Halle or Récamier, Russian medicine compared favorably with that of Europe, or perhaps more accurately, Russian medicine had absorbed and was able to put to use the lessons and ideas which it derived from Europe. In the universal world of science, this marked a considerable development for Russia, and by 1830 Russian medicine stood ready to contribute creatively to the scientific world.

While Russian medical science had developed significantly, it was still unable to perform the tasks which society required. The profession itself was much too small numerically to serve the population, and medical facilities were sadly lacking in all but a few major urban centers. Even in the capitals, existing facilities were scarcely adequate, while in the outlying districts only the military had regularly developed medical centers and hospitals. In St. Petersburg itself the best hospitals were provided for the Army, while those which served the Guards officers were particularly impressive, and, in Granville's phrase, could stand as "fit models for every civilized nation in Europe to imitate." The only establishment superior to that of the Guards was the Hospital for the Poor, which was maintained by the Imperial household. For the rest, Petersburg's hospitals were often badly situated, overcrowded, and in need of interior reform.[62] The situation in Moscow was little better, and though Prince Sheremetev's privately endowed institution commanded respect and excited comment, the hospital services available were scarcely adequate in normal times, and during an epidemic proved utterly inadequate.[63]

It is extremely difficult at this distance to judge the effectiveness of the hospital system. Dr. Hygler, who directed the General Hospital for Troops of the Line, told Granville that the mortality rate was only one in forty-eight, despite crowded conditions and staff shortages. Granville was skeptical of the figure, and rightly so, for the Hospital for the Poor, one of Petersburg's outstanding institutions, reported a mortality rate of 18½ per cent, and Academician Hermann indicated that a 10 per cent death ratio could be expected as a matter of course in a hospital which was not dealing with an epidemic. The figure seemed high, and Granville argued that a hospital whose death rate reached 10 per cent in normal times was probably ill administered.[64]

Whatever the reasons may have been, hospital facilities were lacking, and during the cholera epidemic the provision of adequate centers for treatment remained a major problem. In the provinces, customs offices and military and naval posts had the only reliable facilities, and these were too limited to do more than absorb a part of those requiring help. As a consequence, it was only in such centers as Moscow and Petersburg that anything resembling an integrated program could be developed. This in turn threw a peculiarly heavy burden on non-medical personnel and facilities and contributed to the cholera's social impact.

Medical administration, on the other hand, was highly developed, and the Russian Imperial system created an integrated public health administration during the eighteenth century. The first important steps were taken under Peter the Great, who established governmental offices to deal with quarantine policy, military medicine, and the development of medical education. The Imperial Medical College united functions which had been dispersed earlier in the century, and ultimately the Ministry of the Interior, guided by the Civil-Medical Council, took authority over all aspects of sanitary policy, except for the administration of military medical affairs. The medical administration was primarily concerned with fostering education and developing restrictive policies against major disease outbreaks, and, particularly after the great plague in Moscow in 1771, in laying down basic policies for quarantine, sequestration, and fumigation. By the nineteenth century, a system of reporting on health conditions which used the local police as well as border officials was well established, and, though the government did relatively little in regard to sanitation or housing controls, an elaborate administrative system existed with which to combat epidemic disease. Sanitary policy was regarded as an essential part of government operations and when the cholera appeared the machinery to mobilize the entire system was available.[65]

Some of the problems we have noted emerged when the cholera appeared on the Russian borders, and the Medical Council attempted to rectify known shortages in the Transcaucasus. The first invasion was not serious, and after a brief flurry during September and October, 1823, the disease disappeared. Mortality figures on the first outbreak are unreliable, for the great distance from the centers of Russian administration, failures of medical men to recognize the disease, and the isolationist habits of the non-Russian population all worked against accurate reporting. What figures did come in, however, showed an outbreak of some intensity, for between September 10 and October 4, 392 cases were reported, of which 205 were fatal. The disease stayed within the Astrakhan government, and no effort was made to develop or enforce quarantine measures. Indeed, by the time the Medical Council's special representatives, Drs. Kolinskii and Khotovitskii, had reached Astrakhan, examined conditions, and confirmed the existence of the Indian Cholera, the disease was waning, and the only official action taken was to establish the special cholera council at Petersburg which contributed the recommendations we noted earlier.[66]

The cholera's first appearance on Russian soil went unnoticed by the general population, and its effect was felt in a very limited geographical area. Its appearance did, however, activate the Medical Council, and the instructions which the Council prepared were pressed into service in 1829–1830. Furthermore, a special medical-administrative system for dealing with the cholera was created, and the special cholera council, which disbanded in 1824, was reactivated in 1830. For six years Russia remained free of cholera, but in 1829 the disease reappeared in the Caspian region, and during the next three years spread havoc across European Russia.

Chapter 3

THE CHOLERA RETURNS:
ORENBURG TO NIZHNY, 1829–1830

Although the cholera outbreak at Astrakhan aroused professional interest in European medical circles, and the epidemic's resurgence in 1829 underlined that interest, the cholera played a negligible role in popular thinking until the summer of 1830. The epidemic at Astrakhan was an isolated experience which passed unnoticed, and the possibility of cholera in Central Asia and on the Russian frontiers was given no publicity. There was no reason to publicize events which were little more than unsubstantiated rumor emanating from areas thousands of miles from European Russia, and even events at Orenburg and Astrakhan seemed to belong to another world. In 1829 the cholera epidemic was far more serious than its first visit in 1823, but it was not considered a national problem. Although local newspapers carried cholera news, the first reporting which gained general circulation appeared in *Severnaia pchela* in August, 1830, and was reprinted in the *Journal de St. Pétersbourg* on September 2/14.[1] By that time of course, the cholera was deep into European Russia and was expected momentarily in Moscow.

The government similarly could ignore the cholera until the summer of 1830. Although the Medical Council was actively interested in the Orenburg epidemic, neither the Senate nor the Council of Ministers took any formal cholera measures until June. Tsar Nicholas I was informed that the cholera was encroaching on his lands, but he gave no indication that he took this problem seriously until he returned from Warsaw to Moscow after convening the Polish Diet.[2] The truth was that the cholera offered little to excite official interest, and the formal measures to control it previously had been minimal. Reman had taken an alarmist view in 1823, and as president of the Medical Council was able to make his opinion felt, but his outlook was not widely shared, and the intervening six years had all but obliterated the memory of his protestations.[3] There were many other things to occupy official attention during 1829–1830 which seemed more important than cholera. International questions of the first magnitude troubled the government, and those questions were complicated by revolutions in Europe and growing tension in Poland. The resurgence of the plague seemed a more immediate public health problem than cholera, and through 1829 and into 1830 there was concern over quarantine problems brought on by trade and troop movements in the Black Sea region and on the Balkan frontiers.[4]

Although the cholera stimulated neither public nor official interest, the Central Medical Council continued gathering information and in 1829 opened an investigation of a rumored epidemic among the Asiatic tribes in the Bukhara and Khiva region. Any epidemic in that area was a latent threat to the Empire, for caravans originating in Bukhara regularly passed through Orenburg and entered Russian territory. The Medical Council instructed health officials in Orenburg to investigate, and a special commission under Lieutenant-General Veselitskii was charged with the task. Reports were filed in July and October, 1829, which suggested that although the data were extremely confused, there was a disease among the Kirghiz which might be epidemic cholera. This was not stated as a fact, however, and the commission pointed out that even if it were true, there was little need for concern since cholera was not infectious, and since vast distances separated the reported centers of incidence and the Russian frontiers.[5] The Orenburg commission was correct in suspecting cholera in Central Asia, but it was wrong in viewing the desert wastes as an adequate barrier. The cholera had crossed the Great Wall of China three years earlier, attacked nomadic tribes in Central Asia, and in 1829 came with the caravans to Orenburg.[6]

The Orenburg report had scarcely reached St. Petersburg when the first acknowledged cholera case occurred. On August 26, 1829, a private in the Third Battalion of the Orenburg Line was seized with "bilious vomiting, diarrhea, intolerable pain in the belly, thirst, sunken features, blue lips, yellow sliminess of the tongue, coldness and painful cramps in the extremities, almost imperceptible pulse, extraordinary sinking of the strength, and excessive anxiety...."[7] On September 2, the wife of the Neplevskii school treasurer died after a brief but violent illness. Though no doctor was present, the husband's description strongly suggested cholera. Almost a week later, on September 8, a serf belonging to the Military Governor was seized with the characteristic symptoms and died within twelve hours. Another case occurred on September 9, two more on September 10, and an additional two on September 11. At this point, the local medical board hastily convened and announced to a disturbed community that the cholera was among them and preventive measures were needed.[8]

At first it seemed that Orenburg would have the same experience as Astrakhan, and the cholera would remain concentrated, but on September 28, news was received that the cholera had appeared at Rasypna, a military post sixty-six miles southwest of Orenburg on the Ural. One surmise was that the Tenth Horse Artillery of the Cossack Division, stationed at Orenburg until September 1, had carried the infection with it to Rasypna, although it was popularly believed that a tavern servant who died the day after his arrival was the carrier. Whatever the means, once established at Rasypna, the cholera moved back along the Ural, and on October 8 was reported at Iletsk forty miles southwest of Orenburg. At this point, any apparent pattern of movement disappeared in a deluge of reports; the entire Orenburg region was infected, and by the beginning of November the cholera had reached Bugulma, two hundred miles away in the direction of Kazan.[9]

The Orenburg epidemic puzzled health officials and gave rise to further speculation concerning cholera's cause. Since the theory of direct communication was rejected, the cause was sought in the environment of the city itself. Here, however, the searchers met a dead end. Far from being noxious, the Orenburg region, and especially the city itself, was well located, and neither climate, topography nor physical conditions could explain the disease's outbreak. One physician took the extreme stand that it would be "impossible to conceive a site better calculated for the preservation of human health" than Orenburg, and argued that the town "from the healthiness of its site, its regularity and cleanliness, presents not the slightest source of liability to the disease." [10] It was thought that certain climatic conditions increased the likelihood of an epidemic, and damp, cloudy weather was considered most dangerous, while the suggestion was offered that fewer cases occurred on cold, clear days. This thesis, however, was not fully developed. Physicians exploded one myth, for the epidemic at Astrakhan had suggested that cholera was a hot weather disease, which abated when cold weather arrived.

This agreed with early English observations, but at Orenburg this position was questioned and finally disproved, when cholera outbreaks occurred with the temperature standing at $-35°$ F.[11]

Out of a welter of conflicting arguments, one significant thesis emerged on which there was general agreement: almost all the reports accepted a direct relationship between the mode of life and the cholera's incidence. In an undated memorandum submitted at the request of the Kazan Medical Board, the Orenburg Medical Council emphasized that "the lowest classes, particularly those residing in wet, damp, confined, dirty apartments, are more subject to cholera than others,—the licentious and intemperate more than regular livers,—women, and especially pregnant women, more than men,—and those of middle age more than old people and children." Here was a basic fact for cholera's epidemiology which subsequent experience confirmed again and again, but there was a further problem which the Orenburg Board had to solve. It was easy to understand how drunkeness, debauchery, or poverty could weaken physical resistance and predispose an individual to cholera, but it was more difficult to see why women were more susceptible than men, and even more puzzling, why middle age was more vulnerable than either the old or the young. Clearly there was more involved than mere strength versus weakness, but the best the Board could do was suggest "some obscure internal state of the system, and still more, irregularity and derangement of the digestion." [12]

The concept of predisposition was fully established throughout Europe by the time the first pandemic had run its course. The predisposing causes, however, were only partially attributable to external environment, and by emphasizing "some obscure internal state ... ," the Council hinted the possibility of a cause which was contained in the human organism, and which itself responded to environmental influences. It was this condition, it was argued, which created a receptiveness to cholera, introduced from the outside. This position enabled the Orenburg Board to combine "predisposition" with "contagion" to provide an explanation for cholera's transmission, and they worked out the following formula: "a person who had contracted a tendency to the disease in a place where it prevails, arrives in an uninfected place, there takes ill, and *communicates a diseased condition to the atmosphere of his new residence.* Here the disease increases and spreads, seizing all *whose constitutions are by nature predisposed to receive it."* The Board further pointed out that "Eight instances of such conveyance have been ascertained judicially, and by physicians who were attending to the course of the epidemic in this government." [13]

These conclusions were particularly significant, for they justified quarantine regulations, and underlined the social aspect of the disease. What was more important, however, was that the Orenburg Board outlined a position acceptable within the tenets of contemporary medicine which could serve as the basis for administrative decisions. We have noted that as early as 1819 a bacteriological explanation for cholera's spread was submitted to the Bengal Medical Board, and that in 1831 a similar theory was refused by the Moscow Medical Council.[14] Although the future proved that a bacteriological explanation was correct, the current state of medical science found such a view unacceptable, and either declared that cholera was not contagious, or that it was contagious, but no one knew why. The Orenburg thesis provided a compromise position which could justify moderate quarantine for preventive purposes while stressing the need to improve social conditions, especially among the poor. Thinking similar to this ultimately came to be accepted in both Russia and Europe, and contributed to the development of general public health policies.[15]

Probably the most important public issue which the Orenburg outbreak raised was quarantine policy. Existing government regulations were drawn to fit bubonic plague, not cholera, and though the Central Medical Council's cholera circular of 1823 recommended quarantine, the Council had not defined what constituted effective quarantine procedures. This put Orenburg officials in a dilemma which was not resolved officially until a year after the cholera's appearance. At the epidemic's onset, very little was done to enforce quarantine regulations; there was relatively free movement in the infected areas, and the non-Russian population paid no attention to what regulations existed. On October 9, 1829, the Orenburg Military Governor ordered the establishment of a quarantine, but the prescribed rules reflected both uncertainty regarding cholera's nature and the difficulty of enforcement. A military cordon was drawn around Orenburg and its suburbs in order to examine persons who were leaving the city. Those who exhibited precursory symptoms were prevented from going farther to avoid their falling ill on the journey and bringing "terror and anxiety ... into remote parts of the country." An observation period of seven days was established during which the travellers' luggage was fumigated before being sent on with them. Persons coming to Orenburg who were healthy were forbidden to enter the city "for the sake of their own health and life." Provisioners and farmers with produce for sale were allowed to approach the sanitary barrier in connection with their normal occupations.[16]

These regulations were far milder than those which governed the plague areas and reflected a tentative attempt to meet the cholera's realities. It was fairly certain that cholera was not carried by inanimate objects, and the regulations concerning trade goods and the post were very tolerant and very laxly enforced. The quarantine period itself was short, and the prohibitions on travel were minimal. Somewhat more stringent methods were used in the areas where cholera cases actually existed, and persons who were known to have the cholera, or to have been exposed to it, were supposed to be segregated from the rest of the household. Cholera patients' linens and other apparel were to be washed in brine or lye and then thoroughly dried and their apartments fumigated with vinegar or chloride of lime. Even these measures, however, were applied haphazardly. Apart from segregating individual cases, no attempt was made to use interior cordons sequestering particular districts, though regions in which the existence of cholera was proved were to be quarantined. Quarantine regulations were to remain in force for fourteen days after the last cholera case had ended, and during that period the inhabitants were urged to air their houses, furniture, and belongings.[17]

The Orenburg outbreak was marked by no major social disturbances, and though it cannot be said that the community remained calm, there is no evidence to indicate any notable social reaction. When the cholera first appeared, there was a general exodus which the government made no attempt to suppress, and though individual doctors reported that people hid away with the disease rather than submit to treatment, a completely natural reaction, there was no serious conflict between officials and the populace. The cholera had not yet developed a mythology, and unknown though it was, it had not yet created the fearful image which marked its progress the following year. The Asiatic peoples in particular showed little fear, or even respect, for the disease, and a holiday spirit pervaded the proceedings when the Bukhara and Khiva caravans were inspected and quarantined.[18]

Although the cholera affected the Orenburg community and government generally, its effects were not extreme. Between August, 1829, and Feburary, 1830, the disease attacked 3,590 persons, a figure which indicated a fairly general infection.[19] Of these, however, it was estimated that 2,725 were cured while only 865 died, a mortality ratio of approximately 32 per cent. The number of cases defined an epidemic condition, but the 68 per cent of the cases cured pointed toward moderate optimism regarding effective treatment, and certainly did not seem to justify excessive alarm.[20] In succeeding years, when the cholera developed far greater intensity, an outbreak such as the Orenburg epidemic could well create utter chaos, but in 1829 it still seemed that the cholera could be controlled and that its appearance was not synonymous with a community's destruction.

The Central Medical Council at St. Petersburg summarized the most important lessons learned at Orenburg, and in the process reached some interesting conclusions. The cholera, judging from the Orenburg epidemic, was definitely contagious, and though the Council could not explain the mechanism of infection, they held that sanitary regulations were essential, and they doubted whether the Orenburg quarantine was long enough to be effective. An observation period even of fourteen days was considered insufficient, and it was suggested that known cases occurred well beyond that limit. The fact that cold weather did not appreciably affect the cholera was duly recorded, and the Council noted that the Orenburg medical staff had attempted no preventive measures beyond those embodied in the Medical Council's earlier circular. One fact which received special attention was the need for immediate treatment, and the Council emphasized that the mortality from cholera was worst where the disease was concealed and where cleanliness and ventilation were most often lacking.[21]

The Medical Council consistently took a strong contagionist position throughout the epidemic period, and they held this position regardless of the views expressed by local medical boards. This stand reflected Dr. Reman's influence, and until his death in 1831, the Central Medical Council continued to recommend stringent control measures. The Council criticized Orenburg officials for failing to implement effective controls, and they warned against the results of such lax policies in future.[22] The central government did not share the Medical Council's views, however, and during the winter of 1829–1830 began to review all quarantine policies with an eye to relaxing irksome controls which were also detrimental economically. Black Sea ports had been closed for two years against the plague, but when Count Vorontsov argued in September, 1829, that established quarantine regulations were not sufficient and that the Sea of Azov should be closed, his proposals were flatly rejected. Both Count Zakrevskii, Minister of Interior, and Finance Minister Count Kankrin opposed extending quarantines and pointed out that the result would be to disrupt trade and create unrest.[23]

The point of view which justified the government's decision not to extend the Black Sea quarantines affected cholera quarantine policy. On July 8, and again on August 12, 1830, general regulations appeared which greatly modified quarantine rules for cholera and flatly contradicted the Central Medical Council's recommendations. Indeed, the first decree paid little attention to any of the data so laboriously collected in the previous year, for it argued that cholera spread through the air and therefore was not susceptible to control by quarantine. It was suggested that ships arriving at Russian ports should be quarantined and closely inspected, but that more stringent measures were not actually necessary.

In a more important move, on August 12, the government affirmed full central control over all regulatory measures concerning cholera, and specifically indicated that the quarantine issue was far too important to trust to local authorities. This action came because the Orenburg officials stopped caravans bound for Troitsk and Orenburg in February, 1830. The government pointed out that cholera was not transmitted by direct contact, was not carried by goods, and that the epidemic the preceding year happened six to eight weeks after the caravans' arrival. The Medical Council was not entirely ignored in this decree, for it was recommended that obvious cholera cases, or persons exhibiting preliminary symptoms, should be quarantined, but no other measures were approved. The Governor of Orenburg was specifically ordered not to introduce any other rules, and the cabinet recommended that the staff doctor responsible for the February quarantine be transferred to another post as punishment, a recommendation which Nicholas rejected.[24] The reason for this heated reaction is not difficult to see. The Imperial government regarded trade with Asia as a significant part of its overall effort to expand commercial contacts, and any action which interrupted that trade or affected it adversely had to be avoided. The cabinet believed the Orenburg quarantine had already injured the Asiatic trade, and they were greatly concerned over too zealous a quarantine policy depleting attendance at the great Nizhny fair scheduled for the late summer. In the light of later events, the Imperial government acted with a criminal disregard for the nation's welfare, but it must also be remembered that the men in St. Petersburg had absolutely no experience with the cholera, and there was no substantial reason for them to give great weight to fragmentary and contradictory reports from thousands of miles away. Commercial development seemed far more important at this juncture than a potential epidemic, and economic concerns were more weighty than public health. What is dismaying is that direct experience with cholera did not greatly change the cabinet's attitudes. When more stringent regulations were introduced on August 28–29, 1830, it was done reluctantly, and, more to the point, the Nizhny fair was held in both 1830 and 1831 despite the cholera. Economic factors played a primary role in determining public health policies.[25]

The effect which economic factors had on Russian quarantine policy paralleled similar developments in western Europe, where it was common for commercially interested persons, and governments, to take a strong anti-quarantine position. The political-ideological overtones to the quarantine issue in the west, however, were not repeated in Russia, and no pattern of liberal or conservative interpretations emerged. The public criticized sanitary policies, but there seemed to be no clear identification between political liberalism and anti-quarantine thinking. The same point applies to the contagion controversy on which the quarantine issue turned. In the west, anti-contagion thought came to be identified with political liberalism, but again, this was not the case in Russia. The contagion debate raged throughout the cholera period, but its significance for political ideology was small. It should be remembered, of course, that there was an infinite distance between the *Westminister Review* and English social radicals and the Russian political intelligentsia. England's political sophistication and the long-term existence of political parties created a climate totally different from Nicholaevan Russia and put the issues connected with quarantine and contagion in a quite different frame of reference.

Social stability and the danger of rebellion were more significant for Russian quarantine policy than ideological considerations, and in May, 1830, riots in Sevastopol sharply underlined the potential dangers in too strict sanitary regulations. The port of Sevastopol had been closely quarantined for more than a year against the bubonic plague which had broken out in Turkey. By the end of May, however, the threat seemed to have abated, and the cordons had been withdrawn within the city, with the exception of that which surrounded the section of the town known as the Korabel'naia. This region, a dockside area inhabited by seamen, workers, and their families, was very poor, cramped, and dirty, and well known as a focus of disease. The sanitary regulations were due to expire there early in June, and the expiration was eagerly awaited. Life in the Korabel'naia was hard enough, but under the quarantine regulations it had become impossible. All egress was forbidden, all public gatherings, including ecclesiastical functions, were interdicted; people suspected of infection were subject to virtual house arrest, and even food and water were difficult to get.[26]

Immediately before the expiration of the quarantine rules, medical authorities reported that scattered cases of plague, and several deaths, had occurred. Lieutenant-General Stolypin, provisional military governor of Sevastopol, decreed that further investigations were needed and ordered post-mortem examinations conducted in two suspicious cases. The houses and belongings of the sick were to be fumigated, and the sanitary regulations were to be extended as long as they were necessary. The decision produced an outcry. The sanitary police were prevented from exhuming the body of one suspected plague victim, and the people resisted fumigation orders. Every effort to quiet the district proved unsuccessful, for the opposition was born of desperation and fed on the bitter certainty that deprivation and persecution were an inevitable consequence of sequestration. Police officials who enforced the sanitary regulations were notorious for their brutal methods, and the rumor swiftly spread that the plague was only an excuse to pillage the people.[27]

On May 22, at seven in the evening, a raging mob surged up out of the Korabel'naia, and to the tolling of the great alarm bell, spread swiftly throughout the city. The mob tore down quarantine barriers, smashed open the churches, and threw themselves in a fury on the police and cordon guards. Stolypin showed himself to the crowd in an effort to quiet it, and was murdered, together with several officials. Quarantine posts were ravaged, police offices overrun, and the cordon guards fled the city to hide aboard ships in the harbor or in trenches outside the city's limits. Complete anarchy reigned until the afternoon of May 23, by which time the mob had spent its initial fury; by May 24, order was restored with the hasty arrival of Admiral Greigh, the regular military governor, who was closely followed by Count Vorontsov, the Governor-General of the province.[28] An investigation followed immediately; the supposed ringleaders in the riots were shot, and several hundred sailors were transferred from Sevastopol to Archangel. In his report concerning the outbreak, Vorontsov noted that while punitive measures had been taken, and while the people were doubtless wrong, the administration, particularly on the lower levels, was not guiltless. The clumsy, often brutal handling of the populace by quarantine officials, and especially by the police, worsened popular resentment and contributed directly to the riots.[29]

The Sevastopol riots were a reminder of the danger involved in too hasty or too severe sanitary measures and provided ready evidence that it was unwise to disturb the normal tenor of life without substantial cause. Moreover, the continuing war between lesser officials and the population was a further danger which made any quarantine situation potentially explosive. When combined with the economic issues which were at stake, the social problems inherent in restrictive sanitary policies dictated the moderate approach to cholera quarantine and the centralization of responsibility which crystallized in the decrees of July 8 and August 12.

While these issues were debated, the cholera appeared again, striking Astrakhan on July 3, 1830. This second appearance was far more violent than the first, and it marked the beginning of the epidemic which dominated the Russian interior for eighteen months. The new attack began with a fury unparalleled in Russian experience with the cholera, and, as it spread, it evoked a gathering terror which became as great a danger as the cholera itself. The first cases occurred on a sloop of war newly arrived from Salian, which anchored 90 versts from Astrakhan. The stricken men were taken to the Sedlitovskii quarantine station, and until July 20 all remained tranquil. On that day, however, four persons came down with the characteristic symptoms in the city of Astrakhan itself, and within twenty-four hours more than two hundred deaths had been recorded.[30]

The epidemic at Astrakhan had been heralded by outbreaks in Tauris, Elizabethpol, and Tiflis, but the initial assault was so sudden and so devastating that at first no measures could be taken for its control. The civil governor and the director of police were among the first victims, and with their deaths local administration collapsed. Hysteria swept the city, and the population fled into the surrounding hills. What followed was amazing, for despite anarchy, terror, and death, no violence occurred, and neither pillaging nor looting became a problem.[31] During this anarchic phase, the sick and the well, doctors, medical attendants, and ordinary people were all thrown together without apparent ill-effect. There seemed to be no rational explanation for the seizure of some and the immunity of others, and this led Astrakhan's medical staff to the unwarranted conclusion that cholera was non-contagious and that restrictions were unnecessary. In place of scientific analysis, a quiet fatalism formed their thinking, for they had convinced themselves that those who would take the cholera would take it, and preventive measures were useless. The disease would have its way, and, apart from treating the sick, there was nothing to be done.[32]

The Astrakhan epidemic reached its peak intensity between July 20 and August 15, and during that period the cholera developed a mortality rate which was unsurpassed in any major Russian or European population center during the first pandemic. In the city itself, 3,633 cases were reported, with 2,935 deaths, a mortality percentage of 90.8; while in the province, 5,912 cases were reported between July 4 and August 27, of which 4,856, or approximately 82 per cent proved fatal. A survey of Russian towns in 1825 gave Astrakhan's population as 37,320, while the province of Astrakhan in 1846 had a population of 328,776.[33] Just above 9 per cent of the city population contracted cholera, and approximately 8 per cent of the population died. Compared with the medieval bubonic plague, the cholera affected a relatively small percentage of the total population, and as the cholera spread outward, the percentages grew smaller yet. This, however, was no measure of the cholera's impact, for the tales of its almost certain fatal consequences aroused a terrible fear.

The breakdown in government controls created a peculiar situation whose lessons, had they been read correctly, might well have eased later tensions. Count Zakrevskii asked Senator Lavrov, who happened to be in the district, to direct cholera measures and extended him full powers for that purpose. Lavrov took control at the epidemic's peak and on August 7 reported that more than one hundred persons were dying daily. As late as August 28, however, Zakrevskii had had no further word concerning the Astrakhan situation and could report nothing beyond conjectures to the Tsar.[34] Lavrov's policy was to publicize the methods for dealing with the epidemic, and orders and instructions were published in Tatar, Kalmuk, and Russian. Since the disease had overrun the regular quarantine, the city and surrounding villages were divided into districts; selected local dignitaries were placed in charge, and certain houses were designated as temporary stations, or lazarettes, for emergency treatment. The early panic dissipated itself in flight, and Lavrov's regulations were lenient enough to create no serious resistance. Most important of all, local initiative and local persons were used, and the community actually worked to save itself, a factor which drew it closer together. Chance decreed that restrictive measures were not used at the beginning of the epidemic, while Lavrov's policies made the best of a difficult situation, striking a balance between imposed authority and local initiative. Astrakhan was thus spared the most destructive social effects of the cholera, even while sustaining its most violent attack.[35]

Tiflis experienced an outbreak similar to that in Astrakhan. The cholera arrived after appearances in Baku, Shirvan, and Elizabethpol, but no preparation was made against its coming, and its initial assault was devastating. Those who contracted the disease died in a matter of hours, while those who were spared were utterly demoralized. The people poured out of the city, and the local authorities, far from holding them back, encouraged their flight by announcing that the cholera was not contagious and the best means to escape it was to move to higher ground. It was estimated that at least two-thirds of the city's population left, and the authorities reported that the mass exodus greatly facilitated purification of the atmosphere.[36]

When the cholera reached the settled portions of European

Russia, such open handed measures were considered lax, and stringent quarantine regulations fostered violent outbreaks. By the time the government learned this lesson, hundreds had died in cholera riots, and a general rebellion threatened the Empire. In the Divans of Moldavia and Wallachia, however, Count P. D. Kiselev followed a consistent policy of controlled population removal as "the most effective preventive measure" available against the cholera, and he combined this policy with enlightened and relatively permissive control measures. The Divans suffered terribly from the cholera, but popular unrest was kept within bounds.[37]

The cholera outbreak at Astrakhan was the culmination of the epidemic's northward movement along the Caspian. A similar development occurred to the West, as the cholera spread outward from Persian territory toward Baku and Elizabethpol. By July 21, official reports from this area indicated 4,557 cases with 1,655 deaths. The disease also broke out in Transcaucasia on both banks of the Tesch, at Kizlian, and on the Kuma. By August 8, 268 deaths had been reported in this region, and the cholera was moving on to the territories of the Don Cossacks where it struck the Katchalin-skaia *stanitsa* especially heavily. Finally, the disease was again reported at Orenburg, Guriev, and Uralsk.[38]

At this point the main line of the cholera was following the Volga, and during the 1830 outbreaks, the worst attacks were found along its northern orientation. The westward movement, while it produced some deaths, was not so violent as it was in the following year when the cholera rolled back from west to east. In 1830, using Astrakhan as the beginning point, the cholera moved northward along the Volga and then spread out along the river and canal net beyond Moscow. From Astrakhan it attacked, in order, the provinces of Saratov, Kazan, Nizhny Novgorod, Moscow, Novgorod, and ultimately the Baltic provinces on one side, and Archangel on the other. Petersburg was bypassed in the first wave. In this pattern, the worst mortality was at Astrakhan (90 per cent) and in each succeeding province, the mortality lessened. At Saratov the death-rate was 70 per cent, in Kazan 60 per cent, in Moscow approximately 50 per cent, and in Novgorod, where only 126 cases and 45 deaths occurred, the percentage was near 30. The exception was Nizhny, where 1887 cases were reported, with 1105 deaths for a percentage of 70, or 10 per cent higher than Kazan.[39]

Saratov was the division point between the northern and western routes. From Saratov the cholera moved northward to Kazan and westward into Tambov, Voronezh, Poltava, Kursk, Kiev, Podolia and Kherson. An ascending order of incidence appeared as it moved from east to west. In Tambov in 1830, 184 cases, 66 deaths; Voronezh, 131 cases, 88 deaths; Poltava, 480 cases, 320 deaths; Kursk, 1,017 cases, 656 deaths; Kherson, 5,588 cases, 2,945 deaths. The pattern was quite clear. Even as the cholera diminished in force as it moved north from Astrakhan, so also it intensified as it moved west. In the following year, the patterns were reversed, and the cholera moved from north to south and from west to east. The main line, and the heaviest losses were suffered on the West-East axis in 1831, and as a matter of fact, the 1831 epidemic was much more deadly than its predecessor.[40]

In August, 1830, these patterns were by no means clear, but the government in Petersburg had to act. The cholera attacked Tsaritsyn in the province of Saratov on August 4, and on August 8 was reported in Saratov itself. On August 12, an imperial ukase forbade provincial governors to exercise discretion on quarantine regulations and required clearance from St. Petersburg for all such steps. This placed the responsibility for cholera measures squarely on the central government, but it was not until August 28 that Count Zakrevskii presented a special memorandum on the cholera to the Tsar. The cabinet, moving with remarkable speed, acted on Zakrevskii's proposals the following day, but Zakrevskii then delayed his departure for Saratov until September 9.[41]

The administrative facts behind Zakrevskii's memorandum are important, for a complicated system of public health administration had evolved.[42] The Ministry of Interior was the agency generally responsible for public health decisions, but there were other offices which had to be consulted. Basic policy decisions were formulated by the Tsar in consultation with his cabinet, which comprised the ministerial heads. The Senate approved and published the decisions taken, although this was largely a formality. The Central Medical Council functioned under the Ministry of the Interior and advised both the Ministry and the cabinet on substantive questions, but its recommendations, as we have already seen, were not considered definitive, and were constantly qualified by non-medical considerations.

Although the Ministry of Interior was responsible for many aspects of public health administration, the Ministries of War and Naval Affairs maintained a special medical section. Since the military medical system was more fully staffed and better equipped than the civil, it was essential during epidemic periods that the services co-operate with the civil administration in providing both personnel and facilities. Furthermore, military units were used for cordons in epidemic areas, and the co-ordination of the military and civil sanitary officers posed a serious problem. The Ministry of Finance controlled medical disbursements and shared responsibility with the Ministry of Interior and the Ministry of Foreign Affairs for frontier quarantine policies which affected trade. The Ministry of Public Enlightenment controlled the movement of medical faculty, and so needed to be consulted, as did the Ministry of Interior and the military, when questions concerning personnel shifts arose. Control of standards and local sanitary conditions was vested in the provincial governors through the authority of the Ministry of the Interior, and the latter body retained control over police operations necessitated by sanitary policies.[43]

The Ministry of the Interior was the most important office for medical affairs, but to achieve any order of co-ordination, it was necessary for Interior to work closely with other administrative bodies. This co-ordination was practical on the ministerial level, but the lines of authority diverged as they moved away from the center. Consequently, a special body was deemed necessary to integrate the administrative process and to localize administrative responsibility while simplifying administrative decisions. So long as no emergency existed and there was no need for rapid decisions and immediate execution, the existing system functioned, despite its burden of duplication and contradiction. A crisis, however, required radical revision of the administrative order to achieve clarity and economy of movement.

The establishment of special committees to avoid the complexities of normal administrative practices was a regular feature of Russian government, and Nicholas I was especially quick to use such measures. Nicholas wished to rule as a personal monarch, and the special committee was his chosen vehicle. Unfortunately, Nicholas was very slow to eliminate any agency once it was created, with the result that his efforts to rationalize governmental processes only further complicated them. The cholera committee which Zakrevskii proposed fused several state functions and retained the closest possible ties with the Tsar, but it represented only a paper solution to the cholera threat at the same time that it added to administrative problems by creating an additional, and autonomous, executive agency.[44]

Tsar Nicholas and his view of autocracy were primarily responsible for the cholera commission's administrative weaknesses, and that responsibility began with the men whom Nicholas selected as his ministers. Russian bureaucracy in general, and the Nicholaevan administration in particular, advanced civil servants who were barren of ideas, who were slaves to form, and who possessed the cardinal virtues of loyalty and unquestioning obedience. There were exceptions, of course, including Count M. S. Vorontsov, Count P. D. Kiselev, and Count Kankrin, but the Minister of Interior, Count Zakrevskii, was not of this company. Before his appointment as Governor-General of Finland, Zakrevskii's entire experience was with the army, and he brought a ritualistic faith in organization and chain of command to his administrative work. This faith, unfortunately, was unleavened by creative imagination, and though honest, Zakrevskii was peculiarly unsuited to confront the problems which the cholera presented.[45]

The government took preliminary steps against the cholera on August 28, sending medical instructions to Saratov, Astrakhan, the Caucasus, Orenburg, and the region of the Don Cossacks, while medical personnel were dispatched to Saratov and Astrakhan. Military authorities in the Caucasus were ordered to co-ordinate their efforts with the civil government in the epidemic sectors, and military surgeons and surgeons' aides were detached from regular duties for the cholera campaign. Finally, medical supplies were collected for Saratov and Astrakhan.[46]

Laudable those there efforts were, they were pitifully inadequate, and they were bound to be too late. The cholera was moving more rapidly than the government could act, and in some regions it had either destroyed the existing administration, or created conditions with which the administration could not cope. The government arranged special missions for both Astrakhan and Georgia, which were made necessary by extraordinary circumstances. As we have seen, in Astrakhan the cholera wiped out local government, and the special appointment given Senator Lavrov was an immediate necessity. Georgia was under military administration as a frontier region, and special orders were necessary to co-ordinate civil and military functions. Senators Menshikov and Kutaisov were given the same extraordinary powers for Georgia which Lavrov was given in Astrakhan, and the military was instructed to co-operate. In a further move to strengthen local agencies, an imperial aide-de-camp was sent to help Count Suchtelen, Governor-General at Orenburg, and it was proposed that special funds be made available to Orenburg and Astrakhan. None of this, however, justified Zakrevskii's statement that "the government has taken all police and sanitary measures to guarantee public health," for the steps which had been taken were only the first responses to crisis, and more rational planning was necessary.[47] Furthermore, the government showed no hint of thinking that the cholera would not be stopped short of Moscow. In all the plans presented, in all the actions taken, there was no suggestion of preparatory steps to protect the heart of European Russia. This incredible lack of foresight characterized the government's methods, and was the most eloquent testimony to the blindness, sterility, and formalism which shackled imperial administration throughout the nineteenth century.

Zakrevskii's recommendations have an air of unreality about them, as if the Minister were presenting a theoretical response to an abstract problem. The issues which he treated were organizational, and there was only passing reference to actual shortages of medicine and doctors, and the practical problems of maintaining quarantines within a community. These were questions which would be handled on the scene, yet these were precisely the problems which needed to be solved beforehand. Zakrevskii did treat the administrative problem with some insight, however, and he should be given full credit for recognizing the inadequacy of existing administrative arrangements to combat the cholera. The mistake he made was to attempt to rectify inadequacies by recourse to the same methods which had already proved inadequate. The special powers given to Lavrov, Menshikov, Kutaisov, and Suchtelen were only a stopgap and could not be generalized, for most local officials could not be trusted to exercise discretion. The strangeness of the cholera, its difference from the plague, and the consequent irrelevance of existing sanitary rules left too much latitude for error, yet these same characteristics made initiative and imagination essential. Here was the dilemma. The cholera had created a situation which could not be handled uniformly, a situation which demanded flexibility and initiative. To grant such initiative was beyond Zakrevskii's authority, and to recommend it was beyond his capacity.[48]

The particular issue which summarized the problem was administrative logistics. Zakrevskii pointed out that local authorities were required to request instructions from St. Petersburg on matters which were not covered in existing instructions, but while action on such a request was being taken, the cholera would rage on unchecked. Zakrevskii understood very well that the best efforts in the public welfare would be vitiated by the need to apply to the capital, for the "distance from the capital is itself an obstacle which hinders the campaign at its very origin," but he could not break away from the idea that the central authority must approve each action. Zakrevskii saw this same logistical problem, incidentally, as a major bar to co-operation among provincial officials and the military, and he pointed to the troubles which plagued both Lavrov and Suchtelen in co-ordinating their efforts with each other and with neighboring authorities.[49] What he finally proposed was an ingenious, though completely impractical method for maintaining centralized authority while making it responsive to local conditions. Zakrevskii recommended that the Tsar appoint a commission with full discretionary powers which would take precedence over all civil and military agencies dealing with the cholera. This commission would establish headquarters in the midst of the infection zone, and from there direct the campaign. In essence, Zakrevskii proposed to release the central administration from its stationary role and bring it to the problem, since it took too long to bring the problem to the capital.[50]

Zakrevskii's memorandum was incorporated in an Imperial rescript which was published on August 29 and which approved all his proposals. Nicholas went farther than Zakrevskii, for he absolved the commission from observing collegiate forms and gave it the right to act spontaneously. What this meant in effect was that the commission could act without submitting its plans to the cabinet, though the Tsar still held the commission and its head responsible for any action it undertook. Nicholas also provided a special budget of 50,000 rubles for immediate expenses, with a like amount held in reserve against future needs. In the rescript Nicholas appointed Actual Privy-Councillor Engel as head of the commission, but then changed his mind, and in the Imperial Ukase delivered to the governing Senate on September 4, ordered Zakrevskii to head the commission while Engel was to act as Minister of Interior until Zakrevskii's return.[51]

The functions which the cholera commission performed were clearly specified. All officials in the stricken territories reported directly to the commission, and the commission issued general bulletins which also described its own activities. These bulletins were eagerly awaited, for data on the cholera's spread, incidence, and mortality were desperately needed. Unfortunately, the commission was so overburdened that its reports became routine, and when rebellions broke out, reporting ceased altogether. In addition to publicizing the cholera struggle, the commission was to act as a disbursement center, and all requests for medicines and physicians were directed to it rather than to St. Petersburg. Zakrevskii had included in his recommendations a request for "sufficient" medicines, for he apparently hoped that the cholera commission would bring greater speed and efficiency to the distribution of necessary specifics. As it happened, medical supplies were impossible to obtain, and the commission was bitterly criticized for failing to prevent critical shortages and the attendant profiteering.[52]

Normally, the Medical Council in St. Petersburg would have carried these responsibilities, and, as it happened, the Medical Council ended by dealing with problems of publicity and information. Further, though Nicholas granted the commission autonomy, it still had to clear its requirements for medicines and personnel through the capitol. This meant fruitless squabbling as well as interminable delays, and ultimately it further reduced the commission's effectiveness. Zakrevskii had conceived the cholera commission as both a flying column and a base distribution center. What he failed to take into account was the obvious fact that deficiencies in an area could not be remedied in that area, even though it might be feasible to redistribute personnel from a local center. The commission itself was dependent on the centers of supply, and these were in Moscow and St. Petersburg.

Although Zakrevskii's main concern was with administration, he also viewed the commission as an active agent for combatting the cholera. The heart of the commission was a medical council, chosen by the Commission Chief and composed of four members drawn from the civil and military health services. This council was to be supported by a special faculty of doctors and assistants. This latter group included health officers already in the infected area, or those sent there by the Minister of the Interior, six professors and adjunct professors drawn from the medical faculties of the Universities of Moscow, Kazan, and Kharkov, and ten corps or division doctors. If doctors were not available, the total was to be made up from the best instructed major surgeons available. To this number were to be added fourteen health officers chosen from the faculty of the medical-surgical academies, the members of the sanitary administration, and practising doctors not in service. The appointment of these men lay with the Minister of Public Enlightenment and the doctors-in-chief of the civil and military health services. To this group was joined a complement, not specifically enumerated, of ordinary commissioners, surgeons, pharmacists, and surgical aides recruited from the civil and military services by the Minister of the Interior. Finally, two employees of the Ministry of the Interior were to be designated aids to the commission head. These aides assisted the commission chief in choosing subordinate officials as they were deemed necessary. However, all officials in the locality where the commission was operating were under the commission's jurisdiction, and all retired officials in the district were considered at the commission's disposal.[53]

Since the cholera commission was charged with caring for the sick as well as administering the cholera campaign, it was essential that it be given powers to collect everything necessary for all phases of medical care. Consequently, not only were special talents available for drafting, but the commission had the right to requisition inhabitants' houses for temporary hospitals and to draft military personnel, the interior guard, and, if necessary, the territorial police to serve in the hospitals. If these measures proved insufficient, the commission also had the power to draft men and women, both serf and free, who were paid at the rate of 50 kopeks per day. In all instances, from the top medical personnel to the lowliest drafted serf, service was obligatory, and though all costs of the expedition were underwritten by the Imperial treasury, no individual could refuse to serve.[54]

All preparations were made, and Zakrevskii departed for Saratov on September 9. His task was difficult, and both his instructions and his personality made it worse. The cholera commission had to perform two functions. On the one hand, it was an administrative body which co-ordinated and directed many subsidiary organizations scattered throughout a vast territory. In this respect, the commission was a dispersal center for material and information, a decision center, passing on recommendations sent to it by local authorities, and a channel of communication with the central government at St. Petersburg. These tasks required administrative skills and personnel, and in themselves represented a job for which the commission was badly understaffed. The other task was even more difficult, for in the area where the commission worked, it was empowered to absorb all local functions, to centralize both medical and administrative processes, and to carry on the actual jobs of caring for the sick, collecting medical data, and administering sanitary regulations. In the Saratov region, the cholera commission actually became the local government and took responsibility for all local functions. The only way the commission could perform those functions, however, was to rely directly on the authorities which it superceded. To combine these extraordinary powers with those wielded by local authorities required immense tact and broad understanding. Zakrevskii lacked both qualities, and almost immediately alienated the provincial officials. So bitter did this antagonism become that in the Saratov region effective controls broke down almost at once as Zakrevskii rode roughshod over local officials, who responded by refusing to co-operate and by placing every possible obstacle in the Minister's path. The result was conflict, recrimination, and chaos.[55]

The entire elaborate system which Zakrevskii created reflected the assumption that an anti-cholera campaign and a military campaign were comparable. The center of the epidemic was treated as the spearhead of an enemy drive, while the disease's influence beyond that center was considered a flanking movement which could be countered by strategically placed quarantine posts. The cholera, however, was much more fluid in its movement than any army, and Zakrevskii's commission was both inundated and by-passed. Neither Zakrevskii personally, nor the commission as a whole, grasped the general movement of the disease or was able to do much more than confirm the steps which were taken to deal with it. As a result, the Central Medical Council in St. Petersburg, though lacking the special powers given the cholera commission, played a more significant role in the cholera struggle. Indeed the special cholera commission became an administrative bottleneck which had to be by-passed in the heat of the campaign. Ultimately, even its reports concerned only its own activities, while hastily established medical boards across European Russia reported directly to St. Petersburg.[56]

The very rapidity with which the cholera moved showed the fundamental weakness in Zakrevskii's plans. We have seen that the central cholera commission was created the last week in August. Zakrevskii departed to take up his duties on September 9, was in Moscow on September 14, and only arrived at Saratov around September 20. The cholera appeared near Saratov the first week in August, reached its high point in late August and early September, and the epidemic was over for the year by October. By the time Zakrevskii established himself, the cholera had broken out in Kazan and Nizhny-Novgorod, and was moving westward, farther and farther from the center of control. Zakrevskii probably did his most important work at Kazan, where he moved his headquarters in October, rather than at Saratov. By that time, however, the cholera commission could no longer be regarded as central, and special cholera committees, including the elaborate Moscow organization, were a reality, while Zakrevskii's work had become entirely local. The principle of centralized administration simply could not work, and the government was forced to reorganize its entire campaign on a local basis.[57]

The confusion which the cholera commission was to clarify was actually compounded as the government and the commission developed separate policies. Count Zakrevskii finally took an extreme view of the protective methods required, and in the areas under his control closed all schools, churches, and markets, while employing the most severe sequestration and quarantine measures. Since he lacked the medical personnel to carry out his policies, he employed the army, whose harshness and violence created equally violent resistance. These measures were not those proposed by the government, however, and both the cabinet and the Tsar flatly rejected them when, much later, they were formally presented.[58] On the other hand, there was great confusion over what program to follow.

A Senate ukase dated September 12, 1830, accepted the principle that cholera was an infectious disease and decreed that all persons leaving an infected region should undergo a fourteen-day observation period, during which they were required to wash themselves daily with a chlorine-lime solution. The Acting Minister of the Interior suggested only a five-day detention period for the obviously healthy, but this suggestion was rejected. Since the Medical Council was admittedly ignorant of the way the cholera was transmitted, certain compromises were accepted. It was decided, for example, that everyday articles and travelers' clothes should be inspected and washed with the chlorine-lime solution, but there was to be no delay in the passage of goods, whether baggage or trade goods. In accord with earlier practice, papers and documents carried by couriers and the post were to be fumigated, and on September 20 it was declared that postilions leaving infected regions would be stopped at the quarantine barrier, their pouches inspected and fumigated, and that other postilions would replace them.[59] *Cordons sanitaires* were established around the major areas of infection, and the military and the police were charged with maintaining the barriers on the major land routes leading out of the infected areas. Water traffic was disregarded at this stage, although the later Moscow regulations attempted to rectify that omission. This oversight was very serious since the first cases of cholera at Nizhny-Novgorod broke out among the boatmen, and the rivers, which were major channels of interior communication, also proved to be a major route for the expansion of the cholera.[60]

If the government's quarantine policy seemed haphazard, contradictory, and ultimately unsuccessful, the policy of providing instructions and information for the people was consistent and thorough. The Central Medical Council was responsible for this aspect of the government's work, and the instructions published for the inhabitants of Nizhny-Novgorod show the quality and character of the council's work. The principal symptoms of the cholera were described accurately and in great detail, and though the cholera was recognized as deadly dangerous, the people were told that its effects would be mitigated by following certain preventive measures. The council's recommendations were essentially those written when the cholera attacked Astrakhan seven years before and republished in Orenburg the previous year. People were urged to avoid chills, to dress warmly, and to change wet clothing at once. Sleeping on the wet ground and in the open air either by day or night was thought particularly dangerous, and people were warned not to overload their stomachs. The instructions forebade eating apples, prunes, melons, or cucumbers, and moderation was to be the rule in the consumption of all alcoholic beverages. Though medically incomplete, these regulations contained good advice. Cucumbers, for example, which usually were eaten raw and which often were fertilized with excrement, are capable of sustaining the *vibrio cholerae* for several hours. Cold foods of all kinds are dangerous, especially raw fruits, vegetables, and cold drinks, and the immoderate consumption of alcohol has been proved to be a powerful influence in increasing cholera mortality.[61] Quite rightly, the instructions stressed cleanliness, and baths and frequent changes of linen were considered sovereign preventives. Houses and streets were to be kept as clean as possible, windows were to be kept open in good weather to assure fresh air, while in bad weather householders were to "wash the walls and fumigate as often as possible with vinegar and juniper berries." Fatigue and overwork were also considered predisposing causes and were to be avoided.[62]

If, in spite of the preventive measures described, a case of cholera occurred, an immediate report was to be made to the bureau of police in the quarter where the patient lived. The master of the house was held responsible for informing the police of a suspected case, and punishments were promised if that responsibility were neglected. While waiting for the doctor, the patient was, if possible, to be removed to a separate room which had been purified, while anyone who had to touch the victim was instructed to wash his hands with vinegar. If the patient died, his bed and linen were to be washed and then aired for four days, and it was required that the victim be buried within twenty-four hours. If the doctor arrived before death, he would decide whether the patient should be moved to a hospital. If he was moved, there were no charges either for treatment or for drugs. The instructions concluded with the following statement:

The authorities of the government [of Nizhny-Novgorod], basing their views on the assurance given by physicians who have carefully examined the symptoms and course of the disease which has manifested itself in this city, certify to the inhabitants that they will be preserved from this disease if they conform exactly to the above disposition, and if they will call the physician at the first moment of the disease's appearance; an important means of avoiding the epidemic would be not to sink into discouragement nor give way to anger, but on the contrary to maintain gaity and tranquillity of spirit.[63]

Although the last line could be taken as a tasteless joke, it, and the remainder of the instruction, reflected current medical opinion. And there was good sense behind it. Cleanliness, moderation, avoiding excesses, immediate medical care, and particular concern with diet would be good advice under any circumstances, and in an epidemic period, when physical vitality was doubly important, the advice was doubly good. The point was, of course, that none of this could guarantee freedom from the cholera's effects, and in many cases the advice contradicted popular habits. There was some question whether the government might not have done better to have kept the public instructions to an absolute minimum for, it was argued, the publicity given the instructions together with the daily published mortality figures fostered hysteria without providing any effective controls against the disease.[64] The continuing belief in the efficacy of early treatment, however, made it imperative to distribute information which could enable private persons to recognize the cholera's onset so that they could report it immediately. Beyond the medical aspect, the government's policy of providing full information was theoretically sound. Franz Neumann once wrote that man's personal freedom began with knowledge, for only knowledge could counteract the fear which ignorance induced.[65] The misfortune was that rumor spread faster than facts, that the bulk of the population was too unsophisticated to evaluate the data that was presented to it, and that the government distorted the picture by taking too optimistic a tone. This last was probably the most important point, for the often repeated theme that cholera could be controlled successfully was contradicted daily in the very bulletins which contained assurances. Certainly the government hoped to keep up the people's spirits, but the promise of immunity, when infection was likely, was dangerous and foolish.[66]

By October the cholera's effects on the entire Russian system were felt, and long before October the domestic situation became serious. The annual Nizhny fair was held in an atmosphere of gloom and fear, and merchants were unwilling to buy. The *Commercial Gazette* admitted on October 3 that the fair had been at most a qualified success, and pointed to the interruptions of the caravan routes to Bukhara and Khiva and the cholera outbreaks at Astrakhan, Tiflis and in neighboring regions which prevented Georgian and Persian merchants from participating.[67] By late summer, normal political functions had ceased in Georgia and Caucasia. The courts were closed since the judges had either been called into service against the cholera or had become its victims, and the cabinet recommended that all judicial functions be formally suspended in the cholera area until the disease passed.[68] Recruiting for the army was postponed and then suspended as the cholera disrupted the recruitment areas and recruiters could not be spared from the quarantine lines.[69] Normal financial arrangements were upset, and the cabinet was forced to declare a moratorium on debts and to suspend penalties for non-payment of debts in the cholera territories. When the cholera attacked Moscow, this problem became even more acute, and finally a general moratorium was declared with payments due one month after the cordons were removed. The Moscow merchants pointed out that their connections were all over the Russian empire, and that the cholera had cut off their sources of revenue, making it impossible to cover their liabilities, while the merchants dealing with them were unable to pay their obligations. The government responded by extending the moratorium to three months after the cordons were raised.[70]

A far more serious problem was developing along the Volga, however, for the interruption of normal social, political, and economic activities together with the introduction of extraordinary control measures aroused latent antagonisms which hysteria could turn into rebellion. In the epidemic's early stages, hysteria appeared with the cholera, and people fled in terror. This produced chaos, but no riots. As the cholera reached more settled and more regularly controlled regions, however, the picture changed, and in those areas where dissatisfaction and opposition gathered, cholera gave the spur to violence. The outbreaks which occurred were sporadic and widely separated, but they were serious enough to cause official concern and to require military intervention. In the provinces of Tambov, Kursk, and Saratov the government lost control over the people; riots broke out, and as violence compounded violence, a state of civil war developed.

Tambov and Kursk suffered most from popular disturbances,

though Saratov was not immune, and the Tambov riots were the first to raise the spectre of social revolution. The events which transpired in Tambov bore a close family resemblance to the more violent cholera riots in 1831, and the entire experience in the Volga region should have warned the government against the potentially explosive character of a cholera visitation. As we have seen, the Sevastopol riots in May did affect quarantine rules, but the troubles in the Volga region made little impression on the government. This was due in part to a failure to understand the nature of the revolts, but it also showed a callous immunity to public protests as well as the failure to view social conditions realistically.

The cholera reached Saratov early in August, and on August 10 the governor of Tambov, I. S. Mironov, received word that the disease was communicable and deadly, and that it was on his boundaries. Mironov immediately convened his district council to declare an emergency, to establish quarantine lines on the province's frontiers, and to sequester the city of Tambov itself. The regulations which the Council put into effect required that both persons and goods be held and inspected at the frontier posts, and even letters were fumigated before they were passed.[71] Mironov established a strict quarantine policy from the beginning, but it was a policy which was extremely difficult to enforce. Neither trained doctors nor health officials were available to serve the quarantine posts; consequently, untrained soldiers and police enforced the rules. This created trouble from the very beginning as people were harassed on the quarantine lines, and the soldiers preyed on a helpless peasantry.[72]

After nearly four weeks, the cholera suddenly appeared in a village some thirty versts from Tambov. There again the cholera paused; no cases were reported throughout the neighborhood, and it was not until November 15, more than three months after the quarantines were established, that the first cholera cases appeared in the city. Throughout the entire period, however, the epidemic was expected any moment, and strict control measures were followed. When the disease did break out, it was very mild. Seven deaths from cholera occurred on November 17, and the death toll only reached seventy by December. Included in the deaths were Prince Volkonskii, commander of the garrison battalion, another officer, Captain-Lieutenant Satiri, and fifteen civil officials. Compared with the thousands who died of cholera in Tambov in 1831, however, the initial outbreak was minimal indeed.[73]

The long wait from August to November put an intolerable strain on people's nerves, and proclamations and instructions were daily reminders of the fate which lay ahead. Since the first health regulations went into effect long before the cholera arrived, quarantine stations, military cordons, and roving police added to the peoples' troubles, and as the cholera was slow in coming, people grew suspicious, tension increased, and the populace muttered resentfully. Where was the cholera? If it was not coming, why submit to the indignities of inspection, the annoyances of quarantine, the constant pilfering and mistreatment which accompanied the execution of every minor rule? These conditions fostered clashes between quarantine officials and a restless populace, and the relations between the people and their governmental overlords, never very good, deteriorated rapidly.

The first cholera cases which occurred in the city set into motion a comprehensive plan for controlling the disease, but the relatively small number of cases combined with swelling popular indignation to make the anti-cholera campaign appear to be a full-scale attack on the people. The police, who were charged with bringing suspected cholera patients to the hospital, intensified the public's antagonism by seizing anyone who looked suspicious. Those that were taken, cholera and non-cholera cases alike, were hustled into the hospitals, stripped of their clothes, dosed with calomel and opium, thrust into hot baths, and, when they resisted, were beaten into submission. The hospital was a place of horrors, filled with noise and stench, and for those who believed in contagion, merely to enter it was to flirt with death. Those who denied the cholera's existence faced equally compelling fears of torture, robbery, and murder.[74]

Two days of terror were enough, and on November 17 a crowd headed by the *meshchanin* (*petit bourgeois*), David Il'in, demonstrated outside the hall where the city council was meeting. Il'in took the view that the cholera was less dangerous than the police, and he accused the authorities of fomenting a cholera scare to serve their own devious purposes. Shouting "No cholera!" the crowd surged and eddied around the council hall, and among themselves whispered the dangers of hospitalization, for in hospitals "people are cut up and cooked!"[75] Mironov tried unsuccessfully to calm the agita-

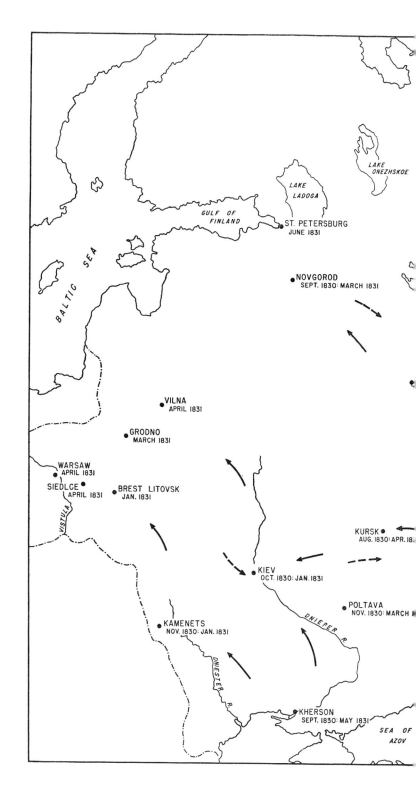

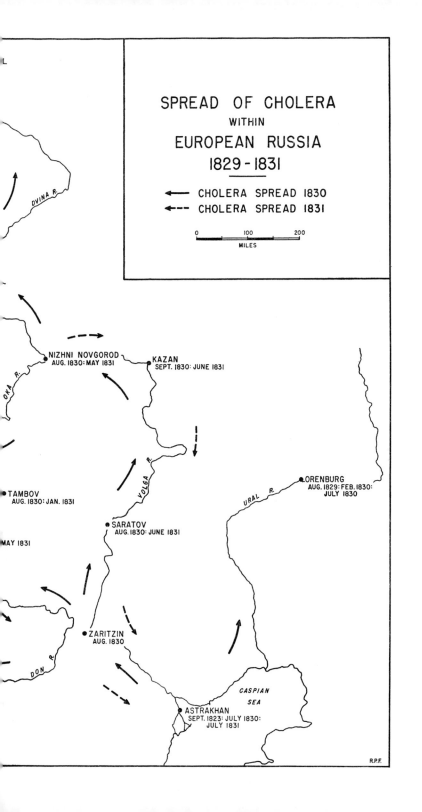

SPREAD OF CHOLERA
WITHIN
EUROPEAN RUSSIA
1829 - 1831

⟵ CHOLERA SPREAD 1830
⟵--- CHOLERA SPREAD 1831

0   100   200
MILES

DVINA R.

OKA R.

NIZHNI NOVGOROD
AUG. 1830: MAY 1831

KAZAN
SEPT. 1830: JUNE 1831

VOLGA R.

ORENBURG
AUG. 1829: FEB. 1830:
JULY 1830

URAL R.

TAMBOV
AUG. 1830: JAN. 1831

MAY 1831

SARATOV
AUG. 1830: JUNE 1831

ZARITZIN
AUG. 1830

DON R.

CASPIAN
SEA

ASTRAKHAN
SEPT. 1823: JULY 1830:
JULY 1831

R.P.F.

tion, but his protests and orders alike passed unheeded, and the mob began to break into quarantined houses. The police were powerless, and as the mob spirit spread, bolder assaults were mounted. By the morning of November 18 the riots had turned to rebellion; the mob controlled the streets; the governor was besieged in his house; and the three-hundred-man garrison in the town was absolutely helpless.[76]

There was nothing comic about this uprising, for between November 18 and November 20 more than two hundred persons lost their lives. Tormented beyond endurance, the people of Tambov rose up to destroy their tormentors. Troops were finally imported to quell the rebellion, but the situation had gotten so completely out of hand that a military occupation was maintained for the better part of two years.[77] The violence of the Tambov outbreak could not be ascribed to the cholera, for it only created the environment in which the riots happened. The long period of suspense, severe quarantine policies and police brutality, and finally an endemic tension between the townspeople and local officials all contributed to an explosive situation. Governor Mironov apparently perceived some of this, but he preferred to report that certain "malicious people" had played upon popular ignorance and had tried to use the people's wrath to advance their hidden purposes. This kind of official scapegoating was pernicious, for it masked the real social and political ills which beset the country and conveyed the erroneous impression that public disturbances, far from revealing internal stresses, were simply the work of the ill-intentioned. Mironov was far closer to the mark when he adverted to popular "dissatisfaction with the methods used against the cholera," but to pursue the point would have weakened his own position before the central government.[78]

Saratov, which was visited before Tambov, suffered far heavier losses from the disease, but was less susceptible to public disorders. The cholera struck there before any preparation could be made, and among the first victims were three of the four available physicians. A clergyman whose letter describing the cholera's onset at Saratov was published in the *Quarterly Review,* described the public reaction: "From this moment, fear and anguish took possession of the public mind. Those who could flee from the city fled; and as the malady was not considered contagious, servants, laborers, Tartars and Russians were permitted to rush into the country." The author's congregation dropped from 550 to 150 as a result of the exodus, and it was further depleted by a death rate which reached 260 per day.[79] Events at Saratov began to unfold as they had done at Astrakhan and Orenburg with free movement by a thoroughly terrified population. Further, the cholera was of such intensity, and the death rate mounted so rapidly, that the people were demoralized. This undoubtedly reduced the social impact of the disease in its early stages. When Count Zakrevskii arrived, however, the cholera was waning, and the public's capacity to resist increased. Zakrevskii implemented his very strict control program on a population which was beginning to revive from a violent shock, and though bitterness and friction resulted, there was no outright revolt. Local officials, however, were embittered by Zakrevskii's methods, and while the Minister had difficulty maintaining order among the people, he was completely unsucessful in gaining the support of Saratov's officialdom. The result was non–co-operation on the official level and a running battle to enforce the quarantine regulations among the people. The Saratov experience was a sour one for both government and people, and it was purely fortuitous that a revolt did not occur.[80]

In Kursk *guberniia* the situation was much more serious. Kursk had been exposed to a threat of plague during 1828 and 1829, and this created great misgivings. The plague never materialized, but the population was still uneasy when the first cholera reports arrived. The plague was only one element which contributed to the unrest in Kursk. For three years, famine had stalked the region, and the government had been unable to alleviate the peasants' sufferings. With first plague and then cholera came the inevitable cordons and quarantines which worsened the food crisis, adding governmental blindness to crop failure as a burden for the people. The populace itself was disposed to disregard the government and its instructions, for this region was deeply influenced by non-conforming religious sects and supported a large population of Old Believers, the direct descendents of those religious nationalists who fought bitterly against Nikon's reforms in the seventeenth century, and who had steadily refused to make their peace with the official church. As conditions in the province worsened, the clergy preached against the government, identifying physicians, quarantine guards, and public health officers with Anti-Christ, while interpreting the cholera as a new punishment visited by an angry God on an erring people, and amulets, charms, and prayers were all used to protect the faithful.[81]

The food shortage was paralleled by shortages in all necessities for an anti-cholera campaign. As in Saratov and Tambov, trained personnel were not available to deal with the disease and man the quarantines, so the task was passed to the military. The people suffered from the brutality of the cordon police as soldiers at check points openly extorted payments from the peasants or refused to let them pass, while the grossest malpractices were common. This, of course, destroyed what effectiveness the quarantine might have had and added to popular resentment. It was estimated at the epidemic's height that there were only twenty-one doctors available for more than a million and a half people, so that it was far more likely that an individual would be mistreated by soldiers than treated by physicians. That the physicians themselves could do little only added to the general despair, for despite the brave words of the official proclamations, the death toll mounted daily.[82] Count Zakrevskii maintained control in Kursk, though at a great price. The sanitary regulations were enforced in an atmosphere of martial law, and the quarantine lines were held with the help of floggings and even executions. The government failed to stop the cholera, but it effectively immobilized the region from Astrakhan to Nizhny, and, what was worse, fostered the additional threat of outright revolution. Kursk and the neighboring provinces suffered as much from the anti-cholera campaign as they did from the epidemic itself, and those areas which cholera attacked ceased to be a functioning part of the empire.

The lower Volga region was just the beginning, for between September and November the cholera blanketed European Russia, bringing dismay and disorder in its train. The disturbances which paralyzed Tambov, Kursk, and Saratov spread broadly to the west and south as cholera moved toward the Polish and Turkish frontiers, and to the west and north as it stretched toward the capitals.[83] The cholera in the provinces set the stage for the Moscow outbreak, the high point of the 1830 epidemic, but it showed as well the latent social issues which exploded in 1831. The atmosphere was growing heavier with the double fear of disorder and disease as the epidemic moved inexorably toward Russia's ancient capital.

Chapter 4

MOSCOW: 1830

The cholera's steady progress up the Volga during August and September threatened both Moscow and Petersburg. The government continued to publish daily reports concerning the cholera's movement, but there was little comfort in them for Moscow's citizens. On September 5, Ferdinand Christine wrote Countess S. A. Bobrinska that it was reported that people died at the rate of fifty a day in Astrakhan, that the situation at Saratov was almost as bad, that the quarantine lines had failed to hold the cholera, and that it was in Tambov and reaching toward Moscow, for "one man died on the road, another at the very gates of Moscow."[1] On that same date A. V. Nikitenko noted in his diary that the cholera had appeared in Saratov, Tambov, and Penza, that it was approaching Vologda, and he went on, "in the capital there is a powerful restlessness. This disease, truly, is a terrible danger in a great city."[2]

It was not only the educated who viewed the cholera's approach with misgivings. In Moscow an oppressive pall of expectancy hung over the people. The plague which had ravaged the city in 1771 had become part of the popular mythology, and the stories of its dreadful effects were revived and circulated. In the public mind, there was little to distinguish cholera and plague, and the contagiousness of the latter was grafted on the rumored morbidity of the former. Hysteria followed, and just as the merchants precipitously fled the Nizhny fair when cholera appeared, the people of Moscow began to shift and murmur and prepare for flight. It was thought that anything could carry cholera, and when the news came that not only was the disease at Nizhny but that merchants and their goods had come from Nizhny to Moscow, terror intensified. The official report summarized the popular reaction:

The world lived in deadly fear of the uncertain future which lay ahead, and the least scraps of information on treating cholera and guarding against it were desperately sought; above all it was feared that some analogy with cholera would be found in the different indispositions which most inhabitants suffered to a greater or lesser degree and which could be equally attributed to the peculiar influence of the atmosphere's epidemic constitution and the expectation of a public calamity.[3]

By September 11, a rising tide of panic which the government was unable to dispel swept the city. Neither medical reassurances nor police intervention could convince the people they could be saved, and as they had fled Napoleon's armies in 1812, the population jammed the Petersburg and Smolensk roads seeking safety. Some 50,000 people joined the retreat, while those that remained either shut themselves up with their private remedies or sought solace in the churches.[4] When the panic broke, Moscow's Governor, Prince Dmitri Golitsyn, was on his estates, but he rushed back to the city to meet the emergency. His first act was to convene the municipal medical council, and, having done so, he made his first public announcement concerning cholera. The people of Moscow were told that the danger of a major cholera outbreak was greatly exaggerated, for neither Moscow nor the province had been infected. Golitsyn also denied that cholera had reached Tula, Kaluga, and Riazan, and he called on the people to calm themselves. Prince Golitsyn's announcement was both false and unavailing. People were convinced that the shadow of death hung over them, and terror mounted. Horses were impossible to find, even harnesses were sold out, while the apothecary shops were stripped of tar, chloride of lime, camphor, and musk. The first terror set off a frenzied rush for safety which was transforming Moscow's staid and quiet populace into a struggling mob.[5]

It is still a mystery when the cholera reached Moscow, but the first officially recognized case occurred on September 14, and the patient died on September 17. Some unofficial reports put the first cases as early as September 6, and it was popularly believed that the epidemic had begun by September 10–11, three days before it was officially verified.[6] When Count Zakrevskii arrived in Moscow on September 14, he immediately published a general instruction covering private and public preventive measures. This instruction was the first public recognition of the emergency, and in it Zakrevskii invited all classes in the city to unite their efforts against the cholera.[7] Zakrevskii's announcement made nonsense of the Governor-General's earlier assurances at the same time that it did nothing to calm the public's distress. The measures presented so optimistically were precisely those which had failed to stop the cholera in the provinces, and the people, believing Moscow was doomed and the government helpless, redoubled their efforts to flee.[8]

If specific evidence were needed that the situation was worsening, that evidence came on September 17, when two more cholera cases were officially verified, and on September 18 when another was announced. These developments, in the words of the official report, "fixed the authorities' attention, while public unrest grew as news of the first case swiftly passed through the city." A new wave of fear swept over Moscow "with the certainty that peril was present," and fears which had been general and hysterical now had a specific referent.[9] It was also on September 18, however, that Prince Golitsyn finally issued a statement which admitted that cholera had reached Moscow and described the government's protective measures. In view of Zakrevskii's earlier announcement, and the events of September 17–18, Golitsyn's statement, which followed a meeting with the city's leading citizens, was anticlimactic. This led Nikitenko to comment sourly a week later that the whole affair was typically Russian: the wealthy fled while the government busied itself with useless regulations.[10]

Although neither Zakrevskii nor Golitsyn can claim credit for it, the cholera's next phase in Moscow brought out a different public reaction. After the exodus, and with the number of cholera cases mounting daily, a new spirit emerged among the people. A general mobilization of available talent followed Golitsyn's announcement; private contributions poured into the newly formed cholera committee, while dozens of volunteers appeared to staff the cholera stations. Alexander Herzen, then a student at Moscow University, praised his fellows' spirit of self-sacrifice as they volunteered for hospital work. For many of them the cholera was a deadly contagion, and it required both courage and devotion to volunteer. Herzen saw this new aspect as the revival of that public spirit which liberated Moscow in the Time of Troubles and which appeared again in 1812 to defeat Napoleon.[11] The *Journal de St. Pétersbourg* tried to publish the contributions of private citizens and organizations toward the cholera work, but soon was forced to give up printing anything more than a sample, for the number contributing became so large that reporting individual donations was impossible. Moscow's citizens gave freely of their time, their money, even their homes, to help in the anti-cholera campaign.[12]

The regulations to protect Moscow and to prevent the spread of the disease embodied the assumption that the cholera was contagious and reflected Zakrevskii's personal belief that only the most stringent regulations could control it. The quarantine system which was announced on September 18 sealed the city of Moscow and the frontiers of Moscow *guberniia,* which were contiguous with the infected areas of Tver, Tula, Vladimir, Kostroma, Riazan, and Yaroslav. All major routes leading from Moscow were closed, with the exception of four observation barriers at Serpukhov, Kolomna, Bogorodsk, and the monastery of St. Sergius. The quarantine rules which Golitsyn put into effect were given him by Count Zakrevskii and flatly contradicted the most recent Imperial decrees. The government had taken the position that cholera could not be transmitted by goods, yet the officials manning the Moscow quarantine barriers were specifically instructed to pay particular attention to merchandise. The government less than a month before had denied contagion, but the Moscow regulations forebade passage of the gates at Bogorodsk and St. Sergius to all travellers, regardless of their mode of transportation, except those arriving by coach. Coach passengers were to be held for observation for fourteen days, then passed through the lines. To get a seat on a "legal" coach required a pass from the Governor-General's office, so a double control over egress from Moscow was established. Needless to say, seats were at a premium, and the competition for them was fierce.[13] Finally, the government had indicated earlier that the post was probably free of contamination, but even here new regulations were written. All posts and official couriers arriving from infected areas were stopped at the barriers, and the mail was inspected and fumigated, after which couriers from Moscow carried it into the city.[14]

If the Moscow quarantine were to work, the neighboring provinces would have to respect it, and Prince Golitsyn asked officials in Tula, Riazan, Vladimir, and Tver to destroy bridges and block water traffic to prevent local people from entering the interdicted regions. Even fishing was covered in Golitsyn's plan. Fishing was considered an essential occupation, but fishermen were required to engage by written declaration not to give passage to any individual and not to touch the opposite shore.[15] Finally, transports which had entered the Moscow district prior to the establishment of the quarantine were allowed to approach the city, but only after having passed quarantine and purification procedures. Those transports presenting themselves at the city gates without having passed quarantine were returned to the quarantine barriers on the frontier.[16]

Golitsyn knew the cholera was already in Moscow when he established his precautionary measures, but he insisted that the outbreak was a minor one and that the regulations he was putting into effect would prevent it from spreading.[17] This was an extraordinarily foolish position, for Moscow's citizens could read in any of a number of journals about the cholera's rapid spread from the frontiers into the heart of Russia, and the official mortality statistics which were published daily bespoke a serious epidemic. It was common knowledge that Nizhny was suffering a violent outbreak, and there was no reason to believe that Moscow could escape. Doubtless Golitsyn feared worsening the public's fears, but his reassurances had little effect when they could be so readily compared with facts.[18]

Prince Golitsyn's early handling of the cholera left much to be desired, and if we judge solely by his published denials and assurances, we must be critical indeed, for these reflected a blind unwillingness to face reality which is staggering in a responsible public official. The deeper failure, however, was the central government's, for it had made no provision for Moscow's protection against the cholera, and had positively forbidden local authorities to take initiative. While this cannot exculpate Golitsyn, it does suggest the difficulties which the official position put in his way, for until Zakrevskii arrived with sanctions from Petersburg, Golitsyn's hands were tied. Even so, four days elapsed after Zakrevskii's arrival before Golitsyn established the Cholera Council and the regulations it was to enforce. Only procrastination accounts for this delay, and here again Golitsyn deserves criticism. When the regulations were finally put into effect, however, Golitsyn handled them with sensitivity and efficiency, and the Moscow Cholera Council was the most effective organization of its kind to be formed in 1830.[19]

Although Prince Golitsyn was credited with the Moscow Cholera Council's success, the Council itself had several important advantages. Unlike the Central Cholera Commission, the Moscow committee developed out of local government, and its existence created no conflict between administrative bodies. A second advantage was that Moscow, because it was the largest city in Russia and a major administrative as well as educational center, had an infinitely larger reservoir of talent on which to draw both for medicine and administration than any other city. Consequently, it was possible to create a medical section numbering twenty-one physicians who oversaw all the work of a large medical staff in both the permanent hospitals and the temporary cholera stations. There were as many physicians serving the Moscow Cholera Council as there were available to serve the whole Volga region, and this undoubtedly was a factor in modifying the cholera's effects.

Russian administration tended toward the a priori and the abstract, a tendency which produced devastating results during the cholera epidemic in the provinces. In Moscow, however, the closest possible connection was maintained between the administration and the people. The Moscow Cholera Council drew its membership from the most influential elements in the city, including the clergy, the military, the nobility, the civil administration, and the city merchants.[20] The representatives of these groups not only sat as the executive section of the Council, but, with the sole exception of the clergy, were also assigned to administrative districts in the city to work with medical personnel. Their work was co-ordinated through daily meetings with the Council's medical section, while their responsibilities in the city brought them into intimate contact with the people. As district inspectors, these men played a very important organizational role, and they were also given broad discretionary powers. Within their districts they were empowered to choose their staffs, and, where facilities were lacking, to establish a lazarette of twenty-five to fifty beds. Most important of all, they were to visit each domicile in which cholera was reported, collect as much information concerning the patients as possible, and decide what measures were needed to protect the neighbors. The district inspectors also were to decide whether a patient needed to be moved to the cholera hospital. A physician accompanied the inspectors on these visits to provide medical advice, but it was the district inspector whose decision was final. Finally, the district inspectors were responsible for inspecting dwellings "to ensure that cleanliness, the first necessity for protection against the disease ,was strictly observed..."

and to convince householders, factory heads, and heads of crafts that they must keep their establishments clean, follow the purification rules strictly, and avoid crowding people together.[21]

The Moscow Council avoided general rules whenever possible and attempted to deal with particular problems as they arose. Enforcement agencies in the administrative districts were under the district inspectors, and the police were never given the broad powers which they received elsewhere. This was a major factor in reducing civil conflict. Naturally, this does not mean that co-operation was complete, or that people lost their fears of the officials. Nor does it mean that brutality, crassness, and venality were banished. But it does suggest that there was a way to bridge the gap between the authorities and the people, and the Moscow Cholera Council was far more sensitive to the public and its needs than organizations less intimately in contact with the people.

One of the few general regulations, and one of the most difficult to enforce, was that requiring a report on all suspected cases. People so feared both officials and physicians that they chose to suffer, sometimes die, in obscurity rather than put themselves in the hands of authority. Appeals and instructions did little good, and the authorities had no choice but to use force. Though abuses resulted, the Council never authorized the mass seizures of suspected cholera patients which triggered the Tambov, and later the Petersburg riots, and since many cholera patients were treated at home, Moscow escaped one of the most destructive aspects of the epidemic. Even when it was necessary to remove a patient, or to displace the inhabitants in a block, the work was carried out in an orderly fashion under supervision, and with precise instructions. Golitsyn's inclination was to moderate the rules, and he had a sufficiently large medical staff to allow discretion. Undoubtedly many cases entirely escaped the doctors, but the alternative would have been a dragnet which could only have created the most violent opposition.[22] Golitsyn resisted the temptation to give carte blanche to the military and police, and his refusal was a major factor in helping Moscow escape anarchy and rebellion.

While the administrative machinery was grinding into operation, the cholera was in the city, and the death rate mounted daily. During the epidemic's first phase, there seemed to be no refuge, and those who contracted the disease died with frightful regularity. In the month of October, 5532 cases were recorded, of which 3107 proved fatal, and in the early part of the period recoveries were few indeed.[23] Given Moscow's contemporary population of near 300,000, the cholera incidence, in absolute terms, was low, but the terror which the cholera inspired more than compensated for the relatively small number of total cases. Tsar Nicholas had watched the cholera's progress with mounting concern, and when the disease was officially announced in Moscow, decided to visit the stricken city. He wrote Prince Golitsyn on September 24 concerning his intention, and Golitsyn inserted the letter in the official cholera bulletin for September 29:

> I have been profoundly affected by the sad news which you send me. Keep me informed by special courier of the disease's progress. My departure will be governed by the intelligence which you transmit to me. I will come to share your dangers and your labors. We must submit to the decree of the Almighty! I approve all the measures you have taken. Thank in my name those people who join their efforts to yours. They are now the foundation of my greatest hopes.[24]

Nicholas' decision to visit Moscow must have followed soon on the dispatch of his letter, for he arrived unexpectedly on September 29. This was the beginning of the worst period of the epidemic, and the Tsar was greeted by an outpouring of public enthusiasm which was all the more passionate for the hectic time the Muscovites were going through. As he passed through the stricken districts on his way to the Kremlin, the people received him with shouts and benedictions: "You are our Father, we knew you would come! Where there is trouble there you are!"[25] The terror of the cholera seemed to be forgotten momentarily; the brutality of the police and the cordon guards, the shrinking fear of the physicians, all this was lost in a rising tide of hope and enthusiasm. The Tsar had come, all would be well. Dr. Markus attempted to sum up the public spirit when he wrote:

> It is difficult for anyone who has not lived in a time of public calamity to understand the mental condition of those who, together with their dear ones, are exposed to mortal danger; each day that passed after September 17 was a day of anguish for every feeling person; but the 29th of that month was a day which history will preserve eternally, as it will remain forever engraved on the hearts of the Muscovites. If ever a sovereign deserved the name, father of the country, His Majesty Emperor Nicholas I has won it by entering a Moscow battered by a devastating plague which had

already cut down thousands of persons while traversing Russia, a murderous plague, at this time still reputed to be eminently contagious, inevitable, whose very approach struck terror into the three hundred thousand inhabitants of the capital, and whose chosen victims neither art nor the most assiduous care could save. The Emperor came there as a father in the midst of his children, he reassured his people who trembled for the very life of their magnanimous sovereign, and he left on October 7, followed by the benediction of all Russians, touched by his heroic devotion.[26]

Baron A. I. Delvig, an engineer with a penchant for poetry, put in verse what Markus attempted in prose, and, from the safety of St. Petersburg, epitomized Nicholas' visit to Moscow in two bits of sentimental doggrel, "Uteshitel'" and "Tsar-otets." For Baron Delvig, Nicholas was the great successor of the great Peter, the Tsar-father who braved death to rescue his people. Pushkin, however, went farther. In his poem, "Hero," published anonymously in *The Telescope* in 1831, Russia's greatest poet honored Nicholas for his courage, but speculated whether, for a ruler courage was enough. Even a tyrant can be brave, but the true successor to the great Peter would possess magnanimity and vision as well as courage.[27] Pushkin raised the crucial point, for ordinary people believed the Tsar was their guardian, their savior, and his very presence fed a flickering hope that the cholera could be arrested and the officials restrained. These hopes, however, were as irrational as the fear which bred them, and more objective, or perhaps more cynical, minds joined Pushkin in speculation. From the time Nicholas entered the Kremlin on September 29 until his departure on October 8, he was surrounded by those very officials whom the people dreaded, and though Nicholas moved through the streets and hospitals of the cholera districts, his only advice was to accept, to obey, to follow directions, and to submit to God's will. Christine observed the Tsar's actions with mixed emotions, recognizing the effect which Nicholas had on the population, but also noting that there was little for the Tsar to do except tighten already stringent regulations.[28] In point of fact, the Tsar sharply criticized the quarantine commanders for breaches which had occurred in the cordons, and ordered Prince Golitsyn to sequester each of the city's twenty quarters. Golitsyn protested Nicholas' order, and a compromise was reached on a cordon around the Tverskaia, the quarter where the highest incidence of cases had occurred.[29] Nicholas could not stop the cholera's ravages, nor would he ameliorate the irksome regulations; yet his coming eased the public mind and momentarily quieted popular distress.

Moscow's physicians found less cause for enthusiasm in Nicholas' visit than did Dr. Markus or Baron Delvig. The personality of the Tsar, who reportedly later solved railroad engineering problems by drawing a straight line on a map, who was described by von Ekstaedt as the epitome of rigidified authority, and who won the sobriquet of Nicholas the Club, appeared clearly when Nicholas assessed the physicians' work. Nicholas measured success in quantitative terms, and his burdensome sense of duty worked against what reason and judgment he possessed. Medical men were supposed to cure, and if they did not do so, Nicholas thought them lax in their measures or inefficient in their practice. From his quarantine at Tver, Nicholas ordered Chief Physician Dr. Pfeller demoted to Ordinary Field surgeon since his hospital showed an extremely high death rate, and the demotion was to remain in effect until such time as there was an improvement in conditions.[30] With the cholera, as with others things, Nicholas' view of what should be blinded him to what was. The man who misgauged English policy in the Near East, since it failed to agree with his idea of what that policy should have been, appeared in the man who tried to defeat the cholera with bayonets, and who thought that medical practice could be improved by punishing physicians whose patients died in the midst of a terrible and unknown epidemic. Nicholas was a ruler, as Prince Lubomirski pointed out, who had both ability and a concern for his people, but who was marked with a tragic flaw—a rigidity and formalism which negated his most positive characteristics.[31]

The Moscow cholera outbreak was the culmination of the 1830 epidemic. Mortality figures were lower than at Astrakhan, and the disease incidence was much smaller than in the south. But other factors gave the cholera in Moscow additional importance. While the epidemic wasted the provinces, it could be considered a remote danger, but when it marched on Moscow it threatened Russia's very life. Although Moscow was not the seat of governent, it was the very heart of Russia; people who merely deplored the cholera on the Volga were overcome by a sense of tragedy when it invaded their ancient capital. For many Russians, the withdrawal of the Moscow quarantine cordons in December meant that the epidemic was over, that they could relax their vigilance and forget their fears, even though the cholera continued its ravages on the frontiers through the winter of 1830–1831. This reaction in itself signified Moscow's importance and the degree to which the city was identified with Russia.[32]

On quite another level, the cholera in Moscow completed the disease's pattern for 1829–1830. Moscow reacted to the cholera much as other Russian cities did during the epidemic's early phases, with the primary difference being that Moscow was far better prepared in every way to face a major crisis. A more responsive administrative system helped Moscow avoid the troubles which occurred in Tambov, while better physical facilities and the availability of personnel and medicines eliminated many issues which were crucial in Kursk, Saratov, and generally throughout the provinces. The only city comparable to Moscow in these respects was Petersburg, but the cholera missed Petersburg in 1830, and when it struck there in 1831, the epidemic had developed a cumulative effect which, in combination with Petersburg's more volatile social situation, greatly intensified its impact. Indeed, the cholera produced far more serious effects generally in 1831 than in 1830, and clearly developed more complex responses.

The superior resources which Moscow possessed were reflected in the medical and administrative data which the Moscow Council collected, and which provided the first intimate view of the cholera's social effects. Throughout the cholera's early history, it was regularly reported that the cholera affected the poor and the indigent, but until the cholera reached Moscow, the meaning of that concept could not be specifically defined. At Astrakhan, Orenburg, and throughout the lower Volga, only the most general pre-epidemic population figures were available, and when the cholera struck, the confusion which followed made collecting statistical information almost impossible. Consequently, the first intimate view of the cholera's sociology appeared with the Moscow epidemic and was published in F. C. M. Markus' *Rapport sur le choléra-morbus de Moscou.*

An interest in population statistics was one universal by-product of the first cholera pandemics, and in western European nations, the 1820's and 1830's saw major developments in the accumulation of population data. Descriptive population statistics were well estab-

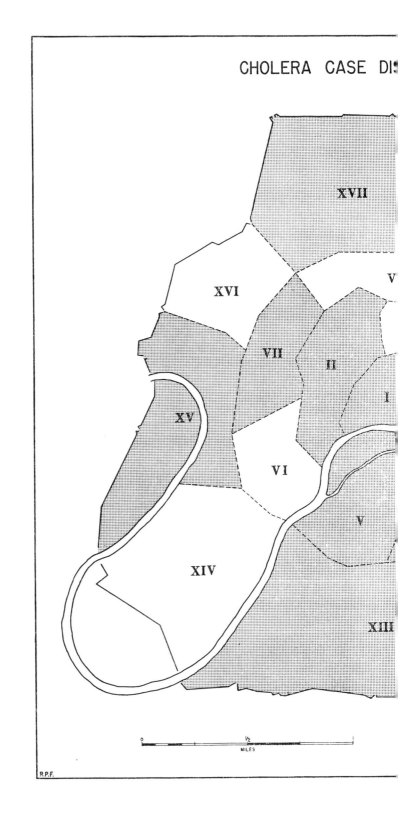

CHOLERA CASE DIS

XVII

XVI

V

VII

II

I

XV

VI

V

XIV

XIII

0   ½
                   MILES

R.P.F.

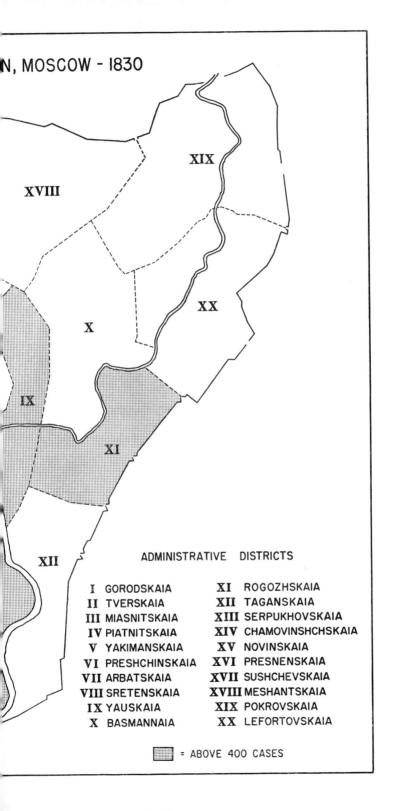

N, MOSCOW - 1830

XVIII

XIX

XX

X

IX

XI

XII

ADMINISTRATIVE   DISTRICTS

I   GORODSKAIA
II   TVERSKAIA
III   MIASNITSKAIA
IV   PIATNITSKAIA
V   YAKIMANSKAIA
VI   PRESHCHINSKAIA
VII   ARBATSKAIA
VIII   SRETENSKAIA
IX   YAUSKAIA
X   BASMANNAIA

XI   ROGOZHSKAIA
XII   TAGANSKAIA
XIII   SERPUKHOVSKAIA
XIV   CHAMOVINSHCHSKAIA
XV   NOVINSKAIA
XVI   PRESNENSKAIA
XVII   SUSHCHEVSKAIA
XVIII   MESHANTSKAIA
XIX   POKROVSKAIA
XX   LEFORTOVSKAIA

= ABOVE 400 CASES

lished among Russian academians by the first decade of the nineteenth century, and there were even some efforts made at statistical analysis.[33] The bulk of the material collected, however, was purely descriptive. During the nineteenth century, the Ministry of the Interior accumulated a vast quantity of population data related to the cholera, but only in isolated instances was this information published. Early Russian students of the cholera, including Pavlovskii and Arkhangel'skii, used statistics available in the archives of the Ministry of the Interior, but their work was primarily concerned with epidemiological problems rather than demographic phenomena, and is of little value for attacking social issues.[34] In more recent years, Soviet historians have done very little with demography as an integral element in social history, and those who have studied the cholera's impact have concentrated primarily on peasant disturbances as evidence for a developing revolutionary pattern.[35] All this gives added significance to Markus' *Rapport,* for it contains a detailed picture of Moscow's population on the eve of the cholera epidemic, and though the statistical data presented are neither so complete nor so analytical as those later collected and published by the Paris population board, they still provide a very useful index for analyzing the cholera's effect.[36]

Russia's former capital sprawled along the Moskva, with the greatest part of the city north of the river on hilly land sloping back from the river itself. With the exception of the river-front districts, the city was relatively dry, and the prevailing architecture, low one- and two-story buildings of wooden construction, gave an impression of space and light which was reinforced by the practice of separating individual dwellings by a yard or garden. The streets were wide, and the great fire of 1812 actually improved conditions by destroying many aged, crowded, and noxious structures. The major recognized sanitary problem was the lack of ventilation characteristic of single-story dwellings. For the rest, however, with the exception of certain areas along the Moskva and its tributary streams, the condition of the city was considered relatively good.[37]

Moscow's population was largely Russian and Orthodox, and the number of foreign residents, as compared with St. Petersburg, was small. The population in 1829 was estimated to be between 296,000 and 305,000. This figure included 22,394 members of the nobility and both active and retired military and civil servants, 4,946 ecclesiatics, and 53,195 people who were engaged in commerce. This last figure covered both merchants and peasants of all designations who were allowed to engage in trade. The general heading of industry covered the members of the twenty-four manufacturing corporations and peasants who were working in industrial enterprises. In all, this group numbered 31,380. Finally, handworkers, including both peasants and domestic workers, made up the largest classification, comprising some 137,166 souls. A miscellaneous category which included 19,546 bureaucratic servants not classified under the nobility, 8,651 members of institutions, including the University and the academies, a garrison of approximately 16,000 men, and 2,691 registered foreigners completed the total.[38]

Moscow was a cross-section of European Russia, and the figures which define the peasant population reflect this fact. When peasants are abstracted from all classifications, their total number was considerably more than half the population: 163,140 as against the total of 295,969. But the matter goes farther than that, for even though the lesser bureaucracy, and especially the bourgeoisie, were defined categories, their attitudes, outlook, and way of life were closer to the "peasant" than they were to the civil or military aristocracy. The latter only comprised, according to Markus, one-sixth of the total Moscow population, and rural Russia gave the pervasive coloration to Russia's second capital.[39]

Moscow's annual mortality rate prior to the cholera epidemic ran about 11,000 or a ratio of approximately 1 : 25. Infant and child mortality were extremely high, and the death rate among women (1 : 23) was markedly higher than that of men (1 : 29). It would be very difficult to specify the social groups which contributed most heavily to the mortality statistics, though the assumption would be that the highest ratios would be found among the domestics and handworkers. This assumption, however, was not borne out by the cholera mortality. In general terms, the Moscow mortality figures compared favorably with western cities, and though they were higher than they should have been, they were lower than contemporary ratios in Paris. Furthermore, the Moscow mortality rates did not show an ascending line, a point which indicated a more stable demographic situation.[40]

Moscow was a major center for trade and industry, and there was a significant working class in the city. This class, however, was not a proletariat, but a peasant population transferred from the land to the city, which retained the outlook and behavioral patterns of the rural world. More than half of Moscow's population were handworkers, people who had no established trade but who performed menial labor of one sort or another. This was not, however, an indigent population in the sense of the Parisian indigents. Although the large labor supply depressed wages, agrarian paternalism partially redressed this condition, and even the destitute were able to find food and shelter in the door yards of the well-to-do. Furthermore, the domestic servant class was extremely large, and there was a ratio of twelve to one between domestic and non-domestic servants. This situation reinforced the paternalistic aspect and further reduced the possibility of a rootless urban mob.[41]

Domestics and hand-laborers together were the dominant population elements in five quarters of the city.[42] These quarters, generally, formed the city's center, represented the oldest sections, and marked the confluence of the city's waterways. Some of Moscow's less favored and most heavily populated sections lay within these quarters, though the quarters themselves showed both topographical and demographic variations. It was this complex which the cholera attacked first, and the quarter which was watched most closely was the Tverskaia, for that was the section hardest hit by the plague in 1771 and it was regarded in 1830 as an endemic problem area.

The plan of the city of Moscow looks like a series of concentric circles moving outward from the Kremlin.[43] The oldest section of the city was the Kremlin and the Kitai-Gorod, lying on the north bank of the Moskva, and forming the administrative unit known as the Gorodskaia. The Belgorod, or White City, surrounded the Kremlin and the Kitai-Gorod, encircling it in a crescent shape, while around the Belgorod lay the Zemlianoi Gorod, or the town of the earthen wall, which completely surrounded the inner sections and included the Yakimanka, the administrative unit south of the Moskva. Beyond this were the Slobody or suburbs.

Six of Moscow's administrative districts, the first through the sixth, were either completely in the river-front area, or were at least on low ground. Four of these districts recorded four hundred or more cases, with more than 50 per cent mortality. The other two, the third and sixth districts, listed 365 and 354 cases with mortality ratios of 54 per cent and 56 per cent, respectively. The cholera first broke out in the Tverskaia (the second district), and in the epidemic's early stages its worst effects were felt in the second and fifth districts, i.e., the Tverskaia and the Yakimanskaia. It soon spread, however, to adjacent districts, reaching parts of the city that were on higher ground, and when the epidemic ended, no district reported fewer than 112 cases.[44]

Although the cholera began in the city's central section, its effects spread generally throughout the populated districts. In the period from September 15, 1830, to January 20, 1831, 8,431 cases were reported, of which 4,588 died. On March 17, 1831, when there were no new cases occurring and the epidemic was finished for the time, this number was adjusted to 8,576 cases, with 4,690 deaths. The case distribution over the city, however, was very even. The Sushchevskaia reported the largest number of total cases, 1,282, but this included the military, most of which were treated in one place. For the rest, nine districts reported between 408 and 689 cases. The Pokrovskaia reported the fewest cases, 112, and only two other districts, the Basmannaia (163) and the Lefortovskaia (151), reported under 200 cases.[45] This distribution reflects two factors. The reports emanated from the place where the individual was treated, so there was not an absolute correlation between incidence and local conditions. On the other hand, a real effort was made to keep the cases in the district where they originated, and to utilize facilities available there, a fact which gives the figures greater meaning than otherwise might be the case. Furthermore, the organization of the city diffused the pattern of living conditions, and each district tended to be a cross section of the city. Consequently, a uniformity between established extremes emerges, since almost all the city was affected, and the intensity of infection was fairly even, with half the city reporting only a little more than half the cases.

The death rate was also remarkably constant in all districts. Only one district, the Presnenskaia, reported a mortality figure below 50 per cent (30 per cent), and the highest death rate reported (68 per cent) was shared by three districts, the Lefortovskaia, the Rogozhskaia and the Srentenskaia. In the remainder, the death rate ranged from 51 per cent to 61 per cent, and in the latter case, the Pokrovskaia, the percentage was on the smallest number of cases reported. Indeed, of the ten districts reporting four hundred or more cases, only one, the Rogozhskaia, was among the top mortality districts. Dr. Markus noted, and Pavloskii's figures bear this out, that the cholera lost intensity as it moved northward.[46] It also should be remembered, however, that communications and controls were more effective in the Moscow region, and this meant that a larger number of cases which were not *in extremis* found their way into the cholera data. The only conclusion that can be drawn at this point is that the cholera affected Moscow generally, and though the heaviest concentration of cases tended toward the heavily populated center, the incidence pattern showed a broad enough distribution to suggest reasonably uniform living conditions throughout the city.

Sanitary conditions were undoubtedly worst in the low, dank areas along the Moskva and the streams and canals connecting with it, and the first recognized cholera case occurred in that neighborhood. This was also the district hardest hit by the plague in 1771, and it was anticipated that cholera would probably claim the largest number of its victims there. As we have seen, the concentration of cases did shade toward the central districts of the city, and it was noticed that the cholera was worst in the low areas first, before attacking districts on higher ground, but the concentration was by no means significant enough to suggest a serious differential in living conditions. Sanitary facilities were primitive throughout, and within the city proper nearly all water sources were polluted. Markus recorded that the streams and canals which flowed through the city, and even the Moskva itself, were so filthy as to be unusable, and he pointed out that most of the city's water came from some 5,000 wells scattered through the city. The wells, however, were very shallow and subject to surface pollution. Since there was no regular system for waste disposal, wells, streams, and canals were almost certain to be fouled. Catherine II had attacked this problem by using aqueducts to bring water from outside the urban circle, but her measures proved inadequate for the general need. Moscow's water supply was clearly questionable, and with no effective waste controls in operation, the cholera could achieve an even extension.[47]

The distribution of cholera incidence by population groups presents a somewhat different picture, for some elements in the population proved more susceptible than others. Here the evidence is more substantial, for the statistical reports made some effort to relate cholera incidence and mortality to class groups. Care has to be used in handing this material, however, for both the cholera reports and the census reports used legal classifications rather than demographic categories, and, as a result, distinctions which are potentially very important were blurred or lost altogether. Contemporary evaluations of the data reflect the problems involved, for diametrically opposed conclusions were drawn from the same basic information. Dr. Lichtenstaedt, for example, held the opinion that the cholera affected the classes equally, and he roundly denied that there was any significant differentiation among them, while Dr. Markus, reached the opposite conclusion, though much less definitely.[48] Part of the reason for this discrepancy was that Lichtenstaedt explicitly accepted the categories in the cholera reports, while Markus made at least an elementary effort to distinguish different population elements on the basis of their "way of life." Unfortunately, Markus did not make the implications of his argument specific, as Lichtenstaedt did, and he did not work out in detail the statistical bases for his claim that the cholera was socially selective in its effects.[49]

Despite the inadequacies of Markus' work, he did recognize the impossibility of using standard census classifications as the basis for meaningful demographic statements. Consequently, when he sought to define the "upper classes," he used a cultural standard, distinguishing between a European and a Russian national style of life. He estimated that perhaps forty-five to fifty thousand people, or one-sixth of the population, could be called "upper class," and he pointed out that its membership would be drawn from the civil and military nobility, but that it would also include members of the lesser bureaucracy, the bourgeoisie, and military personnel below the hereditary noble ranks. We have no idea what proportion he assigned to these latter groups, though they would comprise more than half of the total figure at which he arrived.[50] The "upper classes," as Markus conceived them, were European in dress and diet, and their mode of life contrasted sharply with those of the remaining five-sixths of the population, which wore the Russian national dress and ate a simple diet of bread and "legumes" occasionally enriched with meat and fish. Unfortunately, Markus made no attempt to differentiate grades of existence within the "European" and "national" cultures, though the implication was that the former was luxurious, and the latter unadorned, rough, and natural. Indeed, Markus regarded the Russian way of life as essentially healthy, though he recognized that the river-front and canal districts of

Moscow were damp and dangerous, and Russian houses ill ventilated. Beyond that, he showed no perception of the dangers inherent in the living conditions of the overwhelming part of the Moscow population, and there was more than a touch of pride in his description of the "people," though he deplored some of their habits.[51]

The Europeanized upper classes formed altogether some 16 per cent of the total population of Moscow, according to Markus' calculations, while the cholera mortality tables gave a composite figure of 422 cholera deaths for the nobility, military officers and civil servants, and the merchants of the first guild.[52] This represented 9 per cent of the total number of cholera deaths, a figure well below the given proportion of the population. Lichtenstaedt, who made no attempt at cultural differentiation, used the mortality data to prove that the nobility suffered from the cholera in almost exact proportion to their number in the whole population. He pointed out that the first two classes of the mortality tables gave a total of 307 deaths which represented 6.3 per cent of the cholera's total number of deaths, while the nobility, according to the census figures, comprised 7 per cent of the population.[53] While Markus' approach suffered from a lack of specificity, Lichtenstaedt was too restrictive in his analysis, for he assumed a demographic significance for the legal classifications which simply did not exist. Since we lack any useful correlative data on income, longevity, or living space, which could provide a statistical basis for more specific economic and social differentiation, no final resolution to this argument is possible. In common sense terms, however, Markus' view would seem to give a more realistic definition of those who lived well, and provide some basis for the tentative conclusion that the upper orders of society were markedly less susceptible to the cholera than the lower classes, and this conclusion is supported when we look more closely at other classifications in the mortality tables.

The Moscow garrison was very roughly treated by the cholera, and the disease was especially virulent among auxiliaries, camp followers, and their families. At least 1148 deaths occurred in the military establishment, with 647 active military and 501 inactive listed as casualties. Those classified as being under orders showed a much higher death rate for men as against women, 527 to only 120, while among those not on active duty the reverse was true: 118 men as against 383 women. According to the police registers for 1829, soldiers and their families comprised 27,476 of Moscow's population, but the garrison was expanded in 1830, and the figure probably should be nearer 35,000 for the cholera period.[54] The military suffered 25 per cent of the cholera's total casualties in Moscow, though the entire establishment represented only a little more than 11 per cent of Moscow's population. Despite the work done in military hygiene, the army was one of the depressed segments of Moscow society, and its sufferings during the cholera period stressed the haphazard way that the government provided for its protectors. The health and sanitary standards of the army were miserable, and the non-military adjuncts to the army comprised a part of Moscow's indigent population.

The indications of misery among the military were not entirely unexpected, and at first glance the figures for peasant mortality also seem to conform to a predictable pattern. The tables identify some 1,319 deaths with the peasant serfs, a figure which comprised nearly 29 per cent of the cholera deaths. It is interesting that only eleven factory workers are specifically recorded as victims, and that a mere sixteen appanage peasants are listed. This latter figure is particularly intriguing since the police registers listed 2,847 appanage peasants, and Androssov's table indicated almost half of these were engaged in commerce and industry. Beyond this, domestic serfs and peasants paying *obrok* (quit-rent) added respectively 645 and 264 deaths to the totals, while seignorial serfs contributed an additional 394. The peasant serf population of Moscow was 142,171 or nearly 47 per cent of the city's total population. Yet the peasants contributed only 29 per cent of the cholera deaths. In proportion, the peasant population was clearly less vulnerable than the military, and also proportionately suffered less than the group classed as bourgeois.

It is this latter group which offers one of the most intriguing aspects of the mortality figures. Merchants and burghers formed a substantial part of the Moscow population, and together numbered 48,071, or a trifle better than 16 per cent of the whole. This group suffered 990 deaths, or 22 per cent of the total number. These figures, incidentally, do not include 101 deaths among foreign merchants and burghers. Even leaving crown and industrial peasants entirely out of account, a procedure which raises the percentage figure proportionately, the mortality among peasant serfs represented 1.3 per cent of their number. If the figures on crown and industrial peasants were included, the percentage would sink below one. The percentage figure for the merchant-burgher group was 2.8 per cent, or more than double the peasant figure. By comparison, the burgher class, and particularly the *meshchanstvo,* or lesser bourgeoisie, was more harshly handled than the peasant serfs. Although the burghers altogether made up only 16 per cent of the population, they contributed 22 per cent of the cholera deaths. The peasants, who represented nearly half the city's population, provided only 29 per cent of the deaths. And, finally, the ratio of deaths to population was twice as high among the burghers as it was among the peasants.

These figures are suggestive rather than definitive, for correlative data on income, occupations, non-cholera mortality, and the like are not available in published records. Nevertheless, as Chevalier pointed out, mortality figures define conditions which sap physical resistance, the very conditions that indicate serious social problems. If Chevalier is correct, it would appear that the free merchant group contained elements which lived on an economic margin, which lacked a proper diet, which were subject to the debilitations of poverty. No matter how badly a serf owner discharged his duties, he was still responsible for his people, and those who used serfs in industry often went to considerable lengths to protect the health and welfare of their dependents.[55] No one, however, was particularly concerned about the small shopkeepers, barrowmen, independent coachmen, porters, and their kind. They lacked the income to escape the "margin of existence," and there was no place for them to turn in crisis times. Historians' attention has centered on the peasant serf as the symbol of economic misery and moral degredation, but the cholera showed the existence of a group in Moscow which could be called indigent, a group which combined freedom with economic weakness. In the future this group could only grow, and its existence thirty years before emancipation is provocative.

Despite the mortality among peasants, soldiers, and lesser bourgeoisie, there was little basis for class protests, and this partially explains the relative quiet in Moscow. The antagonisms which existed did not reflect tension between owners and workers, for the bulk of Moscow's population lived in much the same way, but rather the conflict between oppressors and subjects. The terror which the peasant felt was duplicated in the *meshchanin,* and both accepted the protection which religion and the appeal to divine authority offered. Only the smallest segment of the population lived apart, and a common mode of life united the bulk of the people. The reactions that came had to be against the government, against the petty officials who pushed and plundered, and against the physicians who belonged to an alien world. All this indicated a substantial unity in the Russian world, a popular unity which could accept the Tsar as not only the ruler but the father, and a unity affected only incidentally by the Europeanization of Russia's elite. There was little to distinguish the *meshchanin* from the peasant, for their attitudes and reactions were conditioned by the same milieu. These people were still the essence of the Russian system, and major cultural and demographic changes would be necessary before they would be penetrated with anything approaching a lively and general opposition. Groups existed which were exploited and which lived a marginal life confronted constantly by death, but these groups were not sufficiently set apart, not sufficiently unique, to provide a significant core of resistance. The cholera in Moscow suggested the existence of conditions which could become revolutionary, but unlike Paris, or even Petersburg, the sense of exploitation and oppression had not reached the explosive stage. Moscow reflected the stability of old Russia, and the cholera, whose normal effect was to exacerbate tensions, produced only minimal reactions. In this sense the cholera showed a city and a society which still rested on secure foundations.

The cholera declined in Moscow during October and November, and Nicholas celebrated his nameday by raising the *cordon sanitaire* on December 6. *Te Deums* were sung in both capitals to mark the deliverance, and though the cholera continued to ravage the provinces, there was a general feeling that the worst was past.[56] Scattered cholera cases continued to occur in Moscow until March, but these could be ignored, and life in the ancient residence gradually fell back into its normal patterns. The dreadful shadow of silent death had drifted on, and though the cholera returned in 1831, it reserved its most violent ravages for other regions.

Chapter 5

THE SUMMUM: 1831

The cholera was active on Russia's European frontiers during the winter of 1830–1831, but it was quiescent in European Russia itself, and both the public and the government turned to other concerns. This was a misfortune, for the winter quiet was only a respite, not a release, and there was much that needed to be done to secure Russia in case of a recurrence. The experience with cholera in 1830 showed the dangers latent in an epidemic crisis, but Russia learned little from that experience. Indeed, in some respects the situation was worse in 1831 than it had been in 1830 because the cholera had created an image of inevitable, silent death which the government was totally unable to dispel. This aspect of the disease lurked like some obscene monster in the darker recesses of the public mind, requiring only the news of a fresh outbreak to unchain it. The summer of 1830 provided repeated warnings of this danger, but those warnings were consistently disregarded, and the government limited itself to attempting to contain the rebellions which followed.

In every respect, the 1831 epidemic was more serious than its predecessor, and the responses to it were more violent, more extensive, and more revealing. In 1830, the cholera attacked 31 provinces, causing 68,091 cases and 37,595 deaths. In 1831, 48 governments reported cholera cases; the disease incidence was 466,457; and 197,069 deaths were recorded.[1] Although the over-all mortality in 1830 was 13 per cent higher than in 1831 (55 per cent as against 42 per cent), the far larger total number of cases and deaths in the later epidemic had the effect of generalizing the disease's impact, and this was epitomized in a far higher mortality per 10,000 of population in 1831 than in 1830.[2] Finally, the cholera's worst effects in 1830 were felt in the provinces, and the Moscow epidemic marked the disease's most serious penetration into the heartland of European Russia. In 1831, the cholera reappeared with greater intensity in the provinces, but it also attacked the centers of Russian political, cultural and economic life. Both Moscow and Petersburg were affected, the latter especially violently, and the regions which included the two capitals sustained more than 250,000 cases and over 100,000 deaths.[3]

Although the Moscow outbreak was the culmination of the 1830 epidemic, the cholera continued its ravages through the winter months and into the spring. The worst attacks came in the region from Kharkov and Kiev westward and were particularly intense in Volhynia and Podolia. In this area it was as though the 1830 epidemic, extending westward from its beginning point in the lower Volga and Caspian regions, merged with the more violent manifestation of 1831, which rolled back over the south of Russia, intensifying its effects in some places by as much as six times. Pavlovskii noted that Podolia seemed to be the focal point, absorbing the last effects of the 1830 epidemic and providing the initial surge for the more destructive 1831 outbreak, while Volhynia appeared to be the transfer point for the epidemic from the territories of Russia proper into Poland.[4]

The cholera also turned to the south, entering the Divans of Moldavia and Wallachia, where it combined with a new outbreak of plague. Count Kiselev wrote from Bucharest on December 15, 1830, "I am deeply concerned about the cholera morbus which is advancing on the Pruth and which will probably reach these poor provinces...," and his fears were only too well justified. A desperate outbreak disrupted the Divans during the winter and spring and continued through the summer. "After burying three thousand dead at Yassy," Kiselev wrote six months later, "I had to return here [Bucharest] to avert, as far as possible, the misfortunes which menaced this city...." Bucharest was not fated to suffer so serious an outbreak as that at Yassy, and Kiselev was able to report that, "We are already in the fourth week, and to this point the mortality has been only 90 to 100 persons per day. This is only a fifth of that at Yassy, and I rejoice from the bottom of my heart, for this is truly a success, the like of which I would not have dared to anticipate."[5] Kiselev's gratitude for a mere one hundred deaths per day is the most eloquent possible commentary on the ghastly ravages the cholera committed in his territories.

In Volhynia, the large Jewish population was hit very hard, and in the town of Berdichev, for which we have the official figures, the cholera attacked 900 persons, of whom 778 died. The worst of the outbreak occurred between December, 1830, and the end of January, 1831. Although the general mortality in Berdichev was very high, the Jewish population suffered both the highest mortality and the majority of cases. Between December 7, 1830, and January 31, 1831, 630 cases were reported among the Jews, of which 610 proved to be fatal.[6] These figures were terrifying, representing as they did nearly total mortality, and they reflected both the abysmal living conditions in the Jewish settlements and the absolute refusal of the Jewish population either to seek medical aid, or to co-operate with the Russian authorities. Contemporaries professed to be puzzled by the Jews' reactions, and they pointed out that in Germany the Jewish population was much more likely to request medical aid and follow a physician's instructions than were non-Jews. The difference in cultural standards between the Volhynian Jewish population and the Hebrew community in Germany was not recognized, and the vast gulf which separated the Volhynian Jews from their Russian governors was not considered.[7] The terrors which beset the Russian peasant when confronted by the sanitation police or the physician were greatly ramified when cultural and religious differences came into play, and the Jewish community drew in upon itself, hid its troubles from the world, and died of the cholera in terrible profusion.

The cholera had already reached Poland's borders when the revolution broke out in Warsaw in November, 1830, and it began to spread into Poland well before the Russian campaign to suppress the revolution took form. European opinion, however, associated the Russian campaign in Poland with the cholera's spread, and one of the best publicized Russian accounts of the cholera's appearance in Poland gave credence to that thesis. The *Journal de St. Pétersbourg* reported on May 5, 1831, that the cholera reached Brest-Litovsk on March 7, and by March 19 had caused 205 cases and 129 deaths.[8] The implication was that the cholera and the Russian military build-up coincided. Staff-Physician Dr. Schnur, however, in a memorandum on the introduction of cholera into the Polish Kingdom dated May 12, 1831, pointed out that General-Staff-Physician Dr. Schlegel had already identified five cholera cases at Lontzh in western Volhynia at the end of December. Lontzh was the rendezvous point for Imperial troops and had direct communications with Brest-Litovsk, and Dr. Schnur implied that this connection explained the cholera's spread from Lontzh to Brest. Even more to the point, Imperial State Councillor Dr. Peuker reported that throughout the winter the cholera was active among the civilian population, and he suggested that, in all likelihood, it was carried from Volhynia to Brest by non-military personnel. A minor cholera outbreak occurred among the Russian troops quartered in Brest in January, but it was confined to a few scattered cases and had disappeared when the army began to advance in February. The March outbreak, which was reported in the *Journal de St. Pétersbourg* began among the large Jewish community in Brest-Litovsk, and when it came, the garrison was immediately removed. Several cases were reported among the troops as they left Brest, but by that time the disease had reached epidemic proportions in the city itself and had already appeared in nearby villages. The cholera was reported ahead of Russian troops at Miedzyrzyc on March 24, at Biala on March 25, and at Siedlicz on March 30. When Count Dibich reached Minsk on April 27, he found a Polish lazarette with 200 cases, and Dr. Schnur assumed that the disease was transferred from Minsk to Warsaw.[9]

Pavlovskii's detailed study suggests that the cholera was moving toward Poland independently of Russian forces, though the war unquestionably worsened the epidemic.[10] The popular view, however, placed the onus for bringing the cholera to Poland squarely on Nicholas I. It was pointed out that the first cholera cases in Russia's active forces in Poland occurred in the Khoperskii Cossack Regiment on December 8 and 14, 1830, and again on January 13, 1831. This unit had been brought from the Don region where the cholera was active, and the cases appeared immediately on its arrival. As a matter of fact, only five soldiers were taken sick, and the possibility of their having contracted the disease in their new quarters was apparently not considered. The geography seemed significant and that was enough.[11] There is really no need to split logical or logistical hairs, for the case against the Russian government was simplicity itself. The cholera had been in Russia in 1830, and it appeared in Poland in 1831. Since the disease was popularly thought to be contagious, it seemed obvious that the Russians were to blame. This argument actually cut two ways, and Carlist propagandists argued that the cholera reached Poland, and ultimately Europe, because Poland revolted (another variety of infection), and Russia was forced to intervene, thus inadvertantly spreading the disease into Europe. From this standpoint, the Poles, and especially the liberal revolutionaries, were morally responsible for Europe's suffering, although Russia provided the means of transmission.[12]

Among liberals, and particularly Poland's supporters, however, the Russians were tried and convicted of a crime against humanity while pursuing their own ends without regard for culture or morality. Louis Blanc wrote that "borne by the Russians, it [the cholera] appeared on the battlefields of Poland, more murderous than the war itself...," and that Poles fleeing Russia's wrath bore the cholera with them to the West.[13] Polish newspapers cried out against the barbarism of a regime, "which does not merely wage war, but exposes Europe to a contagious disease...," and in a circular dated June 1, 1831, the Polish government charged:

Europe is no longer ignorant of the ally which the Emperor of Russia has called to his assistance for the purpose of consummating the work of exterminating the Polish people...the cholera is general in the Russian army, and each contact with any body of the enemy is dangerous.... We announce to you positive facts, and we ask whether this new consideration does not impose upon the European Powers a new obligation to interpose itself [*sic*] between the Polish nation and the Emperor of Russia, for the purpose of staying the effusion of blood, and of preventing those calamities with which Europe is threatened? [14]

Although no government moved in response to these pleas and charges, the cholera played an important role in the struggle between Poland and Russia. The Russian army suffered the first heavy casualties from the disease, and during April, May, and June the cholera made deep inroads on both Russian personnel and Russian morale. In March, military hospitals in Russia and Poland had only 682 cholera patients, but during April the number jumped to 8720, and 2800 deaths were reported.[15] The units in the Siedlicz area, extending to Miedzyrzyc, Biala, and Brest, were especially hard hit. Hospital facilities were swamped, in many cases the only care available came from a soldier's comrades, and it was estimated that there were no more than four physicians for each 6,000 men. With at least a third of the active army in the lazarettes, the situation was hazardous indeed.[16]

Conditions in the Russian encampments were abysmal, and the

soldiers lived in the midst of mud, squalor, and devastation. Sanitary facilities were primitive, and the Russian command made little effort to combat the hygiene problem. Quarantine regulations were established, and facilities for isolating cholera cases were provided, but these measures left the fundamental problems untouched.[17] Joszef Hardynski described the cholera's coming to the Polish armies as a disaster, but he pointed to the Russian situation as infinitely worse. After the battle of Ignanie, several hundred Polish troops fell ill, and within a few days nearly 1,000 Poles had been lost. But, Hardynski pointed out, "if it was terrible with us, nothing can express the suffering it produced in the Russian camp.... Thousands of those wretched sufferers were left exposed to the open air, and died upon the field." [18] The numbers were exaggerated, but the conditions were not, and Russian morale suffered. When G. I. Filipson entered Siedlicz with his unit in April, the cholera had already commenced its ravages, and Filipson noted that, "there was no sound of joy or even life to be heard; the usually busy streets were empty; every greeting was met with gloom and anxiety." [19] Alexander Lvovich Seeland was less impressed with the cholera, but he was constrained to note the growing evidences of its virulence as his unit moved from Lukov on the way to Siedlicz: "The cholera had claimed many victims and an increasing number of huts were crowded with the sick and the dying; in the quiet woods appeared a large number of unadorned crosses over the graves of the cholera dead, [and] it was seen that the mortality had been very great." [20] Finally, following the battle of Taygrod, Hardynski described the Russian armies as, "wearied and discouraged by the disasters of the campaign, posted in regions which they had devastated, and therefore suffering from scarcity: without hospitals for their sick and their wounded ... and with the cholera ravaging their ranks, that army was in the most precarious situation." [21]

The type of war which Dibich fought in the spring of 1831 did nothing to improve morale, and Filipson commented when Dibich died that he had lost the confidence of both officers and men.[22] This condition worsened the cholera's effect and further reduced the army's efficiency. The Poles also had the cholera in their ranks, but they had fewer cases initially, and their early successes helped to buoy their spirit. Kunz estimated that at the highest point, the number of cholera cases in the Polish army was in the neighborhood of 4,000, but he also pointed out that the Poles "found themselves in the vicinity of Warsaw and because they fought in their own territory [were] in a far better position; the Russians, in an enemy territory, frequently bivouaced in swampy regions, suffered heavily not merely from the cholera, but from nerve fever as well." [23]

The cholera's worst effects in the Russian forces were felt during April and May, although in the latter month the number of new cases dropped markedly. At the same time, the cholera began to take its toll of the Polish civilian population, and the disease also offered opportunities to neighboring powers, especially Prussia, to harass the Polish government with increasingly stringent frontier regulations. The Poles officially protested to Berlin charging that the Prussian border authorities were using quarantine regulations to restrict and constrain the movement of Polish citizens, to interfere with the Polish war effort, and to spy on Poland. The Poles cited medical authorities to support their claim that the cholera did not require the stringent measures that the Prussians had invoked, and they charged Prussia with using sanitary regulations to support the Russian intervention: "... at the end of April, when the cholera appeared in our countries, the Prussian Government hastened to make it a pretext for developing means still more detrimental and even hostile in regard to us, since, on the other side, those methods favored our enemies." [24]

This problem was, of course, less serious than the cholera among the civilian population, for that development weakened Poland's advantage of fighting on her own territory. The Russian forces were reinforced in the early summer when Paskevich took command, and the problems which had plagued the Russians, including the cholera, began to recede. Paskevich complained that the cholera worsened his supply problem, and his agents, Peuker and Tengoborsky, were hindered by the Prussian quarantines in bringing food supplies to the Russian armies, but these were minor considerations. [25] The troubles which the cholera produced in Russia herself during the summer of 1831 only affected the Russian armies in Poland indirectly, and Paskevich was able to reduce Warsaw and end the revolt in August. When the Polish revolution broke out, Poland had held a strong position. That position, however, was eroded during the spring and summer, while the Russian position actually stabilized. [26] As Russian forces regrouped and drove the Polish insurgents back on Warsaw, the cholera epidemic in and around that city reached its highest point of intensity. Between April and September, the province of Warsaw recorded 22,718 cholera cases, and of these 13,103 proved fatal. In the city itself, 5,868 cases occurred, and 2,648 deaths resulted.[27] Even apart from the material effect which such an epidemic had, morale was badly shaken, and the cholera's impact at the very heart of Poland's resistance must be considered seriously when Poland's collapse is evaluated.[28]

While the Russian armies in Poland suffered from the cholera, and their effectiveness for a time was weakened, their discipline remained generally sound. In the areas away from the front, however, the cholera produced disturbances which were especially dangerous for the domestic situation. In the Petersburg military district, the cholera's advance brought restlessness, confusion, and finally a wave of desertions. The officers seemed to be unable to control their men, and it was necessary for Count Benkendorf and Count Essen to intervene. Their efforts brought a momentary respite, but the military camps remained troubled, and finally Nicholas visited the troops.[29] These rumblings in the army were the first indications of the more serious outbreaks which occurred in June and July among the military and civilian populations, and which focused in the Petersburg riots and the revolts in the military colonies.

The 1830 cholera epidemic had claimed the lives of some leading citizens, and the 1831 outbreak in Poland carried off both General Dibich and the Grand Duke Constantine. General Dibich's sudden death on the night of May 28–29, 1831, aroused suspicion and open speculation. Dibich's military failures had lost him favor with the Tsar, and it was noted that Count Orlov arrived at headquarters immediately before the General's death. Ferdinand Christine summarized one popular view when he recorded that, "it was generally believed that poison put an end to his [Dibich's] life...," but there was disagreement whether he had poisoned himself or whether his death was murder.[30] Constantine Pavlovich wrote the Tsar on June 3 that there were four current versions of Dibich's death. One was the cholera story, but the other three were murder by poison, with Count Orlov—and incidentally Nicholas himself—implicated; suicide; and apoplexy. The suicide idea according to the Grand Duke, was most commonly believed, for Dibich was depressed by the reverses his army was suffering and by the Tsar's declining favor. After Count Orlov's arrival, Dibich seemed to be sad and low spirited, and though he was seen at 11:00 P. M. apparently in good health, at one o'clock the following morning he was dead. All these elements seemed to point to suicide.[31] A formal affirmation that Dibich died of cholera was published in the *Journal de St. Pétersbourg,* together with General Count Toll's account of Dibich's last hours: Toll had been summoned to Dibich's bedside when he first became ill, and remained with him until his death.[32] These efforts to scotch the rumors were unavailing, however, and people continued to believe that conspiracy rather than cholera had claimed the General's life.[33]

Taken by itself, there is nothing unusual in malicious gossip following the sudden death of a general who was known to be out of favor. At the same time, the denial that cholera was responsible suggested a reaction which was to become an integral part of the general public's response to the news of cholera deaths. Faced with a disease which was both deadly and unknown, the public mind rejected what it could not understand, and attempted to create a rational explanation for cholera mortality by denying that the disease existed, and by blaming its effects on human agents who were seeking their own destructive and immoral ends. These reactions must be seen in the context of general unrest, for the memory of the 1830 epidemic, new evidences of the cholera's resurgence, the recent revolts in Europe, and the war in Poland had thoroughly disturbed the public mind. Nothing was too fantastic, and rumors of murder by poison spread from hints about individuals to wild stories claiming mass poisonings of whole villages and even cities.

The poison hysteria was actually an effort to rationalize the darkling fears which the cholera's recurrence produced, and since poison was an instrument used by human agents for special ends, the hysteria focussed on particular scapegoats. The most popular villains were Polish agents and foreigners in general, though both physicians and government officials were also included. By mid-summer a mass phobia had set in which affected the educated and the illiterate alike. The former were able to rationalize their stories by reference to public problems and private greed, but for the masses a spirit of evil had entered the land, and no one was immune. The poison scare played a part in the Petersburg cholera revolt, in the risings in the

Novgorod military colonies, in the riots which occurred in Staraia Russa, but it also appeared away from these centers of unrest. Count Benkendorf spoke of the ridiculous fear of poison which overspread the country, and Nicholas himself adverted to it in his published exhortation to the people to calm themselves, a manifest which came after the bloody riots in Petersburg and the military colonies.[34]

The ubiquitous Christine reported from Moscow on July 21 that a wave of arsenic poisonings had swept the region; rumor had it that men had been caught in the act of pouring arsenic into wells, and mass banquet poisonings were whispered. Again, on July 24, Christine reported that the poison panic was continuing, and that an innocent old German and his seventeen-year-old daughter and his fourteen-year-old son, who had been selling whisks and entertaining the crowds with Tyrolean songs for the better part of a month, were suddenly set upon by a mob and desperately beaten. They escaped by diving into Christine's garden where they were given shelter. The reason for the attack was that, "our stupid Muscovites imagined that the whisks concealed poison and that in chasing flies this poison was scattered about and that one breathed it...."[35]

The poison panic reflected an emotional miasma as potent as any "contagious principle" dreamed of by the doctors. The disintegration of morale in the face of an influence which could not be grasped rationally produced an effort to find something which could be understood and which could be associated with a real, and punishable, human agency. Whether there were major outbreaks of arsenic poisoning is questionable, but that people thought there were indicated a violently disturbed state of the public mind. Even Christine, who was anything but an alarmist, refused to deny the arsenic stories, and suggested that undoubtedly the Poles were responsible for the Petersburg riots even as they were probably the ones behind a reported effort to burn down the city of Moscow.[36]

As the cholera spread across Poland, infiltrated the Russian armies, and decimated the Polish civilian population, the fear of another outbreak in Russia itself increased, and that fear became concrete when the cholera appeared at Riga. It had been hoped that the Russian Baltic provinces would escape, but on May 8 the disease broke out, and in twelve days more than 700 cases were reported, of which 400 died. The government reacted promptly to cut Riga off from contact with the other Baltic states and with Russia proper, and preventive quarantines were set up to seal St. Petersburg against the danger. As a major commercial center, Riga had been in contact with the whole of the northern world, and it was difficult to say in what way the cholera reached the city, but the very real danger which existed for St. Petersburg led to initial steps to isolate the capital.[37] These efforts, according to contemporaries, were anything but successful, and the cordons seemed to be established only to be violated. Furthermore, full instructions for the control of trade and commerce through Kronstadt were only presented on June 12, while the establishment of internal sanitary measures was carried out on June 16. Within the meaning of the phrase, we may doubt the accuracy of the announcement in the June 20 *Journal de St. Pétersbourg* that, "At the first news of the cholera at Riga every step was taken to protect St. Petersburg...," for despite the government's knowledge that the cholera was approaching, the efforts made to secure the city were at best half-way.[38] The real pity was that the quarantine measures which were invoked were not stringent enough to provide any assurance that the city was protected, yet they were sufficiently harsh to create public resistance. Freedom of movement was inhibited at a time when the people were becoming restless, yet the restrictions were flexible enough, and the cordons badly enough manned, so that many were able to pass. Ironically, public resentment was equally strong against restraint and the corruption of restraint.[39]

Petersburg had been waiting for the cholera for more than a year, and when the disease failed to arrive in 1830, there was great relief. Nevertheless, fear had built up during those days of waiting, and it returned with redoubled force in 1831. The first cholera case in St. Petersburg was verified on June 15, and on June 16 a special anti-cholera commission was established. The pattern followed that used in Moscow the preceding year, and an assembly of notables joined with the Medical Council to direct the cholera fight. The Military Governor-General of St. Petersburg headed the committee, and he was joined by the Minister of Interior, Count Zakrevskii, the then Minister of War, Count Chernyshev, and Prince Menshikov. The Petersburg commission followed the same organization as the Moscow council. Curators, similar to the district inspectors, were appointed for each of Petersburg's thirteen administrative districts, and these men were responsible for visiting all reported cases and inspecting all dwellings to see that cleanliness was maintained.[40] Physicians were to accompany the curators or their aides on all inspections, and every three administrative districts had over them a physician-in-chief.[41]

It was here that the parallel with Moscow ended. The Moscow cholera committee had maintained close touch with conditions in the stricken portions of the city, and the heaviest responsibility fell on aides and adjuncts who acted as inspectors and who ferreted out and handled suspected cholera cases. In Petersburg, thanks to the greater number of cases which developed, and due perhaps as well to the more extensive police system, the primary burden for discovering the cholera and dealing with it fell on police officers. This was a misfortune, for the cholera was treated like a crime wave, and the police, who lacked the knowledge necessary to discriminate, used suspicious circumstances rather than diagnostic evidence in implementing their instructions. In Moscow the police had acted as an adjunct to the cholera committee, but in Petersburg the police became the most important administrative instrument. The results were devastating.

The people watched these preparations cynically, and from the beginning stubbornly refused to admit that the cholera was real. That reaction was itself a response to fear, but it also indicated a deep seated suspicion of anything associated with the official world. Far from viewing the police and the cholera officials as saviors, the populace saw them as determined enemies who were to be resisted at all costs. The government's efforts were met with sullen opposition, and as the police campaign intensified during the first days of the epidemic, discontent swelled into angry resistance. The populace was in the grip of a growing hysteria to which the police and public health officials were not immune. The resistance which they met called for force to counteract it, and the cholera terror itself drove officials to more frantic efforts. Fear, ignorance, and ingrained brutality combined with officiousness and irresponsible authority to create an intolerable situation. No person was safe on the streets. The sick and the well, the inebriates and the infirm, were collared, dumped unceremoniously into the dreaded cholera carts, and hauled off willy-nilly to the lazarettes, often with whole families trailing the wagons wailing and weeping. It was no wonder that the "arrest" of a cholera patient inevitably was the signal for the gathering of a crowd.[42]

Though the people refused to believe it, the cholera was in the city, and men were dying. The deaths, however, were blamed on the police, on the physicians, on foreigners in general, and the cry of poison was raised again and again. Dimly it was thought that Russia's enemies had found an instrument with which to destroy all true Russians, and blind hatred of everything non-Russian reached fever pitch. Nor was that all, for Petersburgers, like their provincial cousins, feared the hospitals, and went to any lengths to avoid what seemed certain robbery or even murder. Moreover, physicians were believed to practice the black arts, and the news of dissections seemed to prove the darkest and most horrible imaginings. The foreign origin of many doctors only gave credence to these nightmares, and the fear of the non-Russian, the hatred for Russia's enemies, helped to identify physicians with Polish agents in the public mind. The final outcome was utter demoralization and mob violence.[43]

There is no evidence to indicate that the government, or more particularly the cholera committee, was in any way sensitive to the growing public clamor. The attitudes which Zakrevskii exhibited the year before appeared again in Petersburg. Terror was met with force, and the people were left to draw what comfort they could from a mounting number of regulations. Order followed order in bewildering succession. The people were exhorted to be calm, and hysteria was made a crime. The people were ordered to cease drawing drinking water from the canals; the police enforced the order with arrests, but no alternative source of water was provided. The people were ordered to keep warm, to avoid chills, to give up sleeping on the ground, to eschew the "flatulent" fruits and vegetables which were thought to increase the chance of cholera. And each order was followed with an effort to enforce it, and the busy police became busier. The poison scare reached official circles, and a poison prevention campaign was carried on in the midst of the cholera campaign. Charges of poison attempts proliferated, and arrests on suspicion of poisoning became common. Persons carrying powders for protection against the cholera were seized and made to swallow their preparations to prove their innocence, and the flimsiest suspicion was all that was necessary to cause an arrest. The first ten days of the cholera in Petersburg were sheer nightmare, and the government, far from alleviating the terror, actually heightened it.[44]

The first public reactions to the cholera were largely verbal, but as the terror spread, action followed. The police found it harder to perform their duties as hostile crowds gathered around them. Ambulances were seized and upset, the patients liberated, and with each new success, the crowd became bolder. The disaffection centered in the crowded Vasilii-Ostrov and Admiralty quarters, but its influence was felt throughout the city. The high point of popular excitement was reached in the period June 19 to June 26. Special services were held in Petersburg's churches to pray for deliverance, and solemn fast was observed as the power of God was invoked to counter the unknown terror.[45] The services brought people together, and as they left the churches, they gravitated toward the cholera hospitals. On June 21, a large crowd collected before the cholera lazarette on Rozhdestvenskaia Street, shouted abuse at the guards and attendants, and then attempted to storm the hospital. The attempt failed, but the mob milled around until a number were arrested and the remainder dispersed. In other sections, cholera ambulances were attacked; stones were thrown at the cholera hospitals; attacks on the lazarettes were thrown back by armed guards; and a rising tide of disquiet flowed through the city.[46]

By the following morning the situation had become uglier. The crowd was abroad with the morning light, and in the Haymarket district a mob which was numbered in the thousands collected through the day. Its mood was angry yet exalted as it taunted the thirty frightened men who guarded the cholera hospital or flung itself with shouts of "Hurrah! the Cholera!" on ambulances seeking to reach the hospital's haven. One physician, a German, was discovered attending a case, and was left a battered corpse. Others, physicians and attendants, were attacked and beaten, and the police, unable to control the situation, drifted out of the quarter. The mob overran the cholera hospital, liberated the sick and the dead, and with no one to oppose them, controlled the district. Peace was restored only when troops entered the quarter and dispersed the mob. Arrests were made, and more than one hundred persons were imprisoned, but the government was frightened, and further disturbances were expected hourly.[47]

The Haymarket riots were the most serious in the city, but the disaffection was widespread. Compared with the Sevastopol uprising the year before, the Petersburg cholera riots seemed less serious. The fact was, however, that the impact of the cholera itself, combined with the Tsar's intervention, broke the mob's cohesion and preserved the city from even more serious upheavals. The imperial summer residence at Peterhof had been placed under the tightest possible quarantine when the cholera was first reported, and Nicholas was in seclusion there mourning the recent death of the Grand Duke Constantine. Count Benkendorf's reports, however, indicated the unsettled conditions in the city, and when Prince Menshikov brought the news early in the morning of June 23 that the crisis had arrived, Nicholas immediately left for the city to use his personal influence to calm the storm.[48] Peterhof seemed another world from the terror-ridden city, and the court was oblivious to the dangers unleashed in the capital, but Nicholas grasped how serious the situation was, and moved to meet it.[49]

When the Tsar arrived in Petersburg, the aftermath of violence strewed the streets, and it was clear that the danger was not at an end. Knots and clusters of sullen citizens gathered on corners and in the squares, and the atmosphere was heavy with the promise of further trouble. Nicholas first toured the military posts, and then entered the city. All along his line of march he addressed the people exhorting them to calm, quiet, resignation, and obedience. The Tsar moved in a cluster of high officials, but without a military guard, relying on the impact of his personality and the power which he symbolized to protect himself and to quiet the frightened, angry populace. In the Haymarket more than 5,000 people awaited his coming compacted in the square and spilling over into adjoining streets. Nicholas stopped in the midst of them, rose in his carriage and in stentorian tones ordered them to draw nearer, to kneel down and cross themselves, then making the sign of the cross over them, he harangued them, speaking of the shame they had done him before the world, and shouting the rhetorical question, "Are you Poles or French to act so, or are you Russians?" He continued:

At my coronation I swore to maintain order and the laws: I shall keep my oath. To the virtuous I am kind, they will always find me a friend and a father, but woe to evil-doers! I am armed against them! I do not fear you, it is you who fear me! A great burden has been given us by God: a plague. We must take measures to stop its progress. All these measures have been taken by my orders! Therefore it is against *me* that you complain —Me! And I order obedience!

You, peaceful men, fathers of families, I have confidence in you, and I am persuaded that you will always be the first to enlighten the ignorant, to calm the mutinous! But woe unto those who oppose my orders: they will be hunted down without pity!

Now disperse! The plague reigns! It is not well to gather in a crowd— But before all we must reconcile ourselves with God!

If you have offended me by your disobedience, you have offended God still more by a crime: a murder has been committed! Innocent blood has been spilled!

Pray God that he forgive you! [50]

With these words Nicholas dismissed them, the mob gradually dispersed, and Zhukovskii tells us that from this time on there was order, the people were calm, and confidence was re-established. It has become part of the legend of Nicholas I that his personal intervention not only stilled the popular unrest, but that the cholera itself was checked, and fervent admirers of the Tsar have pointed to the Haymarket riots as proving once and for all Nicholas' courage and resourcefulness. This was not entirely fantasy, and the British medical observers in the Russian capital wrote home describing the courageous Tsar whose personal action calmed the mob and allowed the cholera work to proceed uninterrupted.[51]

Following Nicholas' appearance, there were no further outbreaks in St. Petersburg, though unrest continued for several days. The epidemic reached its greatest intensity following the cholera riots, and there can be little doubt that the disease itself was an important element in breaking public resistance and diffusing social antago- nism. The most violent public reactions during the cholera period regularly occurred either before the full impact of the epidemic was felt, or in areas where the disease was of minor importance, or even in regions which the cholera had passed over. During 1830, both the plague riots in Sevastopol and the cholera riots in Tambov occurred in situations which were only incidentally dangerous medically; the revolts in the military colonies and in Staraia Russa did not coincide with a major cholera outbreak; and both the Fast Day riots in London and the cholera riots in Paris, which came in 1832, occurred when the cholera itself was either an anticipated or remembered threat.[52] From this it would appear that the violence of an epidemic outbreak is such that at its height it vitiates every human energy except the drive to survival, and the search for individual security itself can destroy the unity of feeling which holds a mob together. Hysteria, as a mass phenomenon, appears to be worse in anticipation or retrospect, and while individual crimes of violence flourish during a time of intense public crisis, mass reactions tend to break down into their individual components. In these terms, the violence of the cholera epidemic in late June and early July in Petersburg worked to the advantage of the authorities who had to maintain order.

The government was aware that although the Petersburg disturbances had been quieted, potentially dangerous conditions still existed, and within the city it treated the post-riot situation with caution and circumspection. The English delegation which had visited the military hospitals under the guidance of Sir James Wylie offered to take charge of a number of cholera cases, but their offer was refused because of "the violent excitement of the people against all foreigners, more particularly against medical men, whom they lately looked on as emissaries employed by their enemies to poison them. . . ." Barry and Russell noted that on the day of writing (July 4), "the city is now perfectly tranquil, and the poor deluded people beg for the assistance of the very men whom but a day or two ago they would have torn to pieces," but despite this improvement the English doctors were allowed to do no more than observe.[53] A further evidence of the government's caution appeared in publicity policy. Previously, news of major uprisings has been published once the disturbances were over, and those responsible had been punished. The riots at Sevastopol, for example, were given full publicity, and the cholera riots themselves were finally publicized. This was not done until August, however, and the implication seems to be that the government saw a continuing danger for a month or more after the riots had actually happened.[54]

The most significant evidence of the government's concern was the *volte face* which was made in sanitary regulations, and the failure to follow up the Petersburg riots with strict investigations and punishments. Taking the second first, the Sevastopol rioters were severely punished, and those implicated in the riots in the military colonies were subjected to investigation, court martial, and either execution or transportation. The government was equally severe following the Tambov uprising. The Petersburg outbreak, on the other hand, was, to all intents, to be forgotten, and the people let off with a lecture. Undoubtedly, the government was correct in easing rather than tightening administrative controls, and a round of stringent punishments on top of the repressive measures which had set off the riots might very well have ignited further demonstrations. Nevertheless, the government's moderation astonished some contemporaries who felt that the guilty should have been sharply punished, and that the failure to do so only showed weakness.[55]

Nicholas I was notoriously stringent in all matters which affected public security, and in the light of traditional policy, the failure to press an intensive investigation of the Petersburg riots indicated both the weakness of the government's position and the fear of intensifying public resentment. This view is strengthened by the changes which took place in medical policy. Following the cholera riots the hospitals were forbidden to perform post mortems, except in the case of the General Military Hospital, and there only for the purpose of exploring an obscure cause of death, while the police were instructed to release the cordons around infected sections of the city and to moderate their handling of suspected cholera cases. Though the cordons were retained on the routes leading into St. Petersburg, the city itself was relieved of the most repressive regulations, and even the cholera hospitals were opened to free visitation by the members of the patients' families.[56] These decisions cannot be explained by a change in medical opinion, for the Medical Council remained fixed in its view that cholera was contagious, though it moved in the direction of "moderate" or "contingent" contagion, and non-contagion opinions had been ineffectual in the past in qualifying sequestration and quarantine measures. The conclusion follows that the government feared further outbreaks, was by no means sure they could be contained were they to happen, and was willing to contradict its own regulations for fear of further popular demonstrations. Finally, Petersburg was the only place where these amendments to the rules were carried through, and in other areas the former policies prevailed.[57]

The depredations of petty officialdom, which were so apparent in the Petersburg cholera troubles, became a public scandal, and the deep abyss separating the official world from the rest of society was plainly defined. The control measures which were introduced were harsh, but by the standards of contemporary sanitary policies not unduly so. Indeed, Barry and Russell reported to London that the government's precautionary measures were, "liberal, humane, and wise; but the populace is dissatisfied with the indiscriminate removal of their sick to the temporary hospitals."[58] The English observers were overly kind, and they failed to consider the political rigidity behind the regulations, which made literal interpretation mandatory. Count Zakrevskii's well-known theories gave the tone to the Petersburg cholera laws, for they emphasized the closest possible police and military control on every level, and lesser officials were given an open field with no restraints upon them.[59] Unfortunately, the lower orders of Russian officialdom were totally unprepared for such broad responsibilities, and the result was ruthless persecution of those they were supposed to protect. Count Paul Stroganov once described the Russian landholding gentry as brutal, debased, self-seeking, and ignorant, and he argued that Russia could never progress so long as this group was influential.[60] His point could equally have been applied to the lesser bureaucracy, the police, and the military who shared the responsibility for executing domestic policies. This was one of the most serious weaknesses in the Russian system, and it was one which was never eradicated.[61]

In so far as the Petersburg riots focused on the Poles, physicians, and officialdom, they shared common ground with other protests which were made during the cholera years. The public outcry was not against the owners of property or the possessors of wealth, but against the instruments of a mindless political order which was as brutalized as the self-seeking sycophants who served it. The protest was diffused, lacking organization, and possessing only the impetus of emotional reaction. And it was directed against the arm of the state rather than its head, for only a handful of intellectuals could see that the Tsar was the essence of the system, and that responsibility for the nation's daily administration really rested with him. The cholera riots defined the direction of social animus, but they also reflected the occasional and fragmentary nature of social protests. Despite the violence which flared in 1830 and 1831, there was substantial loyalty as well, and the cholera riots exposed conditions which needed to be rectified before that loyalty was finally eroded.

It was believed that the flight from Petersburg carried panic to the outlying districts, and ultimately spread it across European Russia.

Actually, this is doubtful, for the reactions which were exhibited at Reval, for example, paralleled and preceded those at Petersburg and scarcely needed the inspiration of the capital.[62] The poison hysteria appeared everywhere in the forefront and on the flanks of the cholera, and, becoming part of the terror which the cholera's approach generated, created turmoil throughout the area from Moscow to the Baltic. The most serious disturbances, outside St. Petersburg, were the riots which occurred in the city of Staraia Russa and in the Novgorod military colonies. Panic struck there well ahead of the cholera, and latent antagonisms, endemic to the region, exploded into revolution. Nicholas described the genesis of the outbreak in the following terms:

> Crimes alien to the generous and Orthodox Russian population have been committed in the city of Staraia Russa and in the districts of the military colonies of the Corps of Grenadiers, where the peasants, aroused by rumors of poisonings, have vented their suspicions on the doctors and on their own leaders, and have forgotten the obedience prescribed toward the authorities by the Holy Church. . . .[63]

The official report on the uprising gave a more detailed picture and stressed the panic which struck the military colonies in advance of an anticipated cholera outbreak. The panic took the form of a poison hysteria, and the population became firmly convinced that a gigantic conspiracy against them existed, which implicated both the military chiefs of the district and their accomplices, the physicians.[64] What the report did not make clear was the grounds for popular hatred against the military administration. The military colonies were introduced into Russia before the Napoleonic invasion and were modelled on the Austrian frontier colonies. Their initial purpose was to create a self-sustaining militia which would partially alleviate the immense financial burden which the standing military establishment put on an antiquated and admittedly inadequate fiscal system, and at the same time bring discipline and enlightenment to the countryside. There is serious question whether the colonies were even an economic success, though they were represented as such, and in human terms they were a ghastly failure. The colonists lived under the worst possible conditions. Harsh discipline was enforced; an inequitable distribution of land, and especially time for working the land, produced hardships, while individuals lacked even the freedom that a bondsman had. Living conditions were abominable.

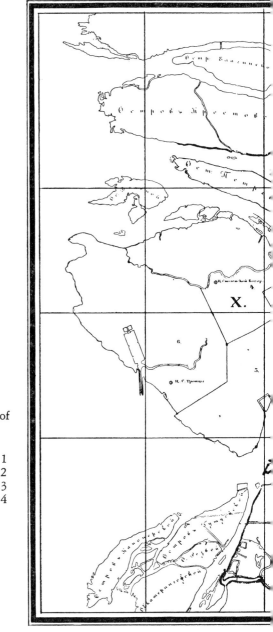

Administrative Districts of
St. Petersburg, 1831

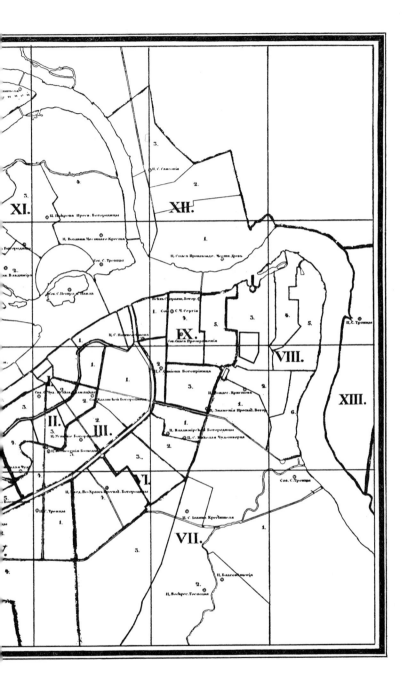

The houses in which the colonists lodged were crowded, badly constructed, and cold. Food was often scarce, and the peasants bitterly resented military discipline and the rigid controls on family life. The military colonies were an especially black mark on the blotted book of Russian social policies, a mark which needed desperately to be eradicated.[65]

Even before 1831, there was widespread disenchantment with the colony system. After the Napoleonic Wars, a series of disturbances rocked the colonies; the Decembrists pointed to them as one significant abuse which needed immediate elimination, and even the nobility resented the special taxes established for their maintenance. Officially, the government expressed its gratification at the colonies' economic success, but there was also a strong feeling that the program needed substantial revision. Several reforms were proposed, each moving farther from the original principle, and in 1827 the French Ambassador, Count de la Ferronnay, reported that Nicholas' most recent proposals "indicated the imminent abandonment of the system of military colonisation." [66]

The riots began in the city of Staraia Russa where relations between the inhabitants and the military had been so strained as to force a decision to move the military headquarters. An amorous soldier, who was thought to be determined to rid himself of an exigent woman demanding marriage as the aftermath of intimacy, provided the spark, for he was seized while bearing spirits of vitriol to his unwanted intended. A physician's declaration that the fumes of this substance, used in cholera fumigations, were harmless went unheeded, and as the police refused to act, a crowd of frightened and angry inhabitants killed the accused while trying to discover his accomplices. The news of the murder, and the alleged poisoning which provoked it, spread like wild-fire. And as it spread it fed on the hysterical fears and well-founded hatreds of the people until it became a roaring blaze consuming everything in its path. Physicians, officers, and administrative officials were wiped out in a dreadful holocaust which scorched every settlement but one in the district, and which only ended when it burned itself out.[67]

The Tsar, convinced that the revolution he had feared in Petersburg had become a reality in the countryside, moved rapidly to counteract the riots' effects and to localize the conflagration. Regular troops were readied, and General-Adjutant Count Orlov, Count Stroganov, and Prince Dolgorukii were dispatched to the trouble centers to disarm the rioters. The peak of the terror had passed, but smoldering resentment against degradation, privation, persecution, and exploitation remained, while the charges of conspiracy and murder were repeated again and again. A delegation of sixty colonists was passed by Count Orlov to interview the Tsar and lay their complaints before him. Nicholas saw them at Izhora, and as they kneeled before him, berated them for their behavior and tried to demonstrate the harmlessness of the medicine which they accused. Though the Tsar thought otherwise, the delegation remained unconvinced, and murder remained to them a more real danger than disease.[68]

Nicholas did not repeat the exercise in moderation which he tried in Petersburg, and he resolved to court-martial the rioters. The units considered most responsible were marched to Petersburg, and the punishments that followed were both public and ferocious. Birches, rods, and the knout were all employed; more than 2500 men were bloodied and beaten, and 129 lay dead when justice's orgy was finally finished.[69] An effort to reform the military colonies came later, and the institution eventually was liquidated. But wrong-doing needed to be punished first, and the mentality which created the conditions and atmosphere which prepared the revolt, shone darkly through the ugly retribution which followed it.

The revolts in Petersburg and the military colonies prepared new terrors which burgeoned with the cholera panic and ignited further explosions throughout European Russia. Public confidence was badly shaken, and horror followed concern as the stories of rebellion and unrest proliferated. At Savidova, a former imperial residence on the great postroad to Petersburg, four thousand peasants burst their bonds, murdered the police master, and rioted through the district, and the news of this uprising only bespoke further and more extended troubles. Tales of Pugachev revived as the nobility confronted the never distant fear of a full-scale peasant rising, and in Moscow Christine compared the riots to the peasant outbreaks in France at the time of the Revolution, and speculated on the possibility of a peasant reign of terror, a true *Jacquerie*, in Russia.[70]

The revolutionary disturbances of 1831 developed out of hysteria about the cholera, but their total effects ran far beyond the disease itself. Nevertheless, the cholera played a crucial role in the psychological mechanism which produced the rebellions by creating public hysteria and eroding social inhibitions. The 1831 epidemic produced social behavior comparable to that in 1830, but the reactions were more intense, and the poison scare suggested more complicated responses than those of the previous year. The cholera in 1830 brought disruption, hysteria, and isolated instances of outright rebellion. In 1831, the revolts were more serious, the evidence of hysteria wider spread, and the strain on the government consequently greater. In both years, however, the social reactions which produced violence occurred in those areas where social problems already existed. Where such conditions did not exist, the terror dissipated itself in religious fervor, in outbursts against popular scapegoats, in looting and destroying, in quackery and pseudo-medical faddism. The second response clearly had elements in common with the first. What distinguished it was its formlessness, its lack of orientation and direction—the absence of a cause. The cholera revolts pinpointed particular issues which threatened Russian stability, while the more general responses indexed the range of popular fears and resentments which provide the psychological substratum of revolution.

One constant in the Russian reactions to the cholera was the hatred of officialdom, but this constant introduced a variable, for apart from the military colonies, popular reactions were most destructive where sanitary controls were most stringent. A policy of *laissez passer* could, as it did in 1829 and early 1830, allow public hysteria to dissipate in flight, but the effort to contain that hysteria, to freeze movement and control the public's behavior, led to serious trouble. Such restrictions produced a focus for hysteria, for quarantine lines and an active sanitary policy were a natural target for public resentment. The classic example of this reaction occurred in St. Petersburg where the cholera riots were directly attributable to the implementation of extreme control measures.

Another element contributed to the Petersburg riots, however, which was potentially more significant than administrative bumbling, for the cholera riots suggested the formation of an urban mob. It is true that the popular attitudes which appeared during the uprising were rural, but this only indicated that the Petersburg mob was not yet indigenous, and that the indigent elements were drawn almost exclusively from the countryside. What is more important, however, is that certain general indications of urban dislocation had also appeared, and these created conditions favorable to social distemper.

Petersburg, among all of Russia's cities, conformed most closely to the urban patterns of contemporary European centers. This is not simply a restatement of the old saw that "Petersburg is Paris without two thousand years of culture," but rather is recognition of some basic demographic facts. One of the most significant of these was population growth, for Russia's first capital has passed through three decades of very rapid expansion. Part of this growth could be laid to commercial development; for during those thirty years Petersburg became Russia's leading northern commercial center —a development which swelled the demand for public services and drew people into the city in search of opportunity.[71] In addition, the building programs associated with the Imperial residence and the development of the capital itself created a continuing demand for labor, while expanding maritime facilities of all sorts required a growing number of people. All this activity was reflected in the population figures, for in 1800 Petersburg had been a city of some 220,000, roughly comparable to Moscow, and indeed somewhat smaller. By 1833, however, Petersburg had more than doubled her population, attaining a figure of 443,000.[72] Moscow grew much more slowly during that same period, and of course was hurt by the Napoleonic invasion. In 1811, Moscow's population was given as 265,000, and by 1830 had reached, at the most, 305,000.[73]

Petersburg's population grew more rapidly than the city's capacity to serve it, although this is not immediately apparent from the descriptions of the capital in the early nineteenth century. Travellers were impressed with the magnificent public buildings, the broad boulevards, and the elaborate dwellings of the great nobility. Some turned their eyes downward and saw that storm sewers had been constructed, and that sidewalks which were raised above street level eased the pedestrians' lot, but these same observers looked past or through the evidences of overcrowding and misery.[74] Yet in 1825, with a stated population of 438,000, Petersburg had but 7,126 dwellings of all kinds. This, on an average, meant sixty-one persons per domicile. By comparison, Moscow, in that same year, for a given population of 241,514 (which may be a low figure), reported 10,000 domiciles, or an average of twenty-four persons per dwelling.[75] Compacted living conditions produce social tensions, and the problems of overcrowding were complicated by the large transient population. Only estimates are available for enumerating this group, but one such placed its number in 1831 at 53,000, and the figure was probably larger.[76] A part of this number was foreign merchants and those connected with their establishments, but a substantial portion represented peasants coming to St. Petersburg in search of work. This latter group especially added to the large lower class population and to the social problems which that population posed.[77]

Other facilities besides housing were lacking in St. Petersburg. We noted in an earlier chapter that the two capitals had the best medical facilities in the Empire, but that those facilities were inadequate. In 1831, Petersburg had 59 formally established hospitals of all types which provided a total of 7,000 beds. Of this number, however, 5,265 were for military units or for military training institutions. At the most there were fewer than 1,000 beds available in the entire city for the general population, and there were a scant 500 beds available for women.[78] With relatively little attention paid to basic sanitary controls, and with medical care almost unavailable for the lower classes, infant mortality averaged 367 deaths out of every 1,000, while the death rate for those between late adolescence and full maturity, a much larger population group, was 397 per 1,000. Academician Hermann commented that, "early maturity ordinarily provided the greatest number of deaths," and explained it, "by the heavy labor of the lower classes, by the efforts of fortuneless employees to advance in their career, by the abuse by more elevated persons of their strength and welfare, and above all at St. Petersburg, by the sudden change of temperature to which this age pays little attention."[79] What he failed to add was that debilitation where strength should have been the rule indicated endemic social maladjustments.

The evidence concerning the peasant revolts in 1831 is clear, and the abuses which the cholera riots defined are well known. In Petersburg, however, an unusual combination of circumstances existed. The lower classes showed the attitudes which were consistent with a peasant Russian background, and their scapegoats differed little, if at all, from those of rural Russia. The biological realities of their existence, however, were different, and the urban conditions under which they lived posed a different kind of problem. It might be suggested that the Petersburg experience with the cholera pointed a new direction and new issues for the autocracy. The serf question was of the first importance, but the necessity of providing for the needs of an urban group was beginning to appear.[80]

Taken altogether, the 1831 cholera epidemic produced a collapse in popular morale which affected every aspect of Russian society. The immediate fear of the disease brought hysteria; the attempt to rationalize the epidemic fostered even more awful fears; and the popular disturbances which attended these reactions added further to the turmoil. The revolutions of 1830 passed Russia by, but the events of 1831 pointed to deep rooted social tensions and basic cleavages in Russian society. As the cholera provided the psychological impetus which brought protests against those conditions, it gave Russia and her Tsar further evidence of the need for fundamental changes.

One important area where immediate reform was possible was administration, and the cholera epidemic clearly indicated the sterile and ritualistic character of Russian bureaucratism at the same time that it provided a shocking lesson in the dangers attendant on unbridled and irresponsible authority. Nevertheless, one practical lesson was learned, and though it happened by default, local officials were allowed a wider scope for initiative and action in 1831 than had been the case in 1830.[81] The Central Cholera Commission, that futile exercise in mobile centralization, was not called into being in 1831, and its former head was only a member of the directing executive of the Petersburg Cholera Council. There was no formal revision of the decree requiring all cholera decisions, and particularly sanitary measures, to be cleared through St. Petersburg, but in practice the rule was forgotten, and local officials and local cholera councils carried the brunt of the campaign. In some cases, administrators were sent out from the capital to perform special tasks, and the areas where revolts occurred were given special handling, but there was no effort to repeat the experiment in co-ordination which was attempted in 1830. The Medical Council of the Ministry of the Interior continued to publish instructions and to advise the Tsar and the Council of Ministers, but this work was done through normal administrative channels, and the Tsar and his advisers continued to make decisions concerning external quarantines, commerce, army recruiting, and other national issues.[82] No blanket authorization for local initiative on cholera questions was ever given, and whatever autonomy local administrators exercised was the result of a grudging admission that the logistics of a cholera campaign did not readily fit a centralized system. Indeed, it was not until the reform period of 1861–1864 that formal steps were taken to approve a degree of local autonomy on questions of sanitary policy and public health measures.[83]

Although the effort to achieve centralization in 1830 created serious problems, it cannot be said that the more relaxed approach of 1831 markedly improved government efficiency. Drug shortages, personnel shortages, and abuses of all kinds were reported through the 1831 epidemic, and the widespread public disturbances further complicated the administrative problem. From the standpoint of the mechanics of administration, the procedures associated with centralization had been a dismal failure. But the horrible debacle for which the Petersburg Cholera Council bore primary responsibility showed just as clearly that a reorientation of administrative principle was not enough. The bureaucratic mentality which failed to grasp social realities on a national scale in 1830 showed itself to be equally insensitive in a limited sphere in 1831. Count Zakrevskii, whose political career shattered on the cholera crisis, attempted to explain his failures by blaming opposition in the Council of Ministers which prevented the implementation of his plans, and by pointing out the failure of local officials to co-operate, as well as the persistent shortages in both men and medical supplies which hamstrung his efforts.[84] Much of what Zakrevskii said in his own defense was true, and there can be no doubt that he was the handy scapegoat needed to explain failures which otherwise raised dangerous and unanswerable questions. What Zakrevskii did not grasp was that the measures he espoused not only did not fit the administrative necessities of the cholera campaign, but they worsened social distress and all but guaranteed public resistance. Though other factors were also influential, the improvement in the public state of mind in Petersburg after the rigid control system was scuttled clearly indicated where one of the major faults lay, but this was precisely the point which Zakrevskii never saw.[85]

Rigid centralization and administrative formalism both symbolized and fostered insensitivity to public reactions and human needs, but the abrogation of that principle did not guarantee responsiveness, and in 1831, as in 1830, the primary administrative failure was human. The continuing tension between public officials and private persons reflected the government's inability to perform fundamental social services and reinforced the popular identification of public servants with exploitation and persecution. This problem did not yield readily to mere institutional reforms, though it was worsened by bureaucratism's impersonal practices, and it was not to be solved simply by granting local autonomy. Perhaps it might be said that the government, including the Tsar, missed the real problem which the cholera raised until it was too late, for the cholera, though a dreadful scourge, was less dangerous ultimately than the reactions which it fostered. The blind assault upon the disease with weapons unfitted to the task, blunted by ignorance, and dangerous mainly to their wielders, was an open invitation to disaster. With neither cure nor sure prevention known, the best that could be done was to ease suffering, preserve public confidence, reduce friction, and foster, harmony. These goals were too little considered and too seldom realized, but they were not unknown, and the French observers in Russia thoughtfully pondered the lessons of the cholera riots:

> We have just read with special interest all the official documents relative to the organization and work of the temporary medical council [in Moscow] presided over by His Excellency the Governor-General Prince Dmitri Golitsyn. This council, by its constant calm, prudent, and courageous conduct, knew how to save Moscow from a peril even more redoubtable than the cholera: we wish to speak of the popular outbreaks which have constantly accompanied the measures which were believed to be repressive of contagion.[86]

The administration's role was crucial, and its failures, especially in 1831, contributed to a wave of unrest which beat against the foundations of the state itself. But those foundations remained strong, and if the government was unable to ease its subjects' plight, it was still capable of containing their resentments. The cholera period also showed, however, that Russia was changing, that new problems were growing out of old, and that new potentialities were gradually unfolding. The misery, ignorance, and degradation of the peasant classes were old and continuing refrains, but new themes emerged faintly with the plight of special segments of Moscow's population and the growing evidence of urban dislocation in St. Petersburg. Russia, though still predominantly peasant and rural, was gaining the foretaste of the problems of urbanization and modernity. Many of the burdens which Russia bore in 1830 and 1831 were both familiar and old, but new paths were opening as well to confuse her stumbling feet.

As summer gave way to fall, the cholera again receded, and though sporadic outbreaks occurred during the winter and spring of 1832, the first epidemic period was finished. The cholera moved on to the West: to Austria and Prussia, the Germanies, France, England, and finally to the Americas, and wherever it appeared it brought dismay, dislocation, terror, and death. The cholera moved like the conscience of the nineteenth century, for it settled in the discreetly veiled cesspools of human misery, and it was difficult to ignore the noxious horrors that its presence brought to view. To the West, reformers stirred, prodded by conscience's pointing finger; but in Russia, the cholera's passing brought only relief and no reforms. The task which Russia's rulers needed to perform had been defined before, and the cholera served to sharpen the lesson's point. The epidemic's final tragedy was that this opportunity, like so many before and after, passed without the lessons being learned, and the victims of both disease and riots died to no purpose. The Russian autocracy showed its greatest strength as it defended itself, its greatest purpose as it destroyed its enemies, its greatest weakness as it prepared for the future.

Chapter 6

RUSSIAN MEDICINE AND THE CHOLERA

The cholera spread destruction and despair throughout Russia, and there was little cause for pride or optimism in the nation's reactions. Private individuals and corporations gave time, money, and property, and the response to danger which followed the hysteria in Moscow showed the public's moral fiber, but this behavior stood out starkly against the darker patterns of administrative bungling and brutality, and the explosive violence of peasant hatreds. Even the successes which the administration scored merely showed old Russia at its best, containing little prospect of social or administrative progress, while the terrible failures which brought the uprisings of 1831 overshadowed the modest successes won in Moscow and the Divans. On balance, the cholera period presented a massive indictment of the autocratic system, of the social and economic foundations on which it rested, and of the men standing at its head. The cholera also, however, brought briefly into public view one aspect of a quiet social revolution which was taking place by means of education. In an earlier chapter, we traced the outlines of medical development in Russia to 1830, and we suggested that the first cholera pandemic marked the maturation of Russian medicine's professional development. Here was one bright spot in the cholera record, one indication of future progress, one hint that Russia was changing from within.

Russian medicine's role in the cholera epidemic has three dimensions of historical significance. First, Russian doctors deserved every recognition for their record of courage and sacrifice. Second, despite immense handicaps, Russian physicians were able to ease suffering and save lives, though their efforts were not always understood or appreciated. Third, and most important, Russian medical writings on cholera showed a sophistication, a dedication to modern, and in the broadest sense liberal ideas which paralleled contemporary Russian creative literature. Here were minds that were emancipated, minds cast in the modern scientific mold, yet minds that were imbued with a humanitarian tradition. The medical profession was very small, but it was part of a new and growing element in Russian society which was drawn from a diversity of social backgrounds, and which represented neither the dominant greater gentry nor the administrative aristocracy. To call this group a middle class without qualification would be misleading, for its basic character was formed through education rather than economics, and its orientation was professional, not commercial. Nor can it, in the special Russian sense, be called an "intelligentsia," though the newly developed professional groups fostered the creative intelligentsia and provided a significant part of its audience.[1] The new professional groups formed a third estate which demanded reform and ended by allying with the revolution.

The Russian medical profession responded nobly to the cholera challenge, and in the face of overwhelming obstacles performed its duties with courage and imagination. The persistent shortage of drugs, the almost complete lack of adequate hospital facilities, the ignorance, insensitivity, and jealousy of administrative officials, and above all, the tragic shortages of trained personnel made its task all but impossible. The people's fears compounded these difficulties, for the terror which the disease inspired intensified deep rooted suspicions of the doctors themselves, and the danger of physical violence was added to the ever present possibility of infection. It required raw physical courage to enter the cholera hospitals or to visit the homes of the afflicted, yet the work was carried forward, and though several gave their lives to the cholera or the mob, there was no slackening of the unremiting effort to stem the disease.[2]

Although it cannot be said that the results which Russian physicians achieved were commensurate either with the enormity of the epidemic or the immense energy spent by individuals to combat it, there were evidences that the doctors' work was not entirely unavailing. Even during the Moscow outbreak, when the first disillusion with current treatments reached positive despair, the mortality rates showed improvement in those instances where full and early treatment could be given, while regions which were totally without medical care, or which lacked any but the most primitive facilities, often showed excessively high death figures.[3] Furthermore, it was only in retrospect that the physicians' real contributions were recognized, and the medical profession itself was terribly aware of its failures. The previous literature had presented the optimistic thesis that cholera, given early discovery, was curable, but the Moscow epidemic brought a rude awakening, and medical men were forced to revise their thinking. The first fifteen days of the Moscow cholera produced a stunning death rate, and during the month of October, toward the end of which the epidemic began to abate, of 5,532 reported cases, 3,107 died.[4] During the epidemic's greatest intensity, no cure produced reliable results, and all seemed to fail far more often than they succeeded. This in itself was bad enough, but a further development during December and January, when the disease was gradually disappearing, completed the scientists' frustration, for in that period every method seemed to work consistently and effectively. Dr. F. C. M. Markus summed up this cruel dilemma in the Cholera Council's formal report:

> After every effort was made without success, or with varied success, the epidemic began to decline, and cures became more frequent day by day. Then complete discouragement followed the illusory belief that the method employed at the moment was that which was to be preferred. If, at the beginning of the epidemic, one were saddened by the lack of success which all methods presented in general, on the other hand, during the epidemic's decline, it was very surprising to see that not only each of these same methods, but even each isolated means, offered numerous cures, and often very promptly.[5]

The disillusion which breathed through the Moscow report was not dispelled in 1831. Violent controversies flared over therapeutic techniques, and no acceptable evidence appeared to settle the contenders' claims. One special report on cholera treatments in Petersburg hospitals listed thirteen separate and distinct methods of therapy, but the mortality statistics which were included in the resumé gave no substantial grounds for preferring any one.[6] Indeed one medical scientist, Professor Diad'kovskii, wrote in 1831 that the controversy over treatments had reached the point where it was obscuring some facts, the most important being that no treatment was so good as its proponents claimed, nor any so bad as its opponents charged.[7] On the latter point, Diad'kovskii himself exaggerated, for some treatments were as bizarre as they were ineffective, lacking any foundation in sense or science. This condition was by no means restricted to Russia, and as late as 1857 it was recorded that medical workers were using nearly every element in the *materia medica* to cure cholera, and often recommended obviously contradictory techniques in the same treatment. The discovery of the *vibrio cholerae* improved therapy, but it was only in the twentieth century that an effective and consistent treatment was developed.[8]

This did not mean that the first cholera epidemic bred only errors, nor should it be taken to suggest that there is nothing of medical interest in this period. Dr. Pollitzer found the roots of several basic ideas in the first pandemic period, and Russian physicians themselves were far better than the strictures which they launched at one another might lead us to believe. Before the fall of 1830, Russian medical publications mirrored views which appeared initially in the Indian cholera reports, but during the Moscow epidemic new ideas began to appear, and by the end of 1831 a core of substantial cholera studies had been published. The best of this work emanated from the Moscow Cholera Council and the Medical Council of the Ministry of Interior, but individual physicians also wrote memoranda and formal scientific papers which contained important contributions.[9] This literature as a whole dealt with more than treatment, presenting a unified attack on the related problems of cause, contagiousness, and cure. The prevailing tone was pragmatic, and the writings summarized current experience, but repeated efforts also were made to develop a "philosophical" analysis which would justify the therapies suggested while giving some basis for classifying the disease. These efforts produced some interesting, provocative, and even valid conclusions.

Progress in scientific knowledge seldom follows a simple line from fallacy to truth, and the cholera problem was no exception. Russian doctors convinced neither their contemporaries nor themselves that their answers were definitive, and many of their arguments missed by an extremely wide margin the truth as it was later revealed. At the same time, those Russian cholera publications which appeared in Europe broadened the base for understanding the disease, and at the very least gave the rest of the scientific world additional suggestions and facts to contemplate. The misfortune was that the best of Russian writings were unknown, or only partially known, in the west, and the most important composite work issued by the Medical Council of the Ministry of the Interior passed completely unnoticed. As a consequence, contemporary medical science missed some of the most trenchant judgments offered by the best of Russia's new medical group, and modern medical histories still have little to say concerning early Russian contributions to the cholera problem.[10]

The first question that demanded an answer was what cholera really was, and it was precisely this question that medical science was unable to answer. There was never any serious doubt that the cholera that attacked Russia was also the disease which had wasted India and the Far East, but this only identified the disease and did not define it. There was confusion initially between the "cholera" as Sydenham described it in the seventeenth century, and the disease that decimated Asia and later Europe in the nineteenth century. Sydenham's cholera was not epidemic, and when Professor Diad'-kovskii wrote the essays on cholera typology for the Medical Council's general treatise, he was very careful to distinguish between what he styled *cholera sporadica* and *cholera epidemico-contagiosa.*[11]

This distinction, which is still valid, led Diad'kovskii to discuss the respective causes of the two diseases, and in doing so to develop the proposition that there was no necessary relationship between them. *Cholera sporadica,* as Diad'kovskii described it, could be taken for a simple case of gastro-enteritis, although both the pre-disposing and immediate causes were different. The pre-disposing causes included an excessively sensitive stomach and intestines, obesity, and other pathological conditions which impaired the functioning of the digestive tract. The *causae excitantes* included too rapid cooling of the body, especially when overheated, indigestible food, immoderate consumption of fruits, vegetables, or sweets, narcotic poisons, and emotional disturbances which affected the digestive organs, and particularly the liver.[12] The immediate cause, then, was irritation of the digestive canal which produced unnatural movement and in turn affected the functioning of all dependent organs. Finally, the disease changed from "nervous-catarrhal" at the beginning to "nervous-inflammatory" in the later stages.[13]

What is interesting here is that the very points which Diad'kovskii stressed as the *causae excitantes* for *cholera sporadica* were the specific elements covered in the public instructions to control epidemic cholera. The repeated instructions to avoid excesses in food and drink, to avoid fruits and vegetables, to avoid sudden chills or the consumption of cold drinks all applied to *cholera sporadica.* Diad'kovskii explained that this was true because there was constant confusion between epidemic cholera and its less dangerous double, and he strongly implied that the recommendations for public protection were aimed at a disease of secondary importance, while controls against epidemic cholera would have to be of a different order.[14]

The cause for *cholera sporadica* was contained within the human organism itself and became operative through environmental influences, but epidemic cholera, in Diad'kovskii's opinion, was produced by the action of a contagious substance which he called the *contagium cholericum.* What this substance was, was unknown, and the way that it was communicated could only be guessed, but Diad'kovskii treated the *contagium* as an autonomous entity which entered the human body and then followed a defined course of development within the host organism. Diad'kovskii defined the cycles of the *contagium* in terms of epidemic patterns, and he noted that each outbreak passed through five stages: the initial period or onset; the period of increase; the summum or culmination; the decline or possible secondary summum; and finally the disappearance. The symptoms of the disease varied in intensity in each stage, as did the mortality which the disease produced, and treatments needed to be tailored to the particular phase of both the epidemic and the individual case.[15] Diad'kovskii could not explain why this pattern occurred, nor could most of his contemporaries, although an early microbe theory which was presented during 1830 argued that the pattern reflected the life cycle of an organism, and that stomach acids actually destroyed the cholera *contagium.*[16]

Although he treated *contagium cholericum* as an autonomus substance, Diad'kovskii was certain that external conditions, or environment, were important in worsening its effects and contributed to its spread. Both weather and topography could create circumstances which would make people more receptive to the cholera substance, but dirty living conditions and an irregular way of life were the most important contributory causes.[17] Such contributory causes, however, again were peripheral to the main fact that cholera was transmitted directly from person to person. It was precisely here that Diad'kovskii's argument was weakest for he was unable to suggest the means of transmission. His reasoning was based on historical evidence concerning cholera's movement, the way the disease attacked some villages and not others, and the appearance of human "carriers" in those places where cholera broke out. All this was too tentative to allow any final conclusions, and Diad'kovskii recognized this fact.[18] The concept of *cholera epidemico-contagiosa* and the related idea of the *contagium cholericum* was near to pure a priorism, though supported with a kind of quantitative data. The problem was that the information used was statistical, geographical, and descriptive, and no method of organic research had yet appeared which could provide the facts, and ultimately the answers, to the problem of cholera's etiology.

Other writers were less modest than Diad'kovskii, and several theories were offered which defined the means of transmission in a variety of ways. One of the most common was the idea that the cholera was the product of a miasma generated by a combination of environmental factors including temperature, humidity, winds, topography, and similar elements. This view gathered strength both in Russia and Europe, and as we noted earlier only the discovery of the *vibrio cholerae* destroyed its influence. Even Diad'kovskii admitted that he was drawn to the miasmal theory, and it was a doctrine that won many adherents. Others tried to explain the cholera by reference to the spoilage of fruits, vegetables, and wheat bread from excessive moisture, and this explanation was often joined to a theory of miasma. In Petersburg, the people were forbidden to draw water from the canals for fear it was contaminated, but no general theory of water as a carrier for cholera was suggested, though it was noted that the disease followed the rivers and attacked the waterfronts. Finally, some convinced contagionists spoke of microscopic "animals" passing through the air and falling on people, thus infecting them. Though this doctrine gained some support, it was generally considered farfetched.[19]

Professor Diad'kovskii's ideas represented one main stream of Russian cholera thinking, though other authors varied particular details. Professor Venediktov, for example, who discussed the efficient cause of cholera as well as the pre-disposing causes, took a position similar to Diad'kovskii's in which he emphasized dirt and depressed living conditions as well as unsuitable foods as pre-disposing causes for the cholera, but he also found the ultimate cause in a *contagium specificum* whose essence was completely unknown, and could very well remain unknown. Indeed, Venediktov pointed out that direct investigation of cholera was very dangerous if not impossible since the contagious substance was the product of a live organism and was probably a weightless gas. The only proofs Venediktov could offer were parallels between the cholera and other contagious fevers, but he did state explicitly a point which was implicit in Diad'kovskii's essays, that the cholera was not absolutely contagious and that there had to be interaction between previously established conditions in the body and the contagion itself to produce the disease.[20]

M. Ya. Mudrov developed a somewhat different approach. Without really attempting to explore the nature of the communicable contagion, he declared the cholera, "moderately contagious"; that is, that cholera, though less readily communicated than some diseases, was still directly communicable through contact with a patient, and particularly a corpse, or by breathing air which had been tainted or which contained the miasma emanating from the dead and dying. The idea that cholera was a miasmal disease had, of course, been suggested earlier, and had produced serious questions concerning the effectiveness of quarantines. Mudrov, however, pointed out that the source of the miasma was in the cholera patients themselves rather than in nature at large, and he concluded that, "it is impossible to repudiate precautions for effective quarantine [just] because cholera is a drifting disease." [21] Mudrov accepted the theory of predisposing causes and argued that there were effective countermeasures to protect the individual against the cholera, the most important being close attention to diet, the avoidance of chilling, and abstinence from intoxicating beverages or cold drinks. Since there was a danger of direct communication, Mudrov also recommended that where home care was provided, those who had to touch a cholera patient smear their hands with grease or oil and that the patient be isolated from the remainder of the family. Finally, he regarded fumigation or thorough cleansing of a cholera victim's room to be a necessary protective measure against the miasma itself.[22]

The Medical Council of the Ministry of Interior generally held to the position that the cholera was the result of the action of a "contagious principle" which developed within the human organism and was transmitted directly through contact, or indirectly through miasma to other organisms. This was essentially the view held by Diad'kovskii, Venediktov, Reman, Mudrov, Lichtenstaedt, and many more. None of those who held the contagionist position, however, overlooked the importance of environment, and though they explored the idea that the *contagium cholericum* was an independent "principle" or organism, they also insisted on the important role played by the individual's way of life. A memorandum presented to the Moscow Cholera Council in April, 1831, summed up the position succinctly. The cholera, it argued, was transmitted, "by means of the vital influence (organic and dynamic) of a sick organism on a healthy one...," but it went on to suggest that, "the contagious character [of the disease] is able mainly to develop in crowded dwellings, dirty and encumbered with inhabitants, [and] in low and wet localities." The memorandum closed with the idea that the cholera, while communicable, was less so than the bubonic plague, and even less than the contagious fevers.[23]

Interestingly enough, the viewpoint called "moderate" or "contingent" contagion was most strongly held in Petersburg, and the greatest opposition to this view developed in Moscow. Only a minority of Moscow physicians clung to contagionist theories, while the majority favored an "epidemic constitution" which, combined with "pre-disposing causes," explained the development and spread of the disease. Dr. Loder argued vehemently that he knew of no instance of the cholera being communicated from person to person, and he cited his own experience in tending the sick as positive proof. Dr. Jeremias Lichtenstaedt attacked Loder very sharply for his stand, but Loder's view remained the majority position.[24] In the official report, Dr. Markus was as outspoken as Dr. Loder, but much more detailed. Markus argued that in all contagious diseases there was a "principle" or "agent" which was transmissible from person to person, and which was endowed with the capacity to give birth to an identical disease. Markus did not identify the agent as an autonomous organism, but saw it as the product of a "pathological state" which was sometimes in a fixed or permanent form and which was analagous to a morbid secretion. At other times the agent existed in a volatile state analagous to vapor, odoriferous particles, or gas, and could transmit itself from one organism to another by means of direct contact or by clinging to certain bodies which could preserve it. All means of transmission, whether mediate or immediate, constituted a common center from which the disease could propagate itself by contact in all directions as human communications made it possible. The cholera, in Markus' opinion, possessed none of these properties, and therefore could not be considered a contagious disease.[25]

The effort to distinguish between a contagious disease and an epidemic disease was common in the arguments over the cholera, but the arguments which Markus adduced did little more than exhibit the limitations of his methodology. His outright denial of the contagious character of cholera was based on reasoning by analogy, and in a long, discursive essay, he attempted to show that the symptoms and characteristic phenonema associated with cholera did not conform to those of diseases which were acknowledged to be contagious, and he concluded that, "We have no right to suppose *a priori* a contagious principle in a disease which shows none of the phenomena attributed to contagious diseases." [26] Markus here was actually developing a theme which had been laid down by the English author, Bell, in his *Treatise on Cholera Asphyxia* (1831), and Markus cited Bell's concluding argument to clinch his own: "It [cholera] has not, therefore, in its mode of attack, in its course or in its termination any of the characters of those diseases which experience enables us to call contagious." [27]

The contagion argument, though heated, was not particularly enlightening, but the question of cholera's cause, which lay behind that argument, had large implications. On the question of the mechanics of transmission, the honors were about equally divided between the contagionist and the non-contagionist camps, but on the fundamental issue of cholera's etiology, those who held to the idea of the *contagium specificum* as an organic, or possibly organic substance were moving in the direction of discovery. Their views were not susceptible of scientific proof, however, and had to remain either a priori assumptions, or simple deductive statements. This raises an interesting point, for, as we mentioned earlier, an advanced microorganismic theory of cholera was developed during the first epidemic and has become the basis for a claim by Soviet medical historians that Russian doctors offered the first valid explanation of the cholera's etiology, an explanation which Koch's work simply confirmed fifty years later. Two men, P. F. Gorianinov and N. N. Malakhov, working independently, developed the view that cholera was produced by "microscopic animals" which were introduced into the intestinal tract, and that the phases of the cholera were the direct result of the life cycle of those animals acted upon by the stomach's digestive juices. Gorianinov's ideas appeared in a book published in St. Petersburg in 1830, while Malakhov presented his theses in a paper submitted to the Medical Council of the Ministry of Interior, and later to the Moscow Cholera Council. Both bodies rejected Malakhov's ideas on the grounds that experimental evidence to support them was lacking, and probably never could be found.[28]

This, of course, was the crucial point, for the difference between hypothesis as the basis for exploratory research and scientific fact grounded in proved experimental data has to be maintained or scientific rigor becomes semantic nonsense. If nothing else, the Russian medical publications showed a high degree of scepticism, and no one theory could be accepted because in every instance, the proofs necessary to its final establishment were lacking. The adherents of particular theories waxed violent in their support and in their attacks on contradictory positions, but even in the official publications it was necessary to present several points of view since the evidence to establish a particular point of view was not available. The refusal to accept as definitive what was at most substantial theory showed both the conservatism and the discipline essential to scientific progress. All through Europe the ideas were gestating that were to lead to the great cholera discoveries, but to tear individual examples, even correct ones, out of their historical context can really serve no purpose other than a variety of antiquarianism.

The arguments which we have discussed were not unique to Russia, and European medicine in general followed the main outlines of the Russian debates. Though concrete evidence was missing, Russian suggestions concerning a viable micro-organism were potentially valuable, and the essays which Diadkovskii and Vendiktov published were as thorough and as thoughtful as any contemporary European work. Theories laying the cholera to micro-organisms also appeared in Europe in this same period, though they were no more popular than those which Russian medical men attempted, and European cholera studies showed the same broad attempt to resolve the contagion issue by reference to conditions as well as specific contagion. Indeed, the emphasis in Europe was more environmental than contagionist, and even in 1849 there was heavy resistance to the arguments offered by John Snow. This resistance was so intense that Koch's discoveries were questioned even after microscopic analysis had definitively demonstrated cholera's cause. The Russian Medical Council's work certainly was the equivalent of contemporary European studies, and there was very substantial evidence in the medical profession at large of a forward looking viewpoint as well as scientific rigor.

Regardless of what caused the cholera and how it was communicated, the most pressing problem was how to cure it, but this question opened the whole difficult and complicated issue of the way the cholera infection affected the human organism. Before 1830, the most common approach to cholera therapy lay in treating particular symptoms as they occurred, especially oral and anal purging, cramps and spasms, the loss of body heat, and the restriction of circulation.[29] The change which occurred in 1830 and 1831 was actually a projection and development of the symptomological approach, which attempted through rationalization and simplification to group cholera symptoms and ultimately to specify a particular condition or set of conditions which accounted for the cholera's effects and which could be treated in itself. This did not mean that the treatment of symptoms as such was neglected, since for the great majority there was no real alternative, and in the hospitals and the cholera stations stimulants, hot baths, massage, bleeding, and depressants were all used to alleviate distress and to keep life in the bodies of the unfortunates transported there.[30]

The most famous cholera cure which this period produced, the "bismuth treatment" developed by a Dr. Leo of Warsaw, was essentially a treatment of symptoms which used three grains of *magisterium bismuthi* with sugar and a drink concocted of infusion of Melissa to soothe the stomach and control the purging. This specific was to be given every two or three hours. To counteract muscular cramps, a special liniment was made up from one ounce of liquid *ammoniae causticae* and six ounces of spirits of angelica. The compound was to be applied hot. The combined bismuth and liniment treatment was to be continued until the secretion of urine together with natural body heat had returned.[31] In Russia, and later in Austria, this treatment achieved near official status, and Nicholas I ordered that it be tried in the Petersburg hospitals in 1831. Although the bismuth treatment has been bitterly criticized for its failures, and has become associated with the Eastern monarchies' attempt to control the cholera by fiat, British medical observers were greatly impressed with it, and recommended it as the most effective single cure which they saw attempted.[32] The primary problem which the Leo treatment posed was that it required constant attention to the individual patient, especially for the repeated applications of the liniment. During the most intense phase of the epidemic, the personnel necessary for this treatment was lacking, only the bismuth preparation was given, and this naturally reduced the treatment's effectiveness.[33]

The attempt to rationalize the cholera's symptoms and develop a "scientific" therapy followed two general lines which were firmly established during the Moscow epidemic and which remained constant through the cholera period. Both schools agreed that the cholera was an active agent which attacked the human organism at a particular point, and both argued that the cholera's effects were produced as that attack made itself felt throughout the system. The cholera's progress was viewed as an organic process, and the problem which was discussed was the nature of that process. The terminology at this distance seems unwieldy, but it was descriptive, as the first school directed its attention to the solid or non-liquid portions of the anatomy, while the second concerned itself primarily with the bloodstream. Each of these schools attempted to develop therapeutic measures which were consistent with the interpretation of the cholera's effect.

The first, or "solid" theory, was by far the most widely held among Russian physicians, for it included the traditional view that the cholera was a variety of intestinal inflammation. In his early essay, Mudrov followed this school and portrayed the cholera as an infection which attacked the stomach and intestines covering them with a mucous phlegm and producing burning sensations, pain, persistent vomiting, and diarrhea. Its effects then spread from the digestive system, paralyzing the nerve centers and ultimately the brain. This paralysis caused the cessation of circulation, a fall in pulse, cramps progressing inward from the extremities, cooling of the body, and the collapse of the vital powers.[34] Dr. Brandeis, a professor at Kharkov, designated the cholera as, "an inflammation of the principal organs of the 'bas centre' with simultaneous exhaustion of the heart's powers." A similar position was taken by M. Herzog, who suggested that the cholera was, "an inflammatory affection of the intestinal tube *in its entire length,* which is distinguished from other partial inflammatory affections of the intestines first by its extension, and then by the fact that it is interrupted in its development," the interruption being produced by spasms, "which appear suddenly because the inflammation, attacking nervous and mucous tissue by preference, rapidly provokes sympathetic reactions in the nerve and blood systems."[35]

The treatment most commonly associated with the intestinal-inflammatory interpretation was a *cura antiphlogistica,* which included bleeding in the early stages of the disease, warm poultices, frictions, and mustard plasters. This, of course, was essentially the so-called "English treatment" which had emerged out of the Indian epidemics. One major difference, however, was that the heavy doses of calomel and opium which had been recommended earlier were discarded, although five to ten drops of laudanum were often suggested to quiet internal distress and give relief from pain. Bleeding, however, was considered the prime requisite for successful treatment.[36] Even the proponents of the intestinal-inflammatory school were taken aback by the results of their treatment during the Moscow epidemic, and the suspicion arose that bleeding, far from being an effective counter-agent, actually increased the cholera's morbidity, and there was a marked switch away from bleeding toward the use of calomel, with or without opium, to which was added "mucilaginous, oily remedies joined with revulsives, and principally every imaginable method of warming the body."[37] Bleeding did retain its adherents, however, and Mudrov returned to the charge in his article on therapy for the Imperial Medical Council's summary collection. Writing in the late winter of 1831, Mudrov praised the *cura antiphlogistica,* argued that when bleeding was not undertaken the majority of the patients died, and minimized any dangers connected with blood-letting. He approved both leeches and the lancet, the former for the rich who could afford them, the latter for the poor who had nothing to give but their blood. Even Mudrov's essay, however, recalled the need for treatments supplementary to bleeding, and stressed the importance of frictions.

liniments, and hot baths to keep the circulation moving, and mucilaginous drinks and opium to quiet the stomach and control internal spasms.[38]

The terrible mortality of the Moscow epidemic, especially in its most intense phase, produced further explanations for the cholera's deadliness which implicitly rejected the idea that the cholera's seat was in the digestive system. The effects which cholera produced on the nervous system, the circulation, and ultimately the heart could not be satisfactorily explained by the spread of inflammation's effects from the digestive tract. One theory which gained a large number of followers in Moscow and came to be widely accepted in Petersburg was propounded by Dr. Loder, among others; it shifted the focus of attention from the intestinal tract and argued that the cholera was a primary infection of the nervous system, "and namely its ganglionary part." Loder reversed the traditional approach, pointing out that the cholera struck the nervous system first, and its primary symptoms then followed from secondary effects on the blood and the digestive organs.[39] At Kharkov, both Dr. Luk and Dr. Blumenthal denied that the cholera's center was in either the intestinal tract or the nervous system, and they settled on the circulatory system as the seat of the disease. Dr. Luk argued that all of cholera's characteristics may be explained, "by a violent spasm in the capillary vessels which compresses the entire blood mass in the organs in the body's cavities...," while Blumenthal held that the arterial system, "deprived of impulse," ceased to perform its functions, while the venous system, "placed on a lower level of vitality, and capable of maintaining slow activity for a long time, even despite a diminished impulse, slowly draws the blood mass toward the central organs." This, in Blumenthal's opinion, produced complete stagnation of the blood throughout the body and gave rise to the blue coloration associated with the cholera. Dr. Keir also subscribed to this view, and defined cholera as a variety of asphyxia.[40]

Dr. F. C. M. Markus went the farthest in trying to define the reason for the cholera's death-dealing powers, and incidentally moved the farthest away from the interpretation that the cholera was essentially an intestinal disease. Markus was partial to the "solids" theory, but he rejected in turn the intestinal, the nervous, and the circulatory systems as the center of the cholera's attack. In a memorandum written in the fall of 1830, Markus outlined a theory that the heart was the true center of the cholera's attack, and that the disease's symptoms and progress were consistent with those of other affections of the heart. For sheer ingenuity, and incidentally as a classic example of the dangers involved in pure deductive reasoning, Markus' ideas deserve a closer look. The Secretary of the Moscow Cholera Council pointed out that the cholera's greatest danger to the human organism came as it altered the movement, not the character, of the blood. The movement affected was of two kinds, first that within the blood itself, "the vitality of this organic liquid," and secondly the relationship between the blood and the pulp of the nerves. The cholera appeared to destroy the blood's vitality at the same time that it radically changed the blood's normal relationship with the nervous system. Markus thought that the blood provided a balance within the total organism, and that as it circulated, it itself went through a continuing process of reintegration as it mixed, separated, and mixed again while serving the different organs. The blood's internal movement depended on both the nervous system and the lymph system, which controlled the process of reintegration, and, "it is evident that the alterations which the blood exhibits can [only] flow from this double source." The alterations in the circulatory system and the integral movement of the blood which the cholera produced meant that the disease attacked the blood system, "by these two sources at once, something which can only take place in the very center of the blood system which is *the heart*." [41] Markus pointed out that all the cholera's symptoms could be compared with those of heart disease; he suggested that the heart was the first part of the body to die, that it was not the *ultimum moriens,* and he concluded his argument with the proposition that the cholera should be renamed and reclassified:

[T]he cholera morbus of our time offers a particular type of heart affection, not inflammatory but nervous, analagous to a paralysis in the sense of the celebrated Reil, and we propose to replace this name of cholera, which only gives an inexact idea of the malady, by that of *Cardiogmus vitalis epidemicus.*[42]

The innovations in treatment which these interpretations of the cholera produced were less striking than the theories themselves, and utilized many elements which were part of the traditional methods. The primary difference was that greater emphasis was placed on stimulation and "the revival of the vital energies." Even galvanism was attempted, with no great success, and it was common for practitioners to employ "opium in huge doses with ether, salts, and spirits of hartshorn, valerian, snakeroot, angelica, and arnica, and even camphor, musk, castoreum, phosphorus, and Dippel-oil." [43] The group which held the spinal marrow to be the disease center were partial to strychnine as their major specific, which they felt would counteract the peripheral spasms in the capillary system which concentrated the blood mass in the center of the body. In addition to strychnine they recommended cold, even iced, drinks combined with very hot baths, but aside from giving their patients a rather severe shock, there is nothing to indicate that their method enjoyed any great success.[44] The *methode excitante* with its heavy emphasis on opium also had only qualified success, and its followers discovered that their patients were prone to a secondary disease which had all the appearances of typhus. This led to the conclusion that stimulants, and particularly opium, were being overused, and the *methode excitante* gradually fell into disfavor.[45]

The second main theoretical approach placed the cholera's "active principle" in the blood stream itself. The most important proponent of this theory was the director of the Gorodskaia cholera hospital, Dr. Jaehnichen. Dr. Jaehnichen collaborated with a chemist named Hermann on a thesis which was presented in a memoir to the Moscow Cholera Council in September, 1830, and during the Moscow epidemic he developed his views further. Jaehnichen argued that the immediate cause of death in cholera was "the coagulation, the thickening of the blood," and utilizing Hermann's chemical experiments, he suggested that this condition was produced by decomposition of the blood itself. The process as he envisioned it was, "A separation of its [the blood's] solid parts (the coagulum) from those which are liquid (the serum) accompanied by a transsu-dation of the latter on the surfaces of the intestines." [46] In building his case, Jaehnichen made extensive use of post mortem examina-tions, and he reported that, "transsudation occurred in every cholera case, including those where diarrhoea and vomiting were not present," and he concluded that, "a spasm of the sphyncters pre-vented the transsuded liquids from being rejected outwardly." Transsudation appeared to be proved by the congestion in the abdominal organs, by the "vascular injection" of the intestinal canal, and Jaehnichen held that the spasmodic state which characterized cholera followed the same laws as those of true hemorrhaging, "because of collapse of the blood system and of the disharmony which may be expected to result from that for the functions of the nervous system." Thus the decomposition of the blood explained the heart's collapse as well as all other symptoms, for the formation of fibrous solids in the heart and in the large blood vessels took place while the patient was still living, but it was the blood's decomposition, "as a consequence of which, as well as the slowing of circulation through the heart, fibrous material attached itself gradually to the inner walls of the heart, and acquired a greater or lesser volume depending on the duration of the illness before its termination by death." [47]

This ingenious theory produced an equally ingenious therapy. The treatment was divided into three phases, each of which responded to a different stage of the disease's progress. The first two phases reflected Jaehnichen's concern with decomposition in the blood, while the third simply represented the standard ideas of keeping the body warm and attempting to alleviate stomach distress, concepts which need not detain us here. In the first stage, or *indicatio radicalis*, the physician should attack the "immediate cause" which lay in the blood stream. Instead of bleeding a patient, it was necessary to replace the elements which were lost from the blood through vomiting and purging. Chemical analysis showed these discharges to be highly acid, and Jaehnichen recommended injections of water and acetic acid which would be made directly into the blood stream. The major problem was that only a small amount of the compound could be introduced, and in one case, a woman far gone with cholera, barely six ounces were forced in. In this instance the injection brought a brief resurgence of the pulse, lasting perhaps a quarter of an hour, but then the patient died. Dr. Jaehnichen based this treatment on experiments which the chemist, Hermann, carried out and reported during the 1830 epidemic. Their combined work exactly paralleled approaches which O'Shaughnessy and Latta developed and published in 1831–1832. Modern authorities generally credit the discovery of the infusion method for treating cholera to Dr. Latta, though Dr. Markus at the time cited Jaehnichen's operation and the theory on which it rested, "to reclaim priority . . . in favor of Russian phusicians, priority claimed later by French and English physicians...." [48] The important point, of course, is not priority, but rather the evidence which this development provides that Russian medicine was generating ideas and methods comparable to the most advanced in Europe. It is equally important to realize that Jaehnichen's light did not shine in isolation, for the potential significance of his treatment was recognized by his Russian colleagues, and it was considered important enough to be included with other methods in the main essays on therapy in the *Traktat*. In this respect, the infusion method gained some currency in Russia, though it was by no means the most popular of the methods which the Medical Council recommended.

The other phase of Jaehnichen's treatment dealt with the *indicatio vitalis*. As the cholera reduced the heart's activity, the flow of blood itself had to be stimulated. Bleeding was called for here, but this procedure was only to be employed in those cases where vomiting and purging had not begun the decomposition process, and where bleeding could still act as a "stimulus" to heart action. When bleeding was no longer feasible, other stimulants could be used, and Jaehnichen particularly favored naphtha compounds in large dosage combined with a great deal of opium. He believed the latter would prevent intestinal secretions which he thought were responsible for restricting circulation. Jaehnichen also recommended "madeira, sub-carbonate of ammonia, concentrated infusion of valerian, phosphorus, cajeput oil, etc." [49]

Both Jaehnichen's theory of the decomposition of the blood and those theories which attempted to specify the focus of the cholera's action in a particular region of the human anatomy were efforts at rationalization which could produce an effective, simplified, and standard therapy. In every instance, however, the theorists were forced to include remedies which were introduced to meet the special conditions which cholera always seemed to engender. In that sense, the pragmatic approach remained a part even of the most strenuous efforts to achieve generalized scientific statements of cause and effect. The natural extension of these tendencies was a full-fledged syncretism such as that developed by Dr. Jeremias Lichtenstaedt, which broke the cholera's progress into six stages each of which affected a different portion of the human anatomy including the intestines, the blood, the main nerve centers, and the heart. The stages were identified through symptoms, and a different therapy was to be applied at each stage. In this way, Lichtenstaedt was able to utilize most of the recommended treatments, combining them into a completed and classified whole.[50]

A similar, though much less formal, syncretism was developed by Professor Diad'kovskii, who presented an intelligent, and highly flexible theory of treatment which avoided hard and fast rules, yet rested on substantial theoretical assumptions. Diad'kovskii was strongly influenced by Jaehnichen's theoretical work and by the views propounded by Bell and Searle that cholera produced a variety of asphyxia, an outlook that was shared by many Russian physicians.[51] Diad'kovskii argued the need to re-establish the oxygen content of the blood through the injection of acetic compounds, and he denied the usefulness of extensive bleeding. He approved bleeding only in those cases where too much blood was present, and he strongly suggested that for small children, the weak, the aged, and the debilitated, bleeding was positively dangerous. He did, however, accept the need to direct the blood away from the body's center to the extremities, and he strongly recommended hot baths, caustic compounds, and frictions for that purpose.[52] The cholera's attack on the nervous system was to be met with Hofmann's drops and mint tea given four or five times a day, and if that gentle approach failed, then opium, ether, or camphor could be used. Diad'kovskii was opposed, however, to the indiscriminate use of strong drugs, especially where there were evidences of inflammation.[53] The real point of Diad'kovskii's essay was that there was some virtue in most of the treatments suggested, and that individual cases of the cholera varied so greatly that generalization was both difficult and dangerous. The treatment had to be tailored to the stage of the disease and the intensity of the particular case as well as to the special symptoms which each case exhibited, and Diad'kovskii pleaded for greater improvisation thus implicitly rejecting the simplifying tendencies which appeared in so much of the cholera literature.[54]

Drs. Barry and Russell went even farther than Diad'kovskii in recognizing that a generalized definition and treatment of the cholera were extremely difficult. Current theories left too many questions unanswered, and the disease itself had taken some unexpected turns. In a letter to the British Medical Board, they warned that a "classic" definition of cholera, such as that given in the

Bombay or Madras reports, was difficult to support in connection with the Russian outbreak, and as one example they pointed to the aftermath of a "true" cholera attack which took the form of a continuing fever and which showed a family resemblance to typhoid. This development, which occurred during the Russian epidemic, seriously affected quarantine policy, for there was literally no way that a person suffering under this phase of the disease could be identified as a true cholera case. The only method they could suggest was little help for quarantine, for that would be to watch the people exposed to such a case to see if they developed the "blue" cholera.[55]

The problem which the English observers raised was only one of many. When Dr. Markus summarized the medical results of the Moscow epidemic, he admitted that the primary contribution which Russian physicians had made was the collection of further data, implicitly recognizing that the basic issues were still unresolved, and Moreau de Jonnès, who wrote a long article for the *Revue des deux mondes* summarizing the Russian cholera work, reached essentially the same conclusions. In his opinion, the Russian physicians, and indeed physicians everywhere, had found no satisfactory rational basis for a cholera treatment, and there were serious difficulties with most of the theories which were presented.[56]

The negative judgment which Jonnès, and so many contemporaries, made on medicine in general and Russian medicine in particular overlooks several significant points. The approach which attempted to control particular symptoms while preventing their advancing into the terrible true cholera offered a great deal that was sensible, and by the end of the first epidemic Russian physicians were increasingly sceptical of general cures, and equally suspicious of the more violent treatments. Dr. Pollitzer could have been describing Russian recommendations for 1830–1832 when he wrote, "it is consoling to find that, at least as soon as the cholera became rampant in Europe, rational methods of treatment were proposed side by side with many others which were useless or even harmful...," and Dr. Griesinger wrote in 1857:

As early as the first epidemics ample experience showed that in the course of the disease, and particularly in its most dangerous stages, nature does more than the physician, that all that can be achieved can be attained with simple means, and that excessive medical zeal is harmful here as in general. We deal with cholera as with typhoid; powerless with our therapy to reach the centre of the morbid process ... we are mainly restricted to assisting the sufferers through it by doing justice to the most urgent—and in the case of cholera almost invariably vital—indications; it also seems possible to retard the incipient morbid process ... and thus to prevent a transition of the still slight initial stage into the strong and dangerous form of the fully developed disease.[57]

Russian physicians were as liable to err as those farther west, and clearly Griesinger's statement could not apply to all, but it did apply, and significantly, for his thesis is precisely that developed by Diadkovskii and the Medical Council. Russian medical men were abreast of current scientific thought, and their published works were in no wise inferior to those appearing contemporaneously in Europe. Indeed, it might be argued that the stress on a single organic cause for cholera in the official publications, and the continued strong contagionist sentiment, provided a more fertile ground for further exploration than the miasmal concepts which dominated western thinking. In this connection we might note the importance which the *Edinburgh Medical and Surgical Journal* attached to the contagionist views of Russian doctors in 1829–1830:

[I]n one particular they [the Russian reports] are especially worthy of attention, as, in opposition to the sentiments entertained by almost every practitioner who has witnessed the East Indian cholera, they have led the Supreme Medical Board of Russia to espouse unreservedly the doctrine of the contagious origin of the disease, and, whether this opinion be right or wrong, will also lead every European state to take measures against its introduction, as if it were really of a contagious nature.[58]

None of this of course, gives grounds for contradicting the view that Russian medical men failed to penetrate the cholera's mysteries, but it does urge the point that advances were made, and at the least the range of approaches to the cholera was broadened. The contagion question was partially resolved as a large area of general agreement emerged between contagionists and non-contagionists. The outright rejection of contagion by Markus and Loder and its equally firm affirmation by Lichtenstaedt and Reman represented the extremes, but a middle or moderate view became popular and was firmly entrenched by 1831. Pre-disposing factors were heavily stressed, and whether one accepted a miasmic theory or one based on *contagium specificum,* all could unite in attacking crowded housing, drunkeness, filth, and debauchery. By 1831, even greater attention was given to living conditions, and the instructions published for St. Petersburg suggested a growing appreciation of the sociology of cholera.[59] It was also possible to justify more moderate police measures on the grounds that the cholera was less contagious than supposed. As we have seen, public violence was the most effective spur to moderating cholera regulations, but it could also be argued that such moderation was not dangerous medically. On the contagion question, the "moderate view" made the best of two worlds and gave wide latitude for social action while admitting frankly that the real nature of cholera's transmission was still enigma.

The Russian work on cholera actually defined the outer limits of European discoveries concerning the disease, and though the next two decades saw many refinements in the original theories, major changes in interpretation became possible only with the development of new microscopic techniques and their application to bacteriological analysis. In terms of assumptions and methods, Russian work on the cholera followed the major lines of European medical thought, and Russian theories were firmly rooted in European medical classics. In turn, British, French, and German commentators were able to use Russian materials. We have seen the degree to which Russian medicine was indebted to the British Indian reports, but the cholera in Russia did not follow the same patterns, and new curative measures as well as new explanations for the cholera's action had to be found. The same development occurred as the cholera moved westward, although the changes in theory and practice were not so marked between France or England and Russia as they had been between Russia and British India. By the time the cholera was finished in Russia, most of the possibilities for analysis inherent in the existing mode of scientific thought had been realized, and when in 1849 Ambrose Tardieu presented a course of lectures on cholera, the issues which he discussed, and the methods which he applied to those issues, were essentially those which we have met in Russian writing on the subject, and which were current in the European medical literature.[60] To suggest this much is not to suggest that Russian theories were original or that Russia "led" Europe. It does suggest, however, that Russia had become part of the European scientific world, that Russian medical scientists were able to use the contributions of other European workers creatively, and that in turn Russian scientific authors could be studied seriously. During the eighteenth century, and the first decades of the nineteenth, the traffic in ideas, including medicine, was from west to east. The cholera marked a major break in that pattern, and the beginning of a new era.

EPILOGUE

The cholera faded from the Russian scene in 1832 to return with renewed vigor a decade and a half later. Nor was that outbreak the last, for all through the last years of the nineteenth century the cholera attacked again and again. Its incidence was an eloquent testimonial to the failures of the Tsarist system, and its recurring ravages symbolized Russia's inability to meet the challenges of modernity. The experiences which Russia had in 1830–1832 were repeated over and over, and through the generations the cholera became part of the Russian folk tradition. It did more, however, for as it attacked the weak, the poor, the demoralized, it also contributed to the alienation of society from the regime. The cholera became one more influence which accelerated the decline of Imperial Russia and helped to erode the government's social foundations by wearing away public confidence. The experiences of 1830 and 1831, when projected for the nineteenth century, leave little doubt that the cholera exacerbated public discontent and contributed to the spirit of dissension and rebellion which developed in the later nineteenth century.

The first cholera epidemic specified the weaknesses endemic in the autocracy and offered a powerful argument for fundamental changes. The administrative failures which Zakrevskii symbolized called the whole system into question and again revealed the vast wasteland of incompetence which existed in the bureaucracy. Even worse, the cholera showed the administration's inability to face political and social realities. Despite Golitsyn's work in Moscow, the bureaucratic leadership, with only minor exceptions, was unimaginative, sterile, and ineffectual. It could not see the mechanical faults which haltered the system, and even the Tsar was more concerned with finding scapegoats than with undertaking needed changes. The Moscow experience strongly indicated that local rather than centralized authority worked best, but the lesson was ill learned, and the bureaucrats, tied to their own interests and unable to throw off the constraining hand of political formalism, were at most able to tinker with the administrative machinery. It was this same problem which helped to emasculate the reform programs at the beginning of the century, and thirty years later it substantially weakened the Great Reforms.

The social reactions which the cholera engendered are particularly important and it would be appropriate to speculate here on the implications of the events we have described. The peasants' revolutionary behavior continued a tradition of peasant rebellion which reached back to the seventeenth century, and the pattern of the cholera revolts was consistent with that of past popular disturbances. The cholera uprisings were the product of local conditions, and like similar riots in Western Europe developed a mythology which reflected contemporary attitudes. Yet the influence of the riots was never more than regional, the rioters contributed nothing to any progressive tradition, and they did not even inspire a literature. No one exalted the Haymarket rioters or the rebels of Staraia Russa, and those who were executed had no afterlife as martyrs to a revolutionary cause. The cholera riots were normal, even predictable occurrences, for Russia had lived for generations in the shadow of peasant risings, and the cholera aroused old fears and old antagonisms. Although predictable, the riots were not inevitable, and we have stressed the particular mechanisms which affected their ultimate issue. But that is not the primary point. What is significant, is that, although educated men criticized the police and the government for their handling of the crises and common people protested their treatment vigorously, the cholera generated no concerted protest—found no ideological point of departure to focus popular antagonism against the regime. The issues which emerged were those which had existed for generations, and they appeared locally, sporadically, and were capable of energizing only limited demonstrations.

One qualification is needed here, for clearly the cholera riots did not take place in a political or cultural vacuum. During the first half of the nineteenth century peasant uprisings occurred with increasing frequency, and during Nicholas' reign they aroused even the bureaucracy to the pressing need for immediate reform. In that respect the cholera riots worsened an already dangerous situation and contributed to the Tsar's reluctant conclusion that serfdom in its existing form had to go. But serfdom and the landholding system it represented were only aspects, though major ones, of a social organization which was identified with the instruments of repressive power. The public reactions in the cholera riots suggest that the state, or better the state's embodiment in officialdom, was the immediate cause for public resentment, while the landholding gentry were attacked only as they were a part of the political order. The peasants feared the unknown, but even more they hated an existence in which they were always something less than human. The soldier and the state official symbolized their plight, and during the cholera riots they drew the people's most violent antagonism.

To the degree that the events of 1830 and 1831 displayed continuity with nearly two centuries of Russian social history, they revealed the static character of Russian society and a significant lack of social development both in attitudes and conditions. The paternalism inherent in an authoritarian regime based on an agrarian economy was evident in the special treatment given workers in factory enterprises, and the only surprising point was the evidence of a depressed and indigent class among the lesser bourgeoisie. No suggestion of a proletariat in the Marxist sense appeared, though in Petersburg there were indications of a mob. Most telling of all, the reactions which were most common among the non-privileged segment of the population transcended such distinctions as serf, crown peasant, or bourgeois. Fear of doctors and foreigners, hatred of officials and police, belief in the Tsar's power to alleviate and protect, and finally a deep and utterly unreasoning religiosity were consistent evidences of a closely knit and cohesive social body whose fundamental reactions showed the existence of an organic culture which was more important than socio-legal distinctions. Given such cultural unity, the increasing tempo of rebellion was objective evidence of the autocracy's debilities and its helplessness in repairing them.

Certain traditional patterns appeared among the privileged as well. In both Moscow and Petersburg the wealthy and the well-born contributed heavily to subscription funds for cholera victims, supported lazarettes and hospitals, and served with the cholera committees. Many, of course, so feared the disease that they ran away, while both quackery and faddism conquered, and in a few cases killed many more. Some dedicated people endangered their lives by their service, but even Alexander Herzen could do no more than praise the spirit which moved them. Many more feared the people, and their attitudes suggested a fundamental alienation from them, yet in none of the Russian cholera literature is there anything to compare with the diatribes against the people which Chevalier recorded among the French bourgeoisie. On the other hand, both administrative and military officials treated the people as a captive population in a conquered country, and the brutal enforcement of sanitary regulations was accompanied by harrassment, thievery, and corruption. These were, for the most part, traditional behavior patterns, and like the reactions of the lower classes, support the idea that Russian society had changed very little in its essentials since the opening of the modern era.

The evidences so far confirm the usual impression that Russian society was static, but the emergence of the Russian medical profession qualifies that view and suggests a significant dimension of social change. The dominant Russian attitudes were those which we have described, but the first decades of the nineteenth century found coming into existence a new group, which by training and inclination was part of neither the peasantry nor the official world, yet it served the former while it belonged to the latter. The impact of eighteenth-century educational reforms were not felt until the nineteenth century, but by 1830 Russian educational institutions had created the nucleus of a new and dynamic social group whose foundations were in the professions rather than in property. Medical men formed an important segment of this group, and in the period we are discussing, were probably the most important element. Culturally, the Russian medical profession identified itself with the main streams of European thought, while its advanced educational status provided a natural association with the Russian creative and political intelligentsia. Yet its function was to listen rather than create, to follow rather than to organize or direct, for medicine's true creativity is in science. Nevertheless, the physicians were part of an immense cultural revolution which was taking place in Russia, and which, by the middle of the nineteenth century, utterly changed the character of Russia's internal life.

Russia's economic system changed very little between 1700 and 1850, although her capacity to exploit primary resources expanded, and this provided an expanding income base. Income, however, was never equal to commitment, and the peculiarities of Russian fiscal methods combined with the inadequacy of administrative operations to produce crisis after crisis. Population also expanded between 1700 and 1850, and particularly in the last thirty years of the period, but this phenomenon, like the expansion of income, only intensified endemic problems without changing their character. In intellectual history, however, a major developmental pattern appeared, and Russia moved steadily from imitation to creativity. The ultimate question is, how could a static, even stagnant, society at the same time produce so varied, so explosive, an intellectual life? The answer, of course, is that the society was not static. The development of modern Western culture depended to a great degree on the contribution of economically defined social groups, most particularly a property-owning bourgeoisie, but that was not the case with Russia. The major creative strain in Russian life was the formation of an educated elite which finally dominated both the cultural and political spheres. This group was drawn from many social strata, and its growth was made possible, not by the accumulation of wealth by individuals, but by the autocracy itself. In fostering technical progress through education, the government prepared an increasing number of citizens to judge it and themselves by new standards, thus creating a cultural *troisième état* between the peasant and the official worlds. The Russian medical profession represented one important element in this third estate, and the emergence of Russian medicine defined aspects both of social development and cultural maturation.

We have stressed the importance of Russian medical development as a proof of the growing maturity of Russian culture in the early nineteenth century, and especially as an evidence of the transition from an essentially imitative culture to one that had become national. The growth of Russian medicine paralleled the development of literature and the arts, and if the most creative period of pre-Revolutionary medicine was a decade behind the golden age of Russian literature, the immense expansion of Russian medical publication and research in the period 1830–1860 indicated massive advances in ideas and techniques, advances which were keeping pace with developments in other cultural areas. Against this record of progress the continued failure of facilities was a constant reminder that the objective environment was largely unchanged, though a new world had come into being within it. Ideas have played a leading role in Russian history, but it has not been an autonomous role, and the changing social foundations which underlay the development of new attitudes require fuller study before we have a balanced view of Russian history in the nineteenth century. The immense literature on the Russian intelligentsia, and specifically the efforts to define the intelligentsia, strike the problem tangentially, but we need to know a great deal more concerning social change in Russia to balance and to put in perspective what we know of intellectual and political development.

The intricate relationships which characterized Russia's growth as a social organism, or series of organisms, in the nineteenth century deserve closer study, yet they have received little attention, and this failure has in part resulted from the lack of a viable point of departure. Though other ways undoubtedly exist, the cholera has provided an opportunity to make one penetration in depth into Russian life, an excursion which has produced certain provisional conclusions. The study of Russian reactions to later epidemics could add information to what we have gathered, but more significantly would provide comparative data through which to judge development in the three key areas which we have defined in this study. This type of data would give us a better appreciation of the mechanisms of social change, and ultimately the historical processes at work in nineteenth-century Russia, processes which provide the historical substructure for the Russia we have come to know today.

REFERENCE

MATTER

APPENDIX
Statistics of Cholera Mortality in Moscow

TABLE A: Survey of Cholera Deaths in the City of Moscow:
September, 1830–January, 1831

Classification	Men	Women	Total
1. Nobility	60	64	124
2. Officers and Civil Officials	106	77	183
3. Clergy	42	51	93
4. Moscow Merchants	68	47	115
5. Foreign Merchants	9	2	11
6. Moscow Burghers	374	365	739
7. Foreign Burghers	54	36	90
8. (Other) Foreigners	31	10	41
9. Regular Guild Members	66	81	147
10. Diverse Middle Class Persons	68	81	147
11. Hospital Cases	66	87	153
12. Active Military	527	120	647
13. Retired Military	118	383	501
14. From the Foundling House	23	40	63
15. Postillions	2	1	3
16. District Police Hospitals	65	24	89
17. Domestics	401	244	645
18. Economy Peasants	163	101	264
19. Appanage Peasants	11	5	16
20. Factory Workers	7	4	11
21. Seignorial Peasants	227	67	294
22. From the Institutions of General Welfare	98	82	180
23. Travellers	8	5	13
24. Unknown	16	14	30
Total	**2610**	**1978**	**4588**

TABLE B: Cholera Mortality in Moscow by Administrative Districts

District	Cases	Deaths	Percentage
1. Sushchevskaia: XVII*	1282	655	51
2. Tverskaia: II	689	365	52.9
3. Serpukhovskaia: XIII	627	321	51
4. Arbatskaia: XIII	547	321	58.6
5. Yauskaia: IX	473	257	54
6. Novinskaia: XV	472	254	53
7. Gorodskaia: I	471	264	56
8. Piatnitskaia: IV	464	270	58
9. Yakimanskaia: V	414	218	52
10. Rogozhskaia: XI	408	280	68
11. Presnenskaia: XVI	377	114	30
12. Miasnitskaia: III	364	198	54
13. Preshchinskaia: VI	354	200	56
14. Chamovinshchskaia: XIV	343	177	51
15. Taganskaia: XII	267	161	60
16. Meshantskaia: XVIII	248	134	54
17. Sretenskaia: VIII	204	140	68.6
18. Basmannaia: X	163	84	51
19. Lefortovskaia: XX	151	105	68
20. Pokrovskaia: XIX	112	70	61

* District number.

NOTES

1   Part of the material in this chapter appeared in two published essays: R. E. McGrew, "The First Cholera Epidemic and Social History," *Bulletin of the History of Medicine,* XXXIV, No. 1 (Jan.–Feb., 1960), 61–73; McGrew, "The First Russian Cholera Epidemic: Themes and Opportunities," *ibid.,* XXXVI, No. 3 (May–June, 1962), 220–44.

2   *Cambridge Modern History,* corrected edition (New York and Cambridge, 1934), X, 788–89; 486–88; 465–74; 613–16. It was noted that both Casimir Perier and General Lamarque died of the cholera, but the epidemic was not otherwise related to the events of 1832–1833. Other historical works have been somewhat more generous in noting the cholera's appearance. See for example: Alfred Stern, *Geschichte Europas,* 10 Bände (Stuttgart und Berlin, 1905), Band I, 160–61; 508–09. N. K. Shil'der, *Imperator Nikolai I: ego zhizn' i tsarstvovanie,* 2 TT. (Sanktpeterburg, 1903), II, 361 ff; Theodor Schiemann, *Geschichte Russlands unter Kaiser Nikolaus I,* 4 Bände, (Berlin, 1904–1919), Band III, 31–37. Some recent studies of the cholera include: Marian A. Patterson, "The Cholera Epidemic of 1832 in York, Upper Canada," *Bulletin of the Medical Library Association,* XLVI (1958), 165–84; C. A. Hutchinson, "The Asiatic Cholera Epidemic of 1833 in Mexico," *Bulletin of the History of Medicine,* XXXII (1958), 1–23; 152–63; Charles E. Rosenberg, "The Cholera Epidemic of 1832 in New York City," *Bulletin of the History of Medicine,* XXXIII (1959), 37–49. For a more detailed discussion of this material, and that cited below, see McGrew, "The First Cholera Epidemic and Social History."

3   See W. L. Langer, "The Next Assignment," *American Historical Review,* LXIII, No. 2 (Jan., 1958), 283–304. Professor Langer's article is abundantly annotated and provides a most useful bibliographical aid as well as presenting a provocative thesis. For a

discussion of some theoretical problems connected with this approach, see: R. E. McGrew, "History and the Social Sciences," *Antioch Review*, XVIII, No. 3 (Fall, 1958), 276–89.

4   A notable example of Langer's thesis is Charles F. Mullett, *The Bubonic Plague in England* (Lexington, Kentucky, 1956). See also Mullett, "Medical History: Some Problems and Opportunities," *Journal of the History of Medicine and Allied Sciences,* I, No. 2 (1946), 189–207. Alexander Vucinich, *Science in Russian Culture; a History to 1860* (Stanford, Calif., 1963), presents an interesting survey and synthesis of Russian science which includes material on medical development.

5   For a full discussion of sources and problems see McGrew, "First Russian Cholera Epidemic: Themes and Opportunities." An admirable introduction to the bibliography of Russian studies in the history of medicine and public health is D. M. Rossiiskii, *Istoriia otchestvennoi meditsiny i zdravookhraneniia: bibliografia* (Moskva, 1956). For current publications see *Meditsinskii referativnyi zhurnal,* Razdel chetverty (Moskva, 1957–1960). See also *Sovetskoe meditsinskoe referativinoe obozrenie.*

6   See, for example, Lawrence Breeze, "English Attitudes toward Russia: 1840–1870" (unpub. Ph.D. diss., Univ. Mo., 1960). Cf. John H. Gleason, *The Genesis of Russophobia in Great Britain* (Cambridge, Mass., 1950).

7   See, among others, Marc Raeff, *M. M. Speransky: Statesman of Imperial Russia* (The Hague, 1957); Nicholas Riasanovsky, *Nicholas I and Official Nationality in Russia* (Berkeley, Calif., 1959); Richard E. Pipes, *Karamzin's Memoir on Ancient and Modern Russia* (Cambridge, Mass., 1959).

8   Quoted in Schiemann, *Geschichte Russlands unter Kaiser Nikolaus I,* III, 37.

9   Charles E. Rosenberg, "The Cholera Epidemic of 1832 in New York City," p. 37.

10 Dr. August Hirsch, *Handbook of Geographical and Historical Pathology,* trans. Charles Creighton, M.D., 1 vol. (London, 1883), I, 1; Hirsch's discussion of the cholera appears on pp. 394 ff. Cf. George Rosen, *A History of Public Health* (New York, 1958).

11 To cite these materials fully would require a separate chapter. Among the famous early reports which reflect the method described were, James Jameson, *Report on the Epidemic Cholera Morbus as it Visited the Territories Subject to the Presidency of Bengal in the Years 1817, 1818, and 1819* (Madras, 1823); *Re-*

port on the Epidemic Cholera which has Raged Throughout Hindustan and the Peninsula of India since August, 1817 (Bombay, 1819). For the way this material was used during the first pandemic, see "Critical Analysis: on Epidemic Cholera," *Edinburgh Medical and Surgical Journal,* XXXVI (1831), 402–16. Cf. Francis Bisset Hawkins, M.D., *History of the Epidemic Spasmodic Cholera of Russia, Including a Copious Account of the Disease which has Prevailed in India, and which has Travelled, under that Name, from Asia into Europe* (London, 1831). For a recent historical account, see R. Pollitzer, M.D., "Cholera Studies: History of the Disease," *Bulletin of the World Health Organization,* No. 10 (1954), 421–61. An extensive popular literature concerning cholera appeared, and the political and economic issues connected with public health regulations gave special importance to the discussions. See Moreau de Jonnès, "Moyens curatifs et hygièniques opposés au choléra-morbus pestilentiel," *Revue des deux mondes,* Part 3 (1831), 149–70; "The Cholera," *Quarterly Review,* XLVI (1831–1832), 170–212; "The Asiatic Cholera," *Fraser's Magazine,* IV, Part 4 (Dec., 1831), 613–25; "Cholera," *North American Review,* XXXV (1832), 92–118. Medical journals began publishing general accounts of the cholera much earlier, but popular interest was aroused only when the disease attacked Europe in 1830. For the cholera in popular literature see Louis Chevalier, *Le choléra: la première épidémie du XIXe siècle* (La Roche-sur-Yon, 1958), "Introduction" and "Le choléra à Paris."

12 See Rosen, *History of Public Health,* pp. 275–78; 285–87. See also below.

13 Chevalier, *Le choléra,* p. 10.

14 Louis Blanc, Chevalier notes, considered the cholera "perhaps the most extraordinary crisis which history mentions," and Chevalier expands on this theme: "In a word, in this troubled Europe of the first half of the nineteenth century, not only was the cholera everywhere considered by the popular classes as an aspect of social inequality, but in the most retarded countries or groups it was denounced as a criminal enterprise of the authorities and the privileged. . . ." *Le choléra,* pp. xv–xvi.

15 R. Pollitzer, "Cholera Studies: Epidemiology," *Bulletin of World Health Organization,* XVI (1957), 809–11.

16 Jeremias Lichtenstaedt, *Die asiatische Cholera in Russland,* quoted in R. Pollitzer, *ibid.,* p. 809.

17 Quoted in R. Pollitzer, "Cholera Studies: Bacteriology," *Bulletin*

of the World Health Organization, XII (1955), 778. Pollitzer makes no mention of the early Russian (1831) micro-organism theory. See below, Chapter 6.

18 *Ibid.,* pp. 778–79.
19 See R. Pollitzer, "Cholera Studies: History," pp. 440–41. S. P. W. Chave, "Henry Whitehead and the Cholera in Broad Street," *Medical History,* II (1958), 93; "The Broad Street Pump and After," *Medical Officer,* XCIX (1958), 347–49; "John Snow and the Cholera Epidemic of 1854," *St. Thomas Hospital Gazette,* LII (1954), 137–44.
20 R. Pollitzer, "Cholera Studies: Epidemiology," pp. 805–06.
21 Pollitzer, "Cholera Studies: History," p. 459.
22 "Epidemic Cholera," *London Medico-Chirurgical Review,* XVI, n.s. (1832), 163. Count P. D. Kiselev to Count M. S. Vorontsov, Bucharest, 15/27 December 1830, *Arkhiv Vorontsova,* XXXVIII, 197.
23 Rauch, "Bemerkung über die Cholera-Epidemic in St. Petersburg," in Jeremias Lichtenstädt, *Mittheilungen über die Cholera-Epidemic zu St. Petersburg im Sommer 1831* (St. Petersburg, 1831), pp. 33; 35 ff.
24 Quoted in S. P. W. Chave, "Henry Whitehead and the Cholera in Broad Street," p. 93. See Rosenberg, "The Cholera Epidemic of 1832 in New York City."
25 M. V. Netchkina *et. al.,* "Le choléra en Russie" in Chevalier, *Le choléra,* p. 154. Cf. McGrew, "First Cholera Epidemic and Social History," pp. 71–72, and below, and L. Pavlovskii, *Kholernye gody v Rossii* (St. Petersburg, 1893), pp. 58–61.
26 For the most recent account see Rosen, *History of Public Health,* Chapters IV and V. One striking example of this awareness was the reconstruction of Paris conceived and executed by Napoleon III and Baron Hausmann. David H. Pinkney, who has done the best recent work on this subject, stresses sanitary and social problems. See David H. Pinkney, *Napoleon III and the Rebuilding of Paris* (Princeton, 1958). See also Louis Chevalier, *Classes laborieuses et classes dangereuses à Paris pendant la première moitié du XIX° siècle* (Paris, 1958). David Eversley, "Le choléra en Angleterre," in Chevalier, *Le Choléra,* p. 188.
27 Eversley, "Le choléra en Angleterre," p. 188.
28 See P. Freour, P. Coudray, M. Serise et M. Jaubertie, "L'épidémie de choléra à Bordeaux en 1832," *Journal de Medicine de Bordeaux,* CXXXV No. 6 (Juin, 1958), 545–49.
29 Eversley, "Le choléra en Angleterre," *passim.*

CHAPTER 2

1   For an appreciation of urban problems, see Louis Chevalier, *Classes laborieuses et classes dangereuses à Paris pendant la première moitié du XIXe siècle* (Paris, 1958). For a substantial survey of the problems and failures in Alexander's reign, see Theodor Schiemann, *Geschichte Russlands unter Kaiser Nikolaus I,* 4 Bände (Berlin, 1904–1911), Bd. I, *passim,* and especially, pp. 351–508. On the peasant problem, see N. M. Druzhinin, *Gosudarstvennye krestiane i reforma P. D. Kiseleva,* 2 TT. (Moscow–Leningrad, 1946); see especially T. I, 186 ff. See also P. P. Evstafev, *Vosstanie novgorodskikh voennykh poselian* (Moscow, 1934). On the Decembrist movement, see A. G. Mazour, *First Russian Revolution* (Berkeley, 1937); M. V. Dovnar-Zapol'skii, *Idealy dekabristov* (Moskva, 1907); M. V. Nechkina, *Vosstanie 14 Dekabria* (Moskva, 1951). See also A. A. Kornilov, *Kurs istorii Rossii XIX veka,* 3 chasti (Moskva, 1918), I, 215 ff. The military colonies are discussed fully in Chap. 5 below.

2   R. Pollitzer, "Cholera Studies: History of the Disease," *Bulletin of the World Health Organization,* X (1954), 421–23. See: J. Macpherson, *Annals of Cholera from the Earliest Periods to the Year 1817* (London, 1872), which Pollitzer cites.

3   C. Macnamara, *A History of Asiatic Cholera* (London, 1876). Quoted in Pollitzer, "Cholera Studies: History," p. 424.

4   Pollitzer, "Cholera Studies: History," pp. 425–27.

5   The following section is based on Dr. August Hirsch, *Handbook of Geographical and Historical Pathology,* trans. Charles Creighton, M.D., 1 vol. (London, 1883), pp. 394 ff., and Pollitzer, *ibid.*

6   See above Chapter 1, note 10. *The Edinburgh Medical and Surgical Journal* published several independent reports concerning epidemic cholera in the East. See William Steuart Anderson, M.D., "An Account of Cholera Morbus Epidemic in India in 1817 and 1818," *Edinburgh Medical and Surgical Journal,* XV (1819), 345–72; John Kinnis, M.D., "Observations on Cholera Morbus and Other Diseases, which Prevailed Epidemically among the Soldiers of the 56th Regiment, Stationed at Port Louis, Mauritius," *ibid.,* XVII (1821), 1–29; C. Telfair, Esq., "Account of the Epidemic Cholera as it Occurred at Mauritius," *ibid.,* pp. 517–26; Dr. William Lloyd, "Case of the Epidemic Indian Cholera Treated Successfully," *ibid.,* pp. 527–29; "Report on the Epi-

demic Cholera of Asia," *ibid.*, XXIV (1825), 180–212; "Official Correspondence on Mr. Henderson's Method of Treating the Indian Cholera," *ibid.*, XXVI (1826), 41–46.

7   See "Cholera Morbus," *Voenno-meditsinskii zhurnal*, Chast' I, No. 3 (1823), 379–435. This survey was the first published in Russian and was almost exclusively based on English sources, especially James Jameson. Interestingly enough, the Russian author did not use the English works themselves, but a series of abstracts which appeared in Hufeland's *Journal der praktischen Heilkunde* in 1822. The reliance on English ideas continued in Russian cholera publications into the 1830's, and Dr. Jeremias Lichtenstaedt noted that although French methods came to be known, the English were preferred. *Die asiatische Cholera in Russland in den Jahren 1829 und 1830* (Berlin, 1831), p. 14. See Lichtenstaedt, pp. 5–19 for official recommendations which reflected the English view. See also: "O kholere: iz sochineniia angliiskago khirurga Serla (Searle), nabliudavshago siu bolezn' v Ost-Indii," *Voenno-meditsinskii zhurnal*, Chast' VIII, No. 1 (1831), 35–52.

8   "Cholera Morbus," pp. 379–96. Cf. General-Staff Doctor Reman, "Poiavlenie vostochnoi kholery na sredizemnom i Kaspiiskom More," *Voenno-meditsinskii zhurnal*, Chast' III, No. 1 (1824), 1–14.

9   "Reports on the Epidemic Cholera," *Edinburgh Medical and Surgical Journal*, XVI (1820), 458; "Review of James Annesley, Esq.,... ," *ibid.*, XV (1826), 180.

10 See "Cholera Morbus," pp. 409 ff. [Reman], "O kholere resprostranenie onoi v rossiiskikh provintsiakh... ," *Voenno-meditsinskii zhurnal*, Chast' III, No. 2 (1824), 160 ff. *Journal de Saint Pétersbourg*, September 2/14, 1830.

11 Dr. Burrel, a military physician who argued strongly for bleeding, noted that no efforts were successful until the English soldiers had been warned that they must present themselves for treatment at the first sign of the disease. "Reports on the Epidemic Cholera," *Edinburgh Medical and Surgical Journal*, XVI (1820), 468–69. Burrel's ideas were conspicuous among those cited in the Russian journals.

12 "Cholera Morbus," pp. 397 ff. gives a very extensive extract of James Jameson's description of a cholera attack; cf. "Nastavlenie o lechenii bolezni nazyvaemoi Kholera (Cholera Morbus), sostavlennoe Meditsinskim Sovetom," *Voenno-meditsinskii zhurnal*, Chast' III, No. 2 (1824), 180–83.

13 "Nastavlenie, etc.," pp. 183–84. Cf. "Reports on Epidemic Cholera," pp. 463–66 for symptoms and post mortem comments.

14 [Reman], "O Kholere"; "Nastavlenie," pp. 184 ff.; "O kholere," *Voenno-meditsinskii zhurnal,* Chast' II, No. 2 (1823), 203–206.

15 See "Cholera Morbus," pp. 427–28. The English position was by no means as clear as this first Russian essay portrayed. In its review of the "Reports on the Epidemic Cholera," the *Edinburgh Medical and Surgical Review* stated: "It appears to us incontrovertible, that it [the cholera] is capable of being transplanted from one place to another as in cases of ordinary contagion or infection, and also to possess the power of propagating itself by the same means that acknowledged contagions do...." XVI (1820), 461.

16 See [Reman], "O kholere," pp. 162–65. For the instructions, see "Nastavlenie," pp. 188–93. The government was slow to define any positive quarantine policy, and when the cholera returned in 1829 and early 1830, local officials were in a quandry as to what line to follow. See below, Chap. 3.

17 [Reman], "O kholere"; "Nastavlenie," pp. 177–93.

18 Anderson, "An account of Cholera Morbus Epidemic in India in 1817 and 1818," p. 358.

19 [Reman], "O kholere."

20 *Ibid.,* p. 160.

21 See Dr. J. R. Lichtenstaedt, *Die asiatische Cholera in Russland in den Jahren 1830 und 1831* (Berlin, 1832), p. 125, n. 56.

22 The results of the Council's work vis-à-vis the Astrakhan outbreak were summarized in a memorandum which was drawn up and published in 1824. The memorandum affirmed a moderate contagionist position, noted that the cholera's cause was unknown, and suggested effective remedies. It was based on reports from the Astrakhan physicians and two under-physicians sent to Astrakhan to investigate the disease. See "Schlussbericht der im Jahre 1823 bei Gelegenheit des Ausbruchs der Cholera in Astrakhan, zu St. Petersburg errichteten und nach dem damaligen Verschwinden der Krankheit im Jahre 1824 wieder aufgehobenen ärztlichen Comitet," Lichtenstaedt, *Cholera in 1830–1831,* pp. 125 ff.

23 Two examples of this early interest may be cited here. The August 24, 1824, report was published in the *Voenno-meditsinskii zhurnal,* Chast' III, No. 2 (1824), 177 ff. and was reprinted in Hufeland's *Journal der praktischen Heilkunde* and abstracted in the *Journal der ausländische Literatur.* Lichtenstaedt republished

the report as the first document in *Die asiatische Cholera in Russland 1829–1830,* where the *Edinburgh Medical and Surgical Journal* found it and summarized it (XXXVI [1831], 118–45) as a part of its long, critical article on Lichtenstaedt's collection. The report was again published in the *Supplement to the Edinburgh Medical and Surgical Journal, Containing Official Reports and Analysis of other Recent Publications on Malignant Cholera* (Edinburgh, 1832), pp. iii–x. Reman's articles cited above had a similar history, being reprinted in Hufeland's *Journal,* June and September, 1824, and extensive abstracts appearing under "Foreign Intelligence," *Edinburgh Medical and Surgical Journal,* XXIII (1825), 222–24; 432–35.

24 See below, Chap. 6, for a full discussion of this point.

25 For a brief survey of pre-Tatar Russian medicine, see: A. F. Nikitin, "Origins of Russian Medicine," *Sovetskaia Meditsina,* XXI, No. 9 (1957), 129–34. See also: Wilhelm Michael von Richter, *Geschichte der Medicin in Russland,* 3 Bände (Moscow, 1813–1817), Bd. I, 1–189. This study is still very useful for the general history of Russian medicine. For early contacts with the West, see D. M. Rossiiskii, *Istoriia otchestvennoi meditsiny i zdravookhraneniia: bibliografiia* (Moskva, 1956), pp. 20–21. This work is valuable both for its introductory survey of Russian medical history and publications, and for its extensive bibliographical listings.

26 Rossiiskii, *Istoriia meditsiny.* See also Alexander Brückner, *Die Aerzte in Russland bis zum Jahre 1800* (St. Petersburg, 1887). Brückner develops the better-known connection with Western medicine, which found physicians of foreign extraction journeying to Russia. See also Nicholas Hans, "Russian Students at Leyden in the Eighteenth Century," *Slavonic and East European Review,* XXXV (1957), 551–62. See also Alexander Vucinich, *Science in Russian Culture: a History to 1860* (Stanford, Calif., 1963).

27 Though monastery records provide the best evidence of early Russian medicine, both the *Russkaia Pravda* of Jaroslav the Wise and municipal records from Novgorod indicate an active interest in public health. Rossiiskii, *Istoriia meditsiny,* pp. 9–15. Cf. Richter, *Medicin in Russland,* p. 24. A. G. Gukasian, *M. Ya. Mudrov. Izbrannye proizvedeniia* (Moskva, 1949), pp. 9 ff. Gukasian points to Mudrov's advanced work in military hygiene and suggests a lengthy tradition for Russian military medicine.

28 The best discussion of Peter's medical reforms is Nikolai Kuprianov, *Istoriia meditsiny v Rossii v tsarstvovanie Petra Velikago*

(St. Petersburg, 1872). See also Richter, *Medicin in Russland,* Bd. III, and Maximilian Heine, *Medicinisches-Historisches aus Russland* (St. Petersburg, 1851). This book celebrated the fiftieth anniversary of the Imperial Medico-Chirurgical Academy of St. Petersburg and contains a history of the Academy. On Bidloo, Kellermann, Köhler, and other western scientists imported by Peter I, see Brückner, *Aertze in Russland.*

29   Brückner, *Aertze in Russland,* pp. 12–14.

30   *Polnoe sobranie zakonov rossiiskoi imperii,* pervoe sobranie, T. XIV, No. 10196. (Cited hereafter as *PSZ* followed by series, volume, and document number.) See also *ibid.,* No. 10354. Heine emphasized the importance of this step for Russian medical development, *Medicinisches-Historiches aus Russland,* pp. 25–28.

31   Brückner, *Aertze in Russland,* p. 68. Almost none of these were Russian-trained. See also Gukasian, *Mudrov,* pp. 12–17. Gukasian attempts to suggest that not only were there Russians practicing medicine, but that the Russian "national" contribution was of a very high order, even superior to the West. It is ironic to see an avowed historical materialist using a romantic *Volk* concept, yet this is what the emphasis on the "innate materialism" of the Russian people becomes.

32   Even in 1830 this tendency was clear. Although key administrative posts were still filled with foreign personnel, e.g., Wylie as head of the Medico-Chirurgical Academy, many of the significant publications concerning cholera, and some of the very important work done to control the disease, were by Russian physicians including Mudrov, Gorianinov, Diad'kovskii, Vendikhtov, *et al.* This was the new generation which was increasingly supplanting the older, and established, foreign imports. Vucinich records the judgment that Russian medical science produced only one major figure—Pirogov—between 1800 and 1850, and stresses over-bureaucratization in this failure (*Science in Russian Culture,* p. 347). Although recognizing later developments, Vucinich emphasizes the weakness of biological science during the period 1800–1830, and he records the stultifying influence which Schellingism had. Unfortunately, he does not discuss the new generation of Russian medical men who appeared in this period, the reaction to Schellingism and the stress on practical, pragmatic, and clinical methods, or the contribution of which the new group was capable (*ibid.,* pp. 336–37). For a detailed discussion and evaluation of the work which this group did in the cholera, and its significance, see below, Chap. 6, *passim.*

33 H. F. Storch, *Picture of St. Petersburg* (London, 1802), pp. 229, 302 ff.

34 It should be emphasized that the increase in "native" Russian participation was significant for a broader realization of Russia's human potential, and a concomitant increase in her ability to train and develop that potential, rather than as the expression of any native creative spirit. It should be quite clear that Russian cultural development was eclectic rather than autonomous, and that by the mid-nineteenth century Russia was coming to depend on her own human resources.

35 D. M. Rossiiskii, *200 let meditsinskago fakul'teta Moskovskogo gosudarstvennogo universiteta* (Moskva, 1955), pp. 57 ff.

36 See *PSZ,* pervoe sobranie, XXX, No. 23185. Cf. Dr. von Embden, "An Historical Sketch of Medicine in the Russian Empire, from the Earliest Period to the Present Time," *Edinburgh Medical and Surgical Journal,* XIII (1817), 464–65.

37 A. B. Granville, *St. Petersburgh: A Journal of Travels to and from that Capital; through Flanders, the Rhenish Provinces, Prussia, Russia, Poland, Silesia, Saxony, the Federated States of Germany, and France,* 2 vols. (London, 1828), II, 256–57.

38 Dr. Ukke, "Epidemii i nashi meditsinskii poryadki," *Vestnik Evropy* (June 1882), pp. 826–52.

39 Brückner, *Aertze in Russland,* pp. 15–16.

40 Granville, *St. Petersburgh,* II, 257–62. Granville's views may be taken seriously, for he was an informed and intelligent observer who enjoyed a wide contemporary reputation. His writings on medicine and public health were voluminous, and he was one of the interesting, even seminal figures in early nineteenth-century English medicine. See C. F. Mullett, "Augustus Bozzi Granville: A Medical Knight-Errant," *Journal of the History of Medicine and Allied Sciences,* III (1950), 251–68.

41 *Rospis' rossiiskim knigam dlia chteniia iz biblioteki Aleksandra Smirdina* (St. Petersburg, 1828), pp. 352–86.

42 See A. F. Bazunov, *Sistematicheskii katalog russkim knigam . . .* (*1825–1869*) (St. Petersburg, 1869), pp. 546–610.

43 See Rossiiskii, *Istoriia meditsiny,* pp. 51 ff. Rossiiskii provides invaluable information for study of Russian medical history per se.

44 *Ibid.*

45 See Gukasian, *Mudrov,* pp. 30–31. Although practical training was lacking, Moscow had become a vital intellectual center, and students in the medical faculty were caught up in the currents of the time which included the idealistic approach to science. See

A. Pypin, *Obshchestvennoe dvizhenie v Rossii pri Aleksandre 1* (Petrograd, 1918), glava VI, pp. 313–62. See also A. K. Kirpichnikov, "Mudrov, Chaadaev, i Vigel'," *Russkaia starina,* XXII, No. 5 (1878), 482–99; M. P. Tretiakov, "Imperatorskii Moskovskii universitet," *Russkaia starina,* LXXV (1892), 533 ff.

46   Rossiiskii, *200 let meditsinskago fakul'teta,* pp. 31–46.

47   Quoted in Gukasian, *Mudrov,* p. 23.

48   N. I. Pirogow, *Lebensfragen: Tagebuch eines alten Arztes, Bibliothek russischer Denkwürdigkeiten,* 3 Bände (Stuttgart, 1894), Band III. Cf. *Russkaia starina,* XIV, Nos. 1 and 2 (September–December, 1875).

49   Granville, *St. Petersburgh,* II, 271 ff. For a general survey of the status of the academy see: *Zhurnal ministerstva vnutrennikh del,* V (1831), 100–52.

50   For the regulations describing and governing these changes, *PSZ,* pervoe sobranie, XXVII, No. 20531; XXXVIII, No. 29057, on Medico-Chirurgical Academy; XVI, Nos. 11964, 11965, on establishment of Medical Colleges. Cf. Heine, *Medicinisches-Historisches aus Russland,* pp. 25–51.

51   Heine, *Medicinisches-Historisches aus Russland,* pp. 25–51; *PSZ,* pervoe sobranie, XXVII, No. 20531.

52   *PSZ,* XXVII, No. 20531 for union of Academies; XXXVIII, No. 29057, return of Academies to the Ministry of the Interior. Heine, *Medicinisches-Historisches aus Russland,* pp. 25–51.

53   On Frank's contribution, Heine, *Medicinisches-Historisches aus Russland,* pp. 36–37. Right to grant Doctor of Medicine at Moscow University, *PSZ,* pervoe sobranie, XXIII, No. 16988.

54   Heine, *Medicinisches-Historisches aus Russland,* pp. 38–51. For the period 1824–1838 Heine listed the following classification of graduates and their respective numbers: Doctor of Medicine and Surgery, 17; Doctor of Medicine, 66; Medical Surgeon, 137; Staff-Physician, 107; Physician, 150; Apothecary, 50; Aides (*Provisoren*), 150. For a survey of the status of the medical department in 1830–1831, see *Zhurnal ministerstva vnutrennikh del,* knizhka III, chast' chetvertaia, pp. 160–92.

55   Granville, *St. Petersburgh,* II, 273. Cf. *Zhurnal ministerstva vnutrennikh del,* knizhka V, pp. 100–52.

56   Sir James Wylie was a Scottish physician who entered the Russian service in 1790 to become one of the leading administrative figures in Russian medicine. In 1799 he was appointed *leibkhirurgus* and *doktor* to Tsarevich Alexander Pavlovich; he was named to the Medical Council and became Inspector of the Medical Section of the Guards in 1805; and in 1808 he was put in

charge of medical affairs for the entire army. That same year he became president of the Medico-Chirurgical Academy. In addition to directing military medical affairs during the liberation campaigns and the later war with Turkey, he founded and edited the *Voenno-meditsinskii zhurnal.* See: Grigorii Gennadi, *Spravochnyi slovar' o russkikh pisateliakh i uchenykh umerskikh v XVIII i XIX stoletiiakh i spisok russkikh knig s 1725 do 1825,* 3 TT. (Berlin, 1876), I, 153. See Heine, *Medicinisches-Historisches aus Russland,* pp. 38–39 for a fulsome description of Wylie's importance to the Academy.

57 See: Lomonosov's correspondence with Shuvalov in June and July, 1754 in *Sochineniia M. V. Lonomosova,* 10 TT. (Moscow-Leningrad, 1948), T. VIII, 172–73. Cited in D. M. Rossiiskii, *200 let meditsinskago fakul'teta,* pp. 10–11. See also: B. N. Menshutkin, *Russia's Lomonosov,* trans. Jeannette Eyre Thal and Edward J. Webster under the direction of W. Chapin Huntington (Princeton, 1952), pp. 81 ff.

58 Rossiiskii, *200 let meditsinskago fakul'teta,* pp. 10–11. Menshutkin writes: "In all probability the elaborately conceived project which was presented by Shuvalov to the Senate also belonged to Lomonosov." *Russia's Lomonosov,* p. 81.

59 Rossiiskii, *200 let meditsinskago fakul'teta,* p. 12. Rossiiskii emphasizes the Russian empirical tradition in medical science, and his enthusiasm for Lomonosov's methodology reflects the belief in materialist philosophy as a progressive force. In this particular instance, Rossiiskii is undoubtedly correct.

60 Rossiiskii, *200 let meditsinskago fakul'teta,* pp. 26 ff., gives an excellent survey of the early Moscow faculty.

61 Rossiiskii (*ibid.*) lists the following members of the medical faculty for the year 1805–1806: F. Politavskii, V. M. Richter, F. Barsuk-Moiseev, F. Hilderbrandt, I. Andreevskii, I. Vensovich, V. Kotel'nitskii, N. Shchegolev, S. Nemirov. See Chap. 3, *passim,* for a discussion of the period 1800–1860.

62 Granville, *St. Petersburgh,* II, 277–301, for an excellent, and informed, view of the Petersburg hospital situation. For a detailed survey, including mortality statistics, number of available beds and related matters for Petersburg, see: P. A. F. K. Possart, *Das Kaiserthum Russland* (Stuttgart, 1846–1851), pp. 318 ff., and especially the tables on pp. 321–23.

63 See F. C. M. Markus, *Rapport sur le choléra-morbus de Moscou,* (Moscow, 1832), pp. 5–56. Markus was Secretary to the Moscow Cholera Council and himself a noted physician. This work represents one of the primary sources for Moscow during the cholera

period, and includes as well excellent background information on population, living conditions, and available facilities. On Markus see Gennadi, *Spravochnyi slovar'o russkikh pisateliakh. . . ,* pp. 291–292. Compare Marcus with J. H. Schnitzler, *Moscou: Tableau statistique, géographique, topographique et historique de la ville et du gouvernement de ce nom* (Saint-Pétersbourg et Paris, 1834), pp. 48–52.

64   Granville, *St. Petersburgh,* II, 278, 295–296. C. T. Hermann, "Données statistiques sur l'état du comité de surveillance génerale en 1811 et 1812," *Mémoires de l'Académie Impériale des Sciences,* Vol. IX, Ser. V, 1819–1820 (St. Pétersbourg, 1824), 533–41, especially 535. Hermann only describes those institutions under the special committee.

65   See *Svod zakonov rossiiskoi imperii,* Izdanie vtoroe, 13 TT., (St. Petersburg, 1833), especially Tom XIII, *passim,* for sanitary and public health administration. See also Karl Geling, *Opyt grazhdanskoi meditsinskoi politsii* (Vil'na, 1842). A wealth of material for all administrative aspects of the development of Russian public health policies is to be found in *Polnoe sobranie zakonov.* Subject index volumes for the first series (to 1825) and volume subject indexes provide a starting point.

66   "Ob otkryvsheisia v g. Astrakhani kholere (Cholera Morbus)," *Voenno-meditsinskii zhurnal,* II, No. 1 (1823), 75–83; [Reman], "O kholere," pp. 159–76. For figures on Astrakhan cholera, L. Pavlovskii, *Kholernye gody v Rossii* (St. Petersburg, 1893), p. 11. Pavlovskii provides excellent summary detail on mortality figures.

CHAPTER 3

1   *Journal de St. Pétersbourg,* September 2/14, 1830. In addition to the brief survey of cholera, this issue carried an article also reprinted from *Severnaia pchela* concerning cholera in Orenburg. The report was dated August 16, 1830. No cholera articles appeared in the *Journal* in 1829, though there were several articles concerning public health generally and plague specifically.

2   Lacroix tells the story that Nicholas was touring through the outlying villages when, on June 13 (N.S.), 1830, he visited a military hospital in the village of Kodin where, he was told, a man had just died of cholera. The doctor in charge of the hospital told Nicholas that he had studied cholera in its first appearances in India and had observed it at Orenburg, that science could not cure it nor quarantine hold it. Nicholas then wrote Zakrevskii

telling him of the threat to the Empire. Paul Lacroix, *Histoire de la vie et du régne de Nicholas Ier,* T. 5 (Paris, 1868), pp. 60–61. Whether this story is true or not, the first formal decision concerning cholera was taken on June 10 (O.S.), 1830, and published on July 8. *PSZ,* vtoroe sobranie, V, i, No. 3785.

3 There is no mention of cholera or Reman in the first series of the *PSZ* (to 1825) nor in the second series (to 1830). The establishment of the cholera council in 1823 apparently was carried out without reference to the cabinet, and neither the outbreaks at Astrakhan nor Orenburg in 1823 and 1829 were considered serious enough to warrant discussion or formal action.

4 See, for example, *PSZ,* vtoroe sobranie, V, i, No. 3733; Count Zakrevskii to Count M. S. Vorontsov, August 4, 1828, *Arkhiv Vorontsova,* XXXVII, 342–43; M. P. Shcherbinin, *Biografiia general-fel'dmarshala kniaza Mikhaila Semenovicha Vorontsova* (St. Petersburg, 1858), pp. 194 ff.; "Mémoires du prince M. Woronzow [Vorontsov] 1819–1833," *Arkhiv Vorontsova,* XXXVII, 65–102.

5 "Beschluss der Medicinalrathes [Petersburg] vom 21 Januar 1830, üher [*sic*] die in Asien herrschenden Krankheiten," in Jeremias Lichtenstaedt, *Die asiatische Cholera in Russland in den Jahren 1829 und 1830* (Berlin, 1831), pp. 85–90. The Medical Council contradicted the Orenburg report on questions of infection and the lack of danger to the empire, but it must be remembered that the Petersburg committee's summary was drawn up after the cholera broke out at Orenburg, an event which the report on diseases in Asia preceded. Cf. *Supplement to the Edinburgh Medical and Surgical Review* (Edinburgh, 1832), pp. x–xiii (cited hereafter as *Supplement*), for an English translation and edition done from Lichtenstaedt.

6 See, for example, Nechkina, "Le choléra en Russie," in Chevalier, *Le choléra: la première épidémie du XIXe siècle* (La Roche-sur-Yon, 1958), who makes this assumption. Cf. "Kholera," *Bol'shaia meditsinskaia entsiklopediia,* T. XXXIV, 269–72; N. F. Kramchaninov, "K istorii bor'by s kholeroi v Rossii v 1829–1830, gg.," *Sovetskoe zdravookhranenie,* IV (1956), 46 ff.

7 "Ueber die Erscheinung der Cholera in Orenburg," in Lichtenstaedt, *Cholera in Russland, 1829–1830,* p. 19; *Supplement,* p. xv.

8 "Ueber die Erscheinung der Cholera in Orenburg," pp. 20–25; Sokolow, "Beschreibung der in Anfange Septembers 1829 in Orenburg erschienenen Cholera," in Lichtenstaedt, *Cholera in Russland, 1829–1830,* pp. 110–17; *Supplement,* pp. xv–xvii. Cf. "Opisanie kholery, v pervykh chislakh sentiabria 1829 g.

iavivsheisia v Orenburge, sostavlennoe shtab-lekarem Sokolo-vym," *Zhurnal ministerstva vnutrennikh del,* knizhka IV (Addendum) (1830), 1–75.

9 Sokolow, "Beschreibung," pp. 117–19; *Supplement,* pp. xvii–xviii.

10 Dr. Reissner, "Gutachten des Operatörs von der Pensa'schen Medicinal-Behörde," in Lichtenstaedt, *Cholera in Russland, 1829–1830,* p. 99. Reissner also pointed out that Pelnitsky's meteorological observations provided no key to the disease. Cf. *Supplement,* p. xx.

11 See Lichtenstaedt, *Cholera in Russland, 1829–1830, passim,* especially pp. 148–49, for Pelnitsky's observations and pp. 152–53, which summarize lessons from Orenburg.

12 "Antworten der Orenburg'schen Aerzte an den Rath der Kasan'schen Aerzte, auf die Fragen über die Cholera," in Lichtenstaedt, *Cholera in Russland, 1829–1830,* pp. 59–60. Cf. *Supplement,* p. xl. The quotation is from the *Supplement.*

13 *Supplement,* p. xlv; "Gutachten der Orenburg'schen Aerzte," in Lichtenstaedt, *Cholera in Russland, 1829–1830,* pp. 91–92. Emphasis added.

14 R. Pollitzer, "Cholera Studies: Bacteriology," *Bulletin of the World Health Organization,* XII (1955), 777.

15 *Ibid.,* pp. 777–79; Pollitzer, "Cholera Studies: Epidemology," BWHO, XVI (1957), 809–12. Cf. George Rosen, *A History of Public Health* (New York, 1958).

16 "Gutachten der Orenburg'schen [*sic*] Aerzte vom. 10. Oktober," in Lichtenstaedt, *Cholera la Russland, 1829–1830,* pp. 41–44. Cf. *Supplement,* pp. xliv–xiv.

17 *Supplement,* pp. xliv–xiv.

18 The following description reprinted from *Severnaia pchela* in the *Journal de St. Pétersbourg,* September 2/14, 1830, provides something of the spirit in which the quarantine was treated: "In the midst of several hundred felt 'kibitkas,' surrounded by a Russian and Khirghiz guard, floated gorgeous cashmir shawls and colored silks which, it was understood, were being aired. Bukhara merchants, richly dressed, strolled about or sipped tea, while some smoked the 'Kalian' and others occupied themselves with their national games. Beyond the military cordon passed troops of camels, horses, and sheep belonging to the Khirghiz; frontier inhabitants and the half-wild Khirghiz with women and children milled about in the midst of our armed Cossacks and profited from the occasion by selling livestock and other things to the Bukharans in quarantine." Cf. L. Pavlovskii, *Kholernye gody v Rossii* (Sanktpeterburg, 1893), pp. 31–33.

19 Pavlovskii, *ibid.,* p. 33. These figures are for the province. In 1848, the population for Orenburg guberniia was given as 1,706-837. Konstantin Arsenev, *Statisticheskie ocherki Rossii* (Sankpeterburg, 1848), pp. 156–58. Pavlovskii estimated the mortality percentage per 1,000 was just 1 per cent, indicating a notably smaller base population figure.

20 In Orenburg proper, the case ratio and the mortality ratio compared against the population, was higher than Moscow's the following year, though by no means so serious as the 1830 outbreak at Astrakhan. (See below.) Orenburg in 1825 was credited with a population of 2,719, exclusive of military personnel. *Statisticheskoe izobrazhenie gorodov i posadov rossiiskoi imperii po 1825 god.* (Sanktpeterburg, 1829). The official reports showed 801 cholera cases in the city and its environs with 121 deaths between September 15 and November 18. "Kurze Nachricht über das Bestehen der Cholera in Orenburg'schen Gouvernement in den Jahren 1829 und 1830," in Lichtenstaedt, *Cholera in Russland, 1829–1830,* table, p. 149. Of the civilian population, approximately 28 per cent were affected, and of these, only 15 per cent died. This mortality percentage was much lower than the epidemic's average (47.5 per cent), but the death ratio of 4.4 per cent was actually higher than the ratio in the government or in those metropolitan centers that later were harder hit.

21 "Schluss," Lichtenstaedt, *ibid.,* pp. 151–154; *Supplement,* pp. liii–lv.

22 *Supplement,* pp. liii–lv.

23 *PSZ,* vtoroe sobranie, V, i, No. 3733.

24 *PSZ,* vtoroe sobranie, V, i, No. 3785; No. 3857.

25 The ambivalence in Russia quarantine policy is nowhere clearer than with regard to the Nizhny fair. There is no evidence to suggest that closing the fair was considered seriously, and in 1831, after Russia had been fully exposed not once but twice to cholera, the fair was held anyway. See below.

26 The Sevastopol uprising is described in detail in Th. Schiemann, *Geschichte Russlands unter Kaiser Nikolaus I,* 4 Bände (Berlin, 1904–1919), II, 409–11. On conditions within the suburb, see the eyewitness account of Father S. Gavrilov, *Russkii arkhiv,* 1867, pp. 137 ff. The uprising was described by Prince M. Vorontsov, especially the measures taken against it and the reasons for the revolt, in his "Mémoires," *Arkhiv Kniazia Vorontsova,* XXXVII, pp. 65–102. The government published a very full account of the revolt in *Journal de St. Pétersbourg,* July 5/15, 1830.

27   The refusal to recognize the plague's existence was the same
reaction which occurred during the cholera in areas where there
was endemic tension. And this reaction was common in Western
Europe as well. It seemed to foreshadow violence, for almost
always the negation of the explanation was accompanied by outbursts against the regime. See R. E. Mc Grew, "The First Cholera
Epidemic and Social History," *Bulletin of the History of Medicine,* XXIV, No. 1 (January–February, 1960), 61–73.

28   The official published account frankly admitted that there were
enough troops in the city to have controlled the mob, but since
they were separated from their officers and had no specific orders,
they simply stood by while the mob ravaged the city. See:
Journal de St. Pétersbourg, July 5/15, 1830.

29   See M. P. Shcherbinin, *Biografiia general-fel'dmarshala kniaza
Mikhaila Semenovicha Vorontsova* (Sanktpeterburg, 1858), pp.
194 ff. Cf. Vorontsov, "Mémoires."

30   "Bemerkungen über die Cholera, welche zu Astrachan im Juli
1830 geherrscht hat, vom Staabsarzt Solomow," Lichtenstaedt,
Cholera en Russland, 1829–1830, pp. 180 ff.; *Supplement,* p. lxi.

31   *Supplement,* p. lxi. The evidence concerning social reactions in
Astrakhan is indirect, and though hysteria clearly followed the
disease, there was no indication of public protests.

32   "Bemerkungen uber die Cholera," in Lichtenstaedt, *Cholera
in Russland, 1829–1830,* pp. 180 ff. These conclusions were
adverted to by two French observers of the cholera in Russia who
applauded freedom of movement in cholera areas and who
regarded restrictive policies inside the country as dangerous as
well as useless. See: Auguste Gerardin et Paul Gaimard, *Du
choléra-morbus en Russie, en Prusse, et en Autriche pendant
les années 1831 et 1832* (Paris, 1832).

33   Pavlovskii, *Kholernye gody v Rossii,* pp. 10–11. For town population, see *Statisticheskoe izobrazhenie gorodov.* Pavlovskii's estimate of Astrakhan's population was 30,000. On the government
population, Arsenev, *Statisticheskie ocherki Rossii,* p. 156.

34   See Zakrevskii's memo to Nicholas concerning the cholera, *PSZ,*
vtoroe sobranie, V, i, No. 3881. The memorandum was published
in full in *Journal de St. Pétersbourg,* September 16/28, 1830.
This memorandum became the basis for the government's handling of the cholera during the fall of 1830, and therefore is of the
first importance. (Cited hereafter as Zakrevskii, *Memo.* Unless
otherwise indicated, the reference is to the *PSZ* document.)

35   See Pavlovskii, *Kholernye gody v Rossii,* pp. 10–11, for brief
comment on measures taken.

36 *Journal de St. Pétersbourg,* September 6/18, 1830.

37 Kiselev to Vorontsov, Bucharest, 18/30 juillet, 1831, *Arkhiv Vorontsova,* XXXVIII, 196–97.

38 Throughout the cholera period, such papers as *Journal de St. Pétersbourg* and *Russkii invalid* regularly published a running tabular account of cholera's incidence and spread. There was no variation among the figures, for they all came from the same source. The figures cited here were presented in Zakrevskii's *Memo.*

39 This view is drawn from Pavlovskii, *Kholernye gody v Rossii,* pp. 49–51. Cf. G. I. Arkhangel'skii, *Kholernyia epidemii evropeiskoi Russii* (Sanktpeterburg, 1874). This study, which was done two decades before Pavlovskii, was based on archival data. Arkhangel'skii's work tended to validate published figures, though he noted they were most reliable in terms of relationships. The Soviet scholar, P. P. Evstafev, was able to show, however, that in the Novgorod military colonies the statistics were doctored to cover the effects of the uprising there. *Vosstanie Novgorodskikh voennykh poselian* (Moskva, 1934). On the whole, however, the patterns which statistics reflect are accurate, though there may be considerable question concerning particular figures.

40 Pavlovskii, *Kholernye gody v Rossii,* pp. 49–51, *et passim.*

41 Zakrevskii, *Memo.*

42 See above, Chap. 2.

43 See Karl Geling, *Opyt grazhdanskoi meditsinskoi politsii* (Vilna, 1842), *passim,* and *Svod zakonov,* 15 vols. series I, XIII, *passim.*

44 Zakrevskii, *Memo.* For the convolutions of "bureaucratism" in Nicholas' Russia see Karl Stählin, "Aus dem Berichten der III Abteilung S. M. hochseigener Kanzlei an Kaiser Nikolaus I," *Zeitschrift für Osteuropäische Geschichte,* VI, VII, Neue Folge, II, III (1931, 1932). The spirit behind this idea is well defined in A. E. Presniakov, *Apogei samoderzhaviia* (Leningrad, 1925). For a summary view, see: M. Miakotine, "Nicolas Ier: l'avènement et les idées de Nicolas Ier," in Paul Miliukov, Charles Seignobos, L. Eisenmann, et al., *Histoire de Russie,* 3 TT. (Paris, 1932), II, 717–29. The most recent general treatment of Nicolas' reign, which deals with both attitudes and organization is N. V. Riasanovsky, *Nicholas I and Official Nationality in Russia* (Berkeley, Calif., 1959), while the problems of organization, personnel, and the autocratic attitude are summarized in R. E. McGrew, "Nicholas I and the Genesis of Russian Officialism" (unpub. Ph.D. diss., Univ. of Minn., 1955).

45 A later contemporary remarked on the development of "nihilism"

as one of the striking characteristics of the Russian intellectual world and he paralleled this by referring to the sterile, and formal administrative type which developed in Nicholas' reign, a type, it was noted, that was epitomized in A. A. Zakrevskii. See "Vospominanie o Konstantine Sergeeviche Aksakove," *Russkii arkhiv,* I (1885), 413. Constantine de Grunwald, who takes his theme from Prince Lubomirski, treats the best of Nicholas' administrators as mediocrities, and the worst as unspeakable. See *La vie de Nicolas Ier* (Paris, 1946). Nicholas himself was aware of the problem of the bureaucratic type, and especially the dishonest one, but he was never able to control it. See Stählin, "Die dritte Abteilung." See also "Pièce remise par S. M. l'Empereur Nicolas le 24 Janvier 1826," *Lettres et papiers du Chancelier Comte de Nesselrode,* 11 vols. (Paris, 1904–12[?]) VI, 283 ff. This is probably the best known statement of Nicholas' concern over administrative personnel.

46 Zakrevskii, *Memo.*
47 *Ibid.*
48 Zakrevskii stressed the extraordinary character of the cholera and he emphasized that extraordinary measures were necessary to meet it, but his concept of the "extraordinary" was limited. See Zakrevskii, *Memo.*
49 *Ibid.*
50 *Ibid.*
51 *PSZ,* vtoroe sobranie, V, ii, No. 3890. Cf. *Journal de St. Pétersbourg,* September 16/28, 1830.
52 Zakrevskii, *Memo.*
53 *Ibid.*
54 *Ibid.*
55 Zakrevskii's failures in the Volga region have become an essential part of his historical personality, and if he is remembered for nothing else, he remains the administrator who was unsuccessful in handling the cholera. See "Kratkoe biograficheskoe vospominanie o grafe A. A. Zakrevskom," *Russkii arkhiv,* 1875, pp. 371–80; "Vospominaniia O. A. Przhetslavskago," *Russkaia starina,* XI (1874), 693–98; "Vospominaniia Andreia Mikhailovicha Fadeeva," *Russkii arkhiv,* Part 3, 1891, pp. 418–23; A. V. Figner, "Vospominanie o grafe A. A. Zakrevskom," *Istoricheskii vestnik,* XX (1885), 665–71. Zakrevskii's side of the story, and his complaints against non–co-operating local officials, may be seen in "Bumagi grafa A. A. Zakrevskago," *Sbornik imperatorskago russkago istoricheskago obshchestva,* LXXVIII (1891), 534–42.

56   *Journal de St. Pétersbourg* maintained a running account of the struggle against the cholera, and Zakrevskii's reports were cited in the same way the reports from other centers were treated. It was the Medical Council in St. Petersbourg, for example, which drew up and published the sanitary regulations for Nizhny-Novgorod. See: *Journal de St. Pétersbourg,* September 25/ October 5, 1830, and it was the Medical Council whose recommendations continued to be the basis for the government's actions. Indeed on December 9, 1830, the cabinet flatly rejected Zakrevskii's recommendations for quarantine and his general sanitary policy. *PSZ,* vtoroe sobranie, I, ii, No. 4177. There was nothing to distinguish the treatment given Zakrevskii's reports and recommendations from those presented, for example, by the military governor-general of Moscow. See *PSZ,* vtoroe sobranie, V, ii, Nos. 4177, 4195.

57   For the spread of cholera, Pavlovskii, *Kholernye gody v Rossii, passim,* and *Journal de St. Pétersbourg,* August–December, 1830, *passim.*

58   See: *PSZ,* vtoroe sobranie, V, ii, No. 4177.

59   *PSZ,* vtoroe sobranie, II, ii, No. 3910. It is interesting that Zakrevskii, though a firm exponent of stringent measures, originally took the position that cholera was not contagious and was not communicated by touching the sick or their effects. The policies which he recommended, however, were appropriate for contagious disease. Zakrevskii, *Memo. PSZ,* vtoroe sobranie, V, ii. No. 3934.

60   *PSZ,* vtoroe sobranie, V, ii, No. 3910. For Moscow, see below, Chapter 4.

61   See R. Pollitzer, "Cholera Studies: Bacteriophage Investigations," *Bulletin of the World Health Organization,* XIII (1955), 1–25.

62   *Journal de St. Pétersbourg,* September 25/October 7, 1830. The item is reprinted from *Severnaia pchela.*

63   *Ibid.*

64   Girardin et Gaimard, *Du choléra-morbus en Russie, . . . pendant les ánnees 1831, et 1832,* pp. 5–12, 131–33. These observers were particularly hard on the optimistic tone which pervaded the instructions. People expected to escape, and when the cholera came, they were doubly horrified.

65   Franz Neumann, *Democratic and Authoritarian State* (Glencoe, Ill. 1957), pp. 202 ff. Perhaps this thesis should be qualified in the light of the point made above that accurate information feeds knowledge and rolls back fear, while inaccuracy only

worsens the hysteria which ignorance begets. It is interesting to see the *Quarterly Review* reporting the cholera and justifying its report in terms of freedom and fear: "If the history of death and human anguish offers little to allay the alarm now oppressing the public, still an accurate, just, and complete account of the impending evil will limit the imagination to reality, and unburden the mind of all those vague and irrational fears which chain down its faculties and leave it paralyzed and helpless in the moments of extremist danger." "The Cholera," *Quarterly Review,* XLVI (1831–1832), 170.

66 See Chapter 2 above for the optimism which the medical profession exhibited in regard to the cholera and the possibility of cures.

67 *Journal de St. Pétersbourg,* October 4/16, 1830. The article cited is reprinted from the *Gazette de Commerce,* October 3, 1830.

68 *PSZ,* vtoroe sobranie, V, ii, Nos. 3940, 4041. The latter extended the period for appeals and appearances for trial in all departments affected by cholera.

69 *PSZ,* vtoroe sobranie, V, ii, Nos. 3950, 3990, 4075; VI, i, No. 4278.

70 *PSZ,* vtoroe sobranie, V, ii, Nos. 4051, 4157; VI, i, No. 4278 (on mortgages). *PSZ,* vtoroe sobranie, V, ii, No. 4157.

71 This action was taken before the decree of August 12, 1830, had reached the governor. That decree, as we noted above, forebade independent action by provincial governors in respect to cholera. *PSZ,* vtoroe sobranie, V, i, No. 3857.

72 The description presented here is based on I. Dubasov, "Kholernyi bunt v Tambove 1830 g.," *Russkaia starina,* XIV (1875), 742–47. Cf. Iv. Yakunin, "Kholera v Tambove," *Vestnik Evropy,* No. 9 (1875), 204–23. Yakunin notes that Zakrevskii whitewashed the Tambov outbreak, and certainly there is no evidence in published official materials that he reported on its seriousness.

73 Pavlovskii, *Kholernye gody y Rossii,* p. 35, gives the following comparative figures: August 24 to November 30, 1830: 184 cases, 66 deaths; January 16 to September 30, 1831: 5718 cases, 2381 deaths. The riots occurred during the first light visitation.

74 I. Dubasov, "Kholernyi bunt v Tambove," pp. 742–47.

75 *Ibid.*

76 *Ibid.,* pp. 744–45.

77 Pavlovskii, *Kholernye gody v Russii,* pp. 345; Iv. Yakunin, "Kholera v. Tambove," pp. 204–23.

78 Dubasov, "Kholernyi bunt v Tambove," pp. 746–47.

79 "The Cholera," p. 180.

80   In a report on the state of Russia in 1830, Benkendorf noted the resistance which Zakrevskii's measures induced and suggested the failure of his mission. He also pointed out, however, that the criticism of Zakrevskii's work in part reflected views in the capital which were critical of the Minister of the Interior and which supported Golitsyn against him. These people greeted the Tsar's rejection of Zakrevskii's policies with satisfaction. "Graf A. Kh. Benkendorf o Rossii v 1827–1830 gg.," *Krasnyi arkhiv,* XXXVIII–XL (1930–32), 136–37. Cf. "Kratkoe biograficheskoe vospominanie Grafa A. A. Zakrevskago," *Russkii arkhiv,* 1865, pp. 371–80; A. V. Figner, "Vospominanie o grafe A. A. Zakrevskom," pp. 665–71; "Kholera v 1830–1831 godakh v Kurskoi gubernii," *Istoricheskii vestnik,* XXV (1886), 132–46; Pavlovskii, *Kholernye gody v Rossii,* pp. 14–16.

81   "Kholera v . . . Kurskoi gubernii," pp. 132–46.

82   *Ibid.* In Kursk, as in Tambov, the 1831 outbreak was worse than that of 1830. From August 30, 1830, to January 23, 1831, there were 1,017 cases, 656 deaths; from April 19 to October 2, 1831, there were 14,535 cases, 6,723 deaths. Pavlovski, *Kholernye gody v Rossii,* p. 91.

83   See for example "Kholera v Malo-rossii v 1830–1831," *Russkaia starina,* XLVII (1885), 209–22; Lichtenstaedt, *Cholera, in Russland, 1829–1830,* pp. 167–79 for overall survey of cholera's spread.

CHAPTER 4

1   "Kholera v Moskve (1830): iz pisem Kristina k grafine S. A. Bobrinskoi," *Russkii arkhiv,* Part III (1884), 137. (Cited hereafter as Kristin, "Kholera v Moskve.")

2   A. V. Nikitenko, *Dnevnik,* 3 TT. (Moscow-Leningrad, 1955), I, 92.

3   F. C. M Markus, *Rapport sur le choléra-morbus de Moscou* (Moscou, 1832), p. 62. (Cited hereafter as Markus, *Rapport.*) Markus was the Secretary for the Moscow Cholera Council, and this work is the single best collection of source data on the Moscow epidemic. Unfortunately, no reports similar in detail and comprehensiveness were published for the other epidemic centers.

4   The best and most detailed account of the early hysteria appears in the eyewitness account of Dr. Theodore Zschokke, *Moskau und Petersburg beim Ausbruch der Cholera Morbus mit Bemerkun-*

gen über die bisher gemachten Erfahrungen von dieser Krankheit (Aarau, 1832). (Cited hereafter Zschokke, *Moskau und Petersburg*.) Zschokke joined the exodus from Moscow, and described the chaotic disorder which attended that emigration.

5   Kristin, "Kholera v Moskve," pp. 137–40; Nikitenko, *Dnevnik*, I, 92–93. Zschokke, *Moskau und Petersburg*, pp. 14 ff. For a general discussion of the cholera in Moscow, see Theodor Schiemann, *Geschichte Russlands unter Kaiser Nikolaus I*, 4 vols. (Berlin, 1909–1911), III, 31–37.

6   Markus, *Rapport*, pp. 57–63. Markus gives a month-by-month summary of health conditions in Moscow in 1830, and a very detailed sketch of the crucial months beginning August, 1830. For a popular view of cholera's arrival, Kristin, "Kholera v Moskve," and Zschokke, *Moskau und Petersburg*.

7   For the report of Zakrevskii's instruction, *Journal de St. Pétersbourg*, October 7/19, 1830.

8   Kristin, "Kholera v Moskve," pp. 137–40.

9   Markus, *Rapport*, pp. 63–64.

10 Nikitenko, *Dnevnik*, I, 93.

11 Alexander Herzen, *Byloe i dumy* (Leningrad, 1947), pp. 70–71. Interestingly enough, Kristin also compared the cholera in Moscow to 1812, but he thought rather of the chaos that surrounded the evacuation on Napoleon's approach. "Kholera v Moskve," p. 137.

12 It was reported in *Severnaia pchela*, in an article reprinted in *Journal de St. Pétersbourg*, October 11/23, 1830, that all the classes of the population were competing zealously to second the government's efforts to meet the cholera threat, that "some volunteer to act as assistants to the commissioners, others donate their houses for hospitals; gifts of money and goods arrive from every part...." *Journal de St. Pétersbourg* began to report the gifts which were made, but the numbers were so large that only partial reporting was possible. See *Journal de St. Pétersbourg*, October 23/November 4, 1830.

13 Dr. Zschokke, who made the journey from Moscow to Petersburg, recorded that those who used normal channels were unable to get a pass, much less a seat on the coaches, and he himself applied directly to Golitsyn for his pass. Zschokke, *Moskau und Petersburg*, pp. 25 ff.

14 For the general regulations, see *Journal de St. Pétersbourg*, October 7/19, 1830; cf. Markus, *Rapport*, pp. 64 ff.

15 Markus, *Rapport*, pp. 64–66. Peasants who aided citizens in escaping quarantine would be sentenced to twenty-five blows of the

knout, while soldiers who violated quarantine rules were subject to court martial. For one such case, see: *PSZ, vtoroe Sobranie,* VI, i, March 10, 1831, No. 4415. Quarantine rules were very unevenly enforced, and neither threats nor punishments could stop the abuses.

16 Markus, *Rapport,* p. 66.

17 See the statements in *Journal de St. Pétersbourg,* October 7/19, 1830, and Markus, *Rapport,* p. 67. Though the wording is slightly different, the sense is the same and stresses in the first that the cholera has appeared "very weakly" and in the second that the cholera exists in Moscow, "although still to a very weak degree." The precautionary measures taken were in both instances presented as necessary to prevent a further extension of the disease, and the reports implied strongly that the situation was under control.

18 Zschokke regarded the official bulletins as arrant nonsense, and he quoted one which stated that the cholera "will not reach Moscow." It was common knowledge that the cholera was a desperately serious matter, yet the government maintained a spurious optimism in the face of its approach. See Zschokke, *Moskau und Petersburg,* pp. 17–19.

19 It should be noted that Golitsyn reported directly to St. Petersburg, and, further, that he had no authority whatsoever outside the Moscow Government. The comparison between Zakrevskii and Golitsyn was made openly and became part of a rising tide of criticism directed against Zakrevskii. See "Lettres de Ferdinand Christine à une dame de sa connaissance, (1830–1831)," *Russkii arkhiv,* Part III (1884), 158. The letter was written in July, 1831, and summarized the anti-Zakrevskii attitude.

20 The organizational structure and the functioning of the committee together with the personnel which served on it are taken from Markus, *Rapport,* pp. 67–70. The names of all participants on the Committee are listed in Markus.

21 Markus, *Rapport,* pp. 70–75.

22 In the *Journal de St. Pétersbourg,* October 18/30, 1830, the mortality figures for the Moscow epidemic were published. In the article the discrepancy between cases reported and cures was noted, and it was suggested that those who finally reached the hospitals were usually in desperate condition, while physicians bewailed the failure of citizens to report at the first indications of the disorder. People feared treatment and refused to submit to it until after their condition was hopeless.

23 Markus, *Rapport,* pp. 76–77.

24 *Journal de St. Pétersbourg,* October 11/23, 1830.

25 L. Pavlovskii, *Kholernye gody v Rossii* (Sanktpeterburg, 1893), p. 19; *Journal de St. Pétersbourg,* October 11/23, 1830.

26 Markus, *Rapport,* pp. 74–75.

27 These poems appear in *Vospominaniia A. I. Del'viga,* 2 TT. (Moscow-Leningrad, 1930), I, 153. A. S. Pushkin, *Sochineniia* (Moscow, 1949), p. 165 for "Geroi," and p. 876 for a brief discussion of the circumstances surrounding the poem's publication. Pushkin's letters contain some interesting observations on the cholera period. Caught in the country and unable to cross the quarantine lines to Moscow, he worked with the sanitation officials while complaining against the chaffing regulations. See: A. S. Pushkin, *Polnoe sobranie sochineniia v desiati tomakh: Pisma,* 10 TT. (Moscow-Leningrad, 1949), X, 307–24. Pushkin's letters from Tsarskoe-Selo describing reactions to the 1831 Petersburg outbreak may be found *ibid.,* pp. 350–75.

28 "Kholera v Moskve," pp. 142–44. Cf. Schiemann, *Geschichte Russlands unter Kaiser Nikolaus I,* III, 33–34.

29 Schiemann, *Geschichte Russlands unter Kaiser Nikolaus I,* III, 33–34.

30 *Ibid.* Paul Lacroix, *Historie de la vie et le règne de Nicholas Ier,* 7 tomes (Paris, 1868), V, 132–33, 137 ff. Lacroix described the public reaction in Moscow as more violently destructive, and then stressed the positive value of Nicholas' presence for the city's morale. In this, as in much else, Lacroix's description is not entirely reliable.

31 Prince Lubomirski, *Souvenirs d'un page du Tzar Nicolas* (Paris, 1869), Preface; McGrew, "Nicholas I and the Genesis of Russian Officialism" (unpub. Ph.D. diss., Univ. of Minn., 1955), in which this characteristic is presented as one of the primary obstacles to the realization of Nicholas' goals.

32 This, in point of fact, was true. By December, except for the western provinces, only scattered cases were reported, and the first serious outbreaks of 1831 began in March and April.

33 According to Soviet writers, Russia also was a leader in the development of statistical concepts. See *Ocherki po istorii statistikii SSSR,* Akademiia Nauk SSSR: Institut ekonomiki, sbornik vtoroi (Moskva, 1957).

34 See Pavlovskii, *Kholernye gody v Rossii* and G. T. Arkhangelskii, *Kholernyia epidemii v evropeiskoi Rossii* (Sanktpeterburg, 1879).

35 Apart from Mme. Nechkina, whose brief article we noted before, P. P. Evstafev has done the most with cholera as a phenomenon

in Russian social history, and though he used archival data, his study concerned the military colonies and used almost no demographic information. See: *Vosstanie novgorodskikh voennykh poselian* (Moskva, 1934). It is interesting that the Akademiia Nauk's *Istoriia Moskvy v shesti tomakh* (Moskva, 1954) also contains very little statistical information which would define demographic phenomena. The history of Russian cities is a field for research in which relatively little has been done, and what has been done is neither so sophisticated nor so complete as the urban history projects in the United States and France. This issue is discussed briefly in J. M. Hittle, Review of Iu. R. Klokman, *Ocherki sotsial'noekonomicheskoi istorii gorodov severo-zapada Rossii v seredine XVIII$_v$* (Moscow, 1960) in *Kritika* I, No. 1 (1964), 15–22.

36 Markus used two sources of population statistics. The first followed the police registers for 1829, while the second was Androssov's then unpublished survey of Moscow's population. See Markus, *Rapport,* pp. 33–35. Androssov's survey was published in 1832, and it was this published work which Schnitzler used in his Moscow survey. See J. H. Schnitzler, *Moscou: tableau statistique, géographique, topographique et historique de la ville et du gouvernement de ce nom* (St. Pétersbourg et Paris, 1834). Other statistical data on Moscow is available, but it is insufficiently detailed to be of use here. See, for example, *Statisticheskoe izobrazhenie gorodov i posadov rossiiskoi imperii po 1825 god* (Sanktpeterburg, 1829); and the article, "Moskva," in *Geografichesko-statisticheskii slovar rossiiskoi imperii,* 5 TT. (Sanktpeterburg, 1863–1885). See also Friedrich Wilhelm von Reden, *Das Kaiserreich Russland: Statistisch-geschichtliche Darstellung seiner Kultur-Verhältniss . . . ,* (Berlin, Posen, Bromberg, 1843). The influence of Androssov's survey may be seen in almost all the published secondary surveys, and, short of using archival data, must be considered the main source for demographic appraisals. More detailed materials are available for later periods. The most useful mortality tables are those published in Lichtenstaedt, *Die asiatische Cholera in Russland in Jahren 1830 und 1831* (Berlin, 1831), opposite p. 390. These are the official mortality figures and are reproduced in part in Table A.

37 Markus, *Rapport,* pp. 5–20. Cf. Schnitzler, *Moscou,* pp. 24 ff.

38 Markus, *Rapport,* p. 35.

39 Markus, *Rapport,* pp. 35–36.

40 Cf. Louis Chevalier, *Le choléra: la première épidémie du XIXe siècle* (La Roche-sur-Yon, 1958), pp. 7–9.

41   See Markus, *Rapport,* pp. 36–37 for general appraisal.

42   Markus lists the Pokrovskaia, Serpukhovskaia, Yauskaia, Gorod-skaia, Miasnitskaia, Sretenskaia, Rogozhskaia, and Piatnitskaia as the main industrial quarters. Cf. pp. 36–37.

43   See map, p. 78.

44   The quarter distribution figures are taken from Lichtenstaedt, *Die asiatische Cholera,* opposite p. 390.

45   See Table B in Appendix which lists the quarters in order of their cholera incidence. The Table is based on data from Lichten-staedt, *Die asiatische Cholera.*

46   Markus, *Rapport,* pp. 75–76. Pavlovskii, *Kholernye gody, passim.* See above: Chapter 3.

47   Markus, *Rapport,* pp. 10–14.

48   Lichtenstaedt, *Die asiatische Cholera,* p. 204. See also *Supplement to the Edinburgh Medical and Surgical Journal . . . ,* February, 1832 (Edinburgh, 1832), pp. xc–xcii. (Cited hereafter as *Supplement.*) Markus, *Rapport,* p. 76.

49   Markus developed his estimate of the upper classes separately from his comments on the cholera's selectivity and his conclusion that the upper classes suffered less than other groups. We have made specific something implicit in Markus' discussion.

50   Markus, *Rapport,* pp. 36–37. According to the police registers, those comprising the nobility numbered 22,394. Markus, *Rapport,* p. 33. Markus' figure for the "upper classes" doubled that number.

51   Markus, *Rapport,* p. 21 ff.

52   See Table A, in Appendix, classes 1, 2, 4.

53   Lichtenstaedt's calculations appear in *Die asiatische Cholera,* p. 204. The figure should be 6.6 per cent: Lichtenstaedt made his calculation on 4,690 deaths, while he should have used the un-adjusted figure, 4,588.

54   See Markus, *Rapport,* pp. 33–35.

55   An interesting example of this may be seen in a report of General Wilson's stewardship of government works near St. Petersburg in which every effort was made to maintain high standards of diet dress, and health generally. *Official Report Made to Government by Drs. Russell and Barry on the Disease Called Cholera Spasmodica as Observed by them during their Mission to Russia in 1831* (London, 1832). (Cited hereafter as Russell and Barry, *Report.*)

56   For the report on raising the quarantine, *Journal de St. Péters-bourg,* December 11/23, 1830. See Kristin, "Kholera v Moskve," pp. 148–49 for attitudes at the end of the epidemic.

CHAPTER 5

1 G. I. Arkhangel'skii, *Kholernyia epidemii Evropeiskoi Rossii v 50-ti-letni period 1823–1872 gg.* (Sanktpeterburg, 1874), p. 2.

2 In 1830 the southern governments had a mortality per ten thousand population of 15.8, the central governments 8.5, the northern governments 0.7. In 1831 the figures respectively were 85.4, 38.8, 15.0. *Ibid.*, p. 5.

3 *Ibid.* The southern governments which had the highest mortality per ten thousand population reported 212,378 cases and 89,703 deaths. The lower population density for the southern governments, 10,506,000, contributed to the exceedingly high mortality percentage ratio.

4 L. Pavlovskii, *Kholernye gody v Rossii* (Sanktpeterburg, 1893), pp. 49–51.

5 *Arkhiv Kniazia Vorontsova,* 40 vols. (Moskva, 1870–1895), XXXVIII, 188–89, 196–97.

6 Jeremias Lichtenstaedt, *Die asiatische Cholera in Russland in Jahren 1830 und 1831* (Berlin, 1831), pp. 122–24. Cf. *Supplement to the Edinburgh Medical and Surgical Journal ...* February, 1832 (Edinburgh, 1832), pp. cxxxii–cxxxiv. (Cited hereafter as *Supplement.*)

7 See Lichtenstaedt, *ibid.,* and *Supplement.* Dr. David Craigie stressed the filthy and crowded conditions among the Jews, but neither he nor Lichtenstaedt showed familiarity with the social, political, and cultural problems of the Jewish community.

8 *Journal de St. Pétersbourg,* May 5/17, 1831.

9 "Report of the Circle Physician Dr. Schnur, on the Propagation of Cholera in the Kingdom of Poland, Dated the 12th May, 1831," *Supplement,* pp. cxxxiv–cxxxvi.

10 Pavlovskii notes the development of cholera in the Russian forces in Poland, but his interpretation of the cholera's movement westward suggests that Poland could scarcely have escaped the epidemic. See also: "Ausbruch der Cholera in Polen...," in Lichtenstaedt, *Die asiatische Cholera,* pp. 220 ff., for a somewhat different view.

11 Alexander Puzyrewsky, *Die Polnisch-russische Krieg 1831,* 3 Bände (Wien, 1892), I, 266–67.

12 Louis Chevalier, *Le choléra: la première épidémie du XIXe siècle* (La Roche-sur-yon, 1958), pp. 15–16.

13 Quoted in *ibid.*

14 Friedrich von Smitt, *Geschichte des polnischen Aufstandes und Krieges in dem Jahren 1830 und 1831*, 3 Bände (Berlin, 1848), II, 117–18. The circular cited appears as Appendix XXI in Francis Bisset Hawkins, M.D., *History of the Epidemic Spasmodic Cholera of Russia; including a copious account of the disease which has prevailed in India, and which has travelled under that name, from Asia into Europe* (London, 1831), pp. 273–75.

15 Puzyrewsky, *Die Polnisch-russische Krieg,* I, 366–67; see also Table III, p. 82.

16 *Ibid.,* pp. 366–67. Cf. von Smitt, *Geschichte des polnischen Aufstandes,* II, 118.

17 See Puzyrewsky, *Die Polnisch-russische Krieg,* I, 374, and von Smitt, *Geschichte des polnischen Aufstan des,* II, 118.

18 Joszef Hardynski, *History of the Late Polish Revolution and the Events of the Campaign* (London [?], n.d.), p. 270.

19 "Vospominanie G. I. Filipsona," *Russkii arkhiv,* Part III (1883), 125.

20 *Errinerungen von Alexander Lwowitsch Seeland aus der polnischen Revolution von 1830–1831,* tr., Georg Freiherrn von Sak. Band II, *Bibliothek russischer Denkwürdigkeiten,* ed., Dr. Th. Schiemann (Stuttgart, 1894), pp. 48–49.

21 Hardynski, *Polish Revolution,* p. 318.

22 "Vospominanie Filipsona," pp. 126–29.

23 Hermann Kunz, *Der polnisch-russische Krieg von 1831* (Berlin, 1890), p. 86. The figures are given on p. 94.

24 "Note officielle du Ministère des affaires étrangères du gouvernement national de Pologne, au cabinet de Berlin," *Les affaires polonaises* (Paris, 1831), p. 14. The Poles reversed here the position taken on cholera's contagiousness; compare this with the circular cited above.

25 Général-Prince Stcherbatow, *Prince Paskévitch: sa vie politique et militaire,* 6 tomes (St. Pétersbourg, 1893), IV, 33, 44–46, 53.

26 Kunz, *Der polnisch-russische Krieg,* pp. 202 ff.

27 Pavlovskii, *Kholernye gody,* pp. 29–31.

28 This discussion should not be considered exhaustive, and further study should prove enlightening on the general problem of the cholera and the Polish defeat. Such a study, however, should be made by a person able to use the city archives in Warsaw as well as archival data on both Polish and Russian national and military development.

29 N. K. Shil'der, *Imperator Nikolai I: ego zhizn' i tsarstvovanie,* 2 TT. (Sanktpeterburg, 1903), II, 364.

30   "Lettres de Ferdinand Christine à une dame de sa connaissance," *Russkii arkhiv,* Chast III (1884), 198. Cf. "Vospominanie Filipsona," pp. 129–30.

31   "Perepiska Imperatora Nikolaia Pavlovicha s Velikim Kniazem Tsesarevichem Konstantinom Pavlovichem," *Sbornik imperatorskago russkago istoricheskago obshchestva,* CXXXII (1911), 224.

32   See *Journal de St. Pétersbourg,* June 6/20, 1831.

33   "Graf A. Kh. Benkendorf o Rossii v 1831–1832." *Krasnyi arkhiv,* LXVI (1931), 135.

34   *Ibid.* For Nicholas' Manifest, see: *PSZ,* vtoroe sobranie, VI, i, No. 4746. Cf. *Journal de St. Pétersbourg,* August 18/30, 1831.

35   "Lettres de Ferdinand Christine . . . ," pp. 157–59.

36   *Ibid.*

37   Lichtenstaedt, *Die asiatische Cholera,* pp. 232–34. The cholera at Riga was particularly violent, and in the first days of the epidemic the progress of the disease was so rapid, and its symptoms so extreme, that medicine could accomplish very little.

38   *Journal de St. Pétersbourg,* June 20/July 2, 1831. A summary of the quarantine orders published June 12, 1831, may be seen in Hawkins, *History of the Epidemic Spasmodic Cholera of Russia,* pp. 25–28. The Riga Medical Board denied that cholera was infectious and stressed attention to a person's way of life. Hawkins, *ibid.,* Appendix X, pp. 234–35.

39   Auguste Gerardin et Paul Gaimard, *Du choléra-morbus en Russie, en Prusse et en Austriche pendant les ánnees 1831 et 1832* (Paris, 1832), pp. 39–51. These observers were especially stringent in criticizing all restrictive measures and showed a particular concern over the opposition and social tension such measures produced. See *ibid.,* pp. 6–7, 11–12.

40   *Journal de St. Pétersbourg,* June 23/July 5, 1831.

41   *Ibid.*

42   Several excellent descriptions of the atmosphere in Petersburg at the cholera's onset are available. This description, and that following, are based on these sources: I. R. Von-der-Hoven, "Bunt na Sennoi ploshchadi v S.-Peterburge," *Russkaia starina,* XLVII (1885), 61–68; Von-der-Hoven, "Kholera v S.-Peterburge v 1831," *Russkaia starina,* XLIV (1884), 391–98, 401–16; N. K. Shil'der, ed., "Imperator Nikolai I v 1830–1831: iz zapisok grafa A. Kh. Benkendorfa," *Russkaia starina,* LXXXVIII (1896), 65–96; A. G. Puparev, "Kholernyi mesiats v S.-Peterburge, iiun 1831 g.," *Russkaia starina,* XLVII (1885), 69–86. See also: N. K. Shil'der, *Nikolai I,* II, 361 ff.; Theodor Schiemann, *Geschichte*

Russlands unter Kaiser Nikolaus I, 4 Bände (Berlin, 1904–1919), III, 141 ff. Paul Lacroix, *Histoire de la vie et du regne de Nicolas Ier,* T. 5 (Paris, 1868), pp. 430 ff., gives a very full account.

43 "Benkendorf o Rossii v 1831–1832," *Krasnyi arkhiv,* XLVI (1931), 136; "Lettres de Ferdinand Christine ...," pp. 149–50. Christine is reporting news sent him from St. Petersburg by Mukhanov where "Terror is the order of the day ..." and "the people have never wished to believe that the disease is in the city and they imagine that healthy people are carried to the hospitals."

44 See especially: Von-der-Hoven, "Kholera v Peterburge v 1831," and Puparev, "Kholernyi mesiats v S.-Peterburge"; Shil'der, *Nikolai I,* II, 366–67.

45 In a letter dated July 5 (June 23, O.S.), 1831, the official English deputation sent to view the cholera in Petersburg commented: "The malady is spreading rapidly. The people are in the midst of a solemn fast;—the streets are thronged with processions and other crowds;—the churches filled all day. The intemperannce likely to follow this fast will add to the violence of the disease." *Official Report Made to the Government by Drs. Russell and Barry on the Disease Called Cholera Spasmodica as Observed by them during their Mission to Russia in 1831* (London, 1832), p. 22. (Cited hereafter as Russell and Barry, *Report.*)

46 Puparev, "Kholernyi mesiats v S.-Peterburge," pp. 402–09; Christine, "Lettres de Ferdinand Christine ...," pp. 150–52; Schiemann, *Nikolaus I,* III, 144–45.

47 Von-der-Hoven, "Bunt na Sennoi ploschadi v S.-Peterburge"; Schiemann, *Nikolaus I,* III, 141 ff.; Puparev, "Kholernyi mesiats v S.-Peterburge," pp. 402–09. Mukhanov, whose letter Christine copies, reported the riots in the capital: "There have been some disorders; hospitals have been forced; patients thrown onto the pavement and the ambulances destroyed; more than ten thousand people gathered on the Sennaia, and that began to become very serious...." "Lettres de Ferdinand Christine ...," p. 150.

48 Schiemann's account, which is meticulous in most details, errs in reporting the dates of the uprising. At the beginning he refers (p. 145) to Monday, July 3 (June 21, O.S.) for the riots in the Rozhdestvenskaia. June 21/July 3, 1831, was a Sunday. See Puparev, "Kholernyi mesiats v S.-Peterburge," p. 405. This is confirmed by the datings in the *Journal de St. Pétersbourg,* which gives June 20/July 2, 1831 as Saturday, and June 23/July 5, 1831, as Tuesday. Schiemann then puts the attack on the

Sennaia "on the following day," e.g., on June 22/July 4, 1831, which is correct. The outrages in the Sennaia were only quieted, by Schiemann's showing, at 8:30 in the evening of June 22. But in the next paragraph, he describes the Tsar's going to Petersburg on the morning of July 4, entering Elagin at 11:00, visiting the parade ground of the Preobrazhenskoe. Two hours elapsed before the Tsar's entourage entered the Haymarket. Were this true, he would have arrived at the beginning of the riots, and quite a different story might be told. Nicholas made his tour of the city on June 23/July 5, 1831. Shil'der has the correct day based on Menshikov's journal. See *Nikolai I*, II, 364. It is interesting that Lacroix makes the same mistake as Schiemann, for he cites Nicholas' departure as 6 o'clock in the morning, July 4 (June 22, O.S.), *Histoire de Nicolas I*, V, 433. The error may very well stem from the same entry in the Tsarina's diary: "Da begab sich der Kaiser am 22 juni in die Stadt....," quoted in Schiemann, III, 147, n. 1. Further confirmation of the correct dating is to be found in Mukhanov, who reported: "It was on Monday the 22nd that all this happened, and yesterday, Tuesday the 23rd, the disturbances began again and the Emperor arrived ... and harangued the people...." "Lettres de Ferdinand Christine ...," p. 150.

49   For the atmosphere at Peterhof see: "Iz pis'ma V. A. Zhukovskago k Printsesse Luize Prusskoi," *Russkii arkhiv*, 1866, pp. 339–43. See also: A. Th. von Grimm, *Alexandra Feodorowna, Kaiserin von Russland*, 2 Bände (Leipzig, 1866), II, 60–63. The entry in the Tsarina's diary cited above (note 48) reveals her outlook on the cholera riots which she saw in terms of Menshikov's phrase: "Yesterday the Emperor had some sublime moments."

50   The speech cited was that reported by Menshikov on his return to Peterhof and which Zhukovskii retailed to Princess Louise. This is undoubtedly embellished. See "Iz pis'ma V. A. Zhukovskago." The reference to the French and Poles, as well as to Nicholas' shame before the world, are taken from Schiemann's account which he based on written reports by Menshikov and Benkendorf. Schiemann, *Nikolaus I*, III, 146. Schiemann refers to the myth which grew up around the Haymarket incident and specifically referred to "the poet Zhukovskii's letter." The speech Zhukovskii gives is quoted because, in this writer's opinion, it catches Nicholas' spirit—the emphasis on order, the appeal to the family, the warning to the disaffected, and the stress on religious values.

51   Drs. Barry and Russell dated their second report July 16 (July 4, O.S.), 1831, and noted "much of this favorable change is

owing to the noble conduct of the Emperor who harangued the mob in the Haymarket, and told them they ought to be most grateful to medical men who risked their own lives to save theirs." Russell and Barry, *Report*, p. 28. The equestrian statue of Nicholas I which was erected facing the Isaac Cathedral in 1859 has four small bas reliefs on the base portraying great moments in the Tsar's reign. The second of these shows Nicholas calming the mob in the Sennaia. Perhaps it is fitting that two of the four deal with rebellions, the other being the Decembrist uprising.

52 See above Chaps. 3 and 4. See also Chevalier, *Le choléra,* pp. 17, 179 ff. Cf. McGrew, "The First Cholera Epidemic and Social History," *Bulletin of the History of Medicine,* XXXIV, No. 1 (Jan.–Feb., 1960) and "The First Russian Cholera Epidemic: Themes and Opportunities," *ibid.,* XXXVI, No. 3 (June, 1962).

53 Russell and Barry, *Report,* p. 28.

54 *Journal de St. Pétersbourg,* August 18/30. No other mention of the riots is to be found before this issue published the Tsar's manifest. Schiemann points out an even graver problem, for, he suggests, the people took Nicholas' speech on the Haymarket as a kind of justification for their view that the cholera did not exist. According to Schiemann's view, the Tsar mentioned Frenchmen and Poles, but he said nothing about the cholera, and this added to rumors which remained current after the riots. Schiemann, *Nikolaus I,* III, 147–49. In the light of other evidence, Schiemann's point should be qualified, but it is not unlikely that the Tsar's speech was misunderstood.

55 Arrests, of course, were made during the riots, but no full-scale investigation was undertaken, and no effort to punish the people for their misdeeds was made. On the contrary, it seemed that the Tsar had made concessions, had given the people a gift by relaxing the restrictions which already existed. Christine commented that in his opinion this was unwise, for, he noted, "concessions made in the wake of a popular disturbance are a dangerous example," and he remarked, after quoting Prince Yussupov on the revolt in the military colonies, that, "as there is still no exemplary punishment for the Petersburg 'journées,' probably these most recent ones expect the same immunity," and he concluded that a ruler must be feared as well as loved. "Lettres de Ferdinand Christine . . . ," pp. 152, 159–60.

56 See *Journal de St. Pétersbourg,* July 2/14, 1831; July 4/16, 1831; July 7/19, 1831, for personnel changes and revision of quarantine policy. Changes in local sanitary policies including the

relaxation of police measures are reported in Russell and Barry, *Report,* pp. 29–30. The English recorded that, "We have been cautioned not to enter, for the present, into minute personal inquiries as to the origin of the disease. Even the government authorities, in consideration of the state of popular feelings, have forbidden all dissections, except at the General Military Hospital; and even these, except in cases of medico-legal doubts as to the cause of death" (p. 29). See Girardin et Gaimard, *Le choléra-morbus,* pp. 31–37 for a discussion of the Admiralty Quarter. "Lettres de Ferdinand Christine...," pp. 151–52.

57 A general relaxation of quarantine policy as it affected inland commerce was announced in *Journal de St. Pétersbourg,* July 4/16, 1831, and special arrangements were also announced so that the Nizhny Fair would be held as scheduled. *Journal de St. Pétersbourg,* June 27/July 9, 1831. Cf. *PSZ,* vtoroe sobranie, VI, i, No. 4760. Controls remained strict, however, outside the capital, and Russell and Barry reported the violent breaking of a quarantine barrier some thirty miles away on July 2/16, 1831. *Report,* p. 30. This movement was part of a major emigration which followed the relaxation of the quarantine rules in the city and which saw at least 10,000 people depart. Schiemann, *Nikolaus I,* III, 147.

58 Russell and Barry, *Report,* p. 25. The French observers were stringent in denouncing the uselessness of the rules and were quick to indicate the public's resistance, but their criticisms were not against the regulations as such, though they never went so far in approval as did Russell and Barry. See Gerardin et Gaimard, *Du choléra-morbus,* pp. 11–12.

59 This characteristic held true throughout the epidemic. Officers who were reprimanded or punished were guilty of *too lenient* an interpretation of the rules, or were guilty of infractions of the rules themselves. See, for example, Von-der-Hoven, "Kholera v S.-Petersburg v 1831," pp. 392–93; N. K. Shil'der, *Nikolai I,* II, 367–70. On the other hand, it was said concerning quarantines on vessels bound for Petersburg, "It is now, however, generally known, and acknowledged, by those acquainted with the facts, that even these trifling precautionary interruptions were in many cases omitted or evaded." Russell and Barry, *Report,* p. 24.

60 See Velikii Kniaz Nikolai Mikhailovich, *Graf Pavel Alexandrovich Stroganov,* 3 TT. (S.-Petersburg, 1903), I, 108–10. The members of Alexander's secret committee, in common with reformers throughout the nineteenth century, recognized the great

need for effective administrators, and this could be considered one of the main themes in Russian reform thought.

61   The sense of apartness, and the ineffectual quality as well as the venality of officialdom forms a consistent theme in nineteenth-century Russian literature. Though never the villain, the *chinovnik* is always there—ubiquitous, obsequious, authoritarian when it is possible, and always venal. A most interesting study, and a most enlightening one, could be done on the official in Russian literature. Professor Sidney Monas discussed this problem in a paper delivered to the American Historical Association in 1964.

62   Shil'der makes the point that during the flight from Petersburg after the cholera riots the rumors of poisoning were carried throughout Russia and especially to the Novgorod military colonies. *Nikolai I,* II, 370. The poison hysteria, however, was a function of the cholera and was more profound than any particular manifestation. Thus the following description of the Reval reaction could have been generalized for much of Russia: "At the appearance of this malady, the people of Reval, as in other Russian cities, were firmly persuaded they were poisoned; their defiance became extreme; they rejected medical aid, refused even the food which was distributed to them, showed an insurmountable aversion for the hospitals, and began to contradict the powerful voice of authority." Gerardin et Gaimard, *Du choléra-morbus,* p. 6.

63   *Journal de St. Pétersbourg,* August 18/30, 1831. *PSZ,* vtoroe sobranie, VI, i. No. 4746.

64   See P. P. Evstafev, *Vosstanie novgorodskikh voennykh poselian* (Moskva, 1934), p. 95. Evstafev argues that the government used the cholera to cover up the real causes for the revolt, which lay in the conditions in the colonies themselves, and he points out that the cholera mortality tables contained deaths which were part of the rebellion rather than the epidemic. His point is well taken, but it should be stressed that the cholera hysteria was the immediate factor which triggered the revolt.

65   *Ibid., passim.* This study provides an excellent summary of the history and problems of the military colonies. See also: "Vospominaniia doktora I. I. Evropeusa," *Russkaia starina,* VI (1872), 272 ff.; A. Dolgorukii, "Novgorodskie dvoriane i voennye poseliane," *Russkaia starina,* VIII (1873), 411–14. For a brief description of the colonies, P. A. F. K. Possart, *Das Kaiserthum Russlands,* 2 Theilen (Stuttgart, 1840–1841), I, 465 ff.

66   "Rapport sur les colonies militaires en Russie," St. Pétersbourg,

22 avril, 1827, in Theodore Schiemann, *Nikolaus I,* II, Anlagen, 415–22. The quotation is on p. 422. A. G. Mazour, *The First Russian Revolution: The Decembrist Movement* (Berkeley, Calif., 1937), pp. 37–45. Mazour takes a moderate view of Arakcheev and his work. See "Le comte Aleksej Andreevič Arakčeev," *Le monde slave* (juin, 1936), 365–90. Evstafev, *Vosstanie,* pp. 96–112.

67 Schiemann, *Nikolaus I,* III, 149–53; Evstafev, *Vosstanie,* pp. 114 ff.

68 Schiemann, *ibid.;* Evstafev, *ibid.*

69 Shil'der, *Nikolai I,* II, 370–71; Schiemann, *Nikolaus I,* III, 152–53. See also: L. A. Seriakov, "Moia trudovaia zhizn'," *Russkaia starina,* XIV (1875), 164 ff.

70 "Lettres de Ferdinand Christine . . . ," pp. 159–60. See "Gr. A. Kn. Benkendorf o Rossii v 1831–1832, gg." *Krasnyi Archiv,* XLVI (1931), 135–37; Schiemann, *Nikolaus I,* III, 153–54. See also: N. K. Shil'der, (ed.), "Imperator Nikolai I v 1830–1831 gg.," and N. M. Druzhinin, *Gosudarstvennye krestiane i reforma P. D. Kiseleva,* 2 TT. (Moskva-Leningrad, 1946), I, 186 ff. for general discussion of unrest.

71 See Ch. Th. Herrmann, "Des progrès de la population en Russie par gouvernements . . . ," *Mémoires de l'académie impériale des sciences de St. Pétersbourg,* series V, Tome VIII (1817–18), 352 ff., especially 356–59.

72 For Petersburg's growth see *Geografichesko-statisticheskii slovar' rossiiskoi imperii,* 5 TT. (Sanktpeterburg, 1873), IV, 450. It is interesting that the rate of growth slowed considerably in the early 1830's.

73 These figures are from Possart, *Das Kaiserthum Russlands,* II, 449.

74 Baron Storch celebrated Petersburg's public monuments and institutions in Heinrich F. Storch, *Gemälde von St. Petersburgh* (Riga, 1793) and thirty years later Granville portrayed the city with an amazing lack of sensitivity to public problems. His visit, which took place in the depths of winter, came at a time when many outward appearances would be masked by the snow. See A. B. Granville, *St. Petersburgh . . . ,* 2 vols. (London, 1828), *passim.* Other travellers were less uncritical, though often the points they seized on—the police system, the weather, the dampness of the city's situation—were not relevant to the point at hand. It might be argued that early nineteenth-century voyagers were sufficiently acclimated to misery that unless it was picturesque, they could simply ignore it. See, for example, Captain James Abbott, *Narrative of a Journey from Heraut to Khiva, Moscow, and St.*

Petersburg, 2 vols. (London, 1867); Robert Bremner, *Excursions in the Interior of Russia* ... (London, 1839); Le Marquis de Custine, *La Russie en 1839,* 4 TT. (Bruxelles, 1843). When Custine was not too busy dripping vitriol, he was a perceptive observer. J. G. Kohl, *Petersburg in Bildern und Skizzen* (Dresden und Leipzig, 1845); Leitch Ritchie, *A Journey to St. Petersburg and Moscow* ... (London, 1836), etc.

75 *Statisticheskoe izobrazhenie gorodov i posadov Rossiiskoi imperii po 1825 god* (Sanktpeterburg, 1829). Some sections of Petersburg were much more crowded than others. Count S. S. Uvarov reported that in the Admiralty Quarter there were 39,975 inhabitants in 233 dwellings, or an average of 171 persons per house. Gerardin et Gaimard, *Du choléra-morbus,* pp. 31–32.

76 The estimate cited is from Possart, *Das Kaiserthum Russlands,* II, 282.

77 Ch. Th. Hermann cited a total of 42,449 non-domiciled population in Petersburg in 1832. Of these, 37,442 were Russian, the remaining 5,037 foreign. See Ch. Th. Hermann, "Recherches statistiques sur les mariages, les naissances et les décès des habitants de St.-Pétersbourg depuis 1808 jusqu' à 1831," *Mémoires de l'académie impériale des sciences de St. Pétersbourg,* VI series, Sciences politiques, histoire et philologie, II (1833), 547–83. The figures cited are on p. 559.

78 Possart, *Das Kaiserthum Russlands,* II, 321–23. Cf. "O delakh meditsinskago departmenta," *Zhurnal ministerstva vnutrennikh del,* III (1831), 160 ff.

79 Ch. Th. Hermann, "Recherches statistiques sur les mariages ... ," *Mémoires de l'académie impériale des sciences de St. Pétersbourg,* Ser. V, VIII (1817–18), pp. 575–77. Hermann distinguishes two age groups: 15 to 30, and 30 to 45.

80 It is interesting that both the French and English observers pointed out that workers engaged on projects in the capital were far less seriously affected by the cholera than the non-working population. The cholera, for example, was particularly violent among the people who were living on boats in the Rozhdestvenskaia, and it was actually impossible to determine the number of deaths in this crowded sector, as in the Admiralty, since the people hid their dead and buried them most secretly. These, of course, were the quarters where the worst cholera troubles occurred. See Gerardin et Gaimard, *Du choléra-morbus,* pp. 31–33; Russell and Barry, *Report,* pp. 43 ff., esp. pp. 79–80. Although we can go no farther on the basis of published material, evidences of basic urban problems appear to be present in

Petersburg, and it could well be that unpublished sources would be extremely rich for defining further the nature of those problems and their larger significance. For example, one of the most important indices for abnormal urban conditions is evidence on murder, suicide, armed robbery, and other crimes against persons and property. This type of information is slight, fragmented, and overgeneralized in published sources, and often is of questionable accuracy. See, for example, Hermann's articles on suicide and murder in the Russian Empire in series VI, Tomes I, II, and III of the *Mémoires* of the Academy of Sciences of St. Petersburg.

81 Even in Petersburg where a cholera council was formed, it appeared for a time that no special administrative dispositions would be made, and that if the cholera had been overadministered in 1830, it was going to be underadministered in 1831. With some asperity, Dr. Reman, the chief of the Civil-Medical Council, reported on June 14: "With respect to this object, nothing more is at present required from the Civil General-Staff Physician [himself] than the appointment of medical officers to the quarantines, and to the boundaries of observation, formerly not in any degree falling under his direction, he not even having been appraised of the original establishment of the quarantines." Russell and Barry, *Report,* pp. 33–34.

82 The way the government carried on every operation may be seen in *PSZ,* vtoroe sobranie, VI, i, No. 4618 on grace periods for foreclosure procedures; No. 4715, on grace periods for payment of loans; No. 4724 on salaries of medical and pharmaceutical functionaries whose services were co-opted for the cholera struggle.

83 The regulations governing the organization of the Medical Department and public health administration which were published in 1832 showed no significant revision from the centralized procedures which were followed in the cholera epidemic. See *Svod zakonov rossiiskoi imperii poveleniem gosudaria imperatora Nikolaia Pavlovicha sostavlennyi,* Izdanie vtoroe (Sanktpeterburg, 1833), T. XIII, *passim.* Although the cholera did not immediately produce major administrative reforms, it showed the need for them, and in at least one case—Moldavia and Wallachia—hastened their development. See A. P. Zablotskii-Desiatovskii, *Graf. P. D. Kiselev i ego vremia,* 2 TT. (Sanktpeterburg, 1882), I, 371 ff.

84 "Bumagi grafa Arseniia Andreevicha Zakrevskago: zapiska o prichinakh, kotoryia, krome bolezni ...," *Sbornik imperatorskago russkago istoricheskago obshchestva,* T. 78, pp. 534–42.

85   Gerardin et Gaimard, *Du choléra-morbus,* pp. 31–38.
86   *Ibid.,* pp. 21–22.

CHAPTER 6

1   For a summary statement of this thesis, see McGrew, "The Russian Intelligentsia from Radishchev to Pasternak," *Antioch Review,* XXIII, No. 4 (Winter, 1963–64). This view should be compared with Martin Malia's view of the intelligentsia in R. E. Pipes, ed., *The Russian Intelligentsia* (Cambridge, 1960).

2   The most serious physical threats to the physicians occurred during the cholera riots in the summer of 1831, although the people's fear of the hospitals and doctors was amply attested in the earlier outbreaks. Among the physicians who died of cholera were the head of the Medical Council of the Ministry of Interior, Dr. Reman, and the well-known physician, M. Ya. Mudrov. It should also be remembered, however, that the disease mortality among physicians and aides seemed to be relatively low, a point which was used by non-contagionists to support their position.

3   Markus' table, "Malades du cholera á Moscou...," covering September, 1830–March, 1831, shows the following figures for persons treated in hospitals as opposed to those who remained in private dwellings: of the latter, 1515 cases were reported, 1008 died. In the temporary hospitals, 5352 cases were treated, 2899 deaths were recorded; in public establishments, 1709 cases were treated with 783 deaths. F. C. M. Markus, *Rapport sur le Choléra-morbus de Moscou* (Moscou, 1832). (Cited hereafter as *Rapport.*) The opportunity for regular medical care and supervised treatment in private dwellings was definitely restricted. Cf. Jeremias Lichtenstaedt, "Vollständige Übersicht der Cholera-Kranken in der Residenzstaedt Moskau...," *Die Asiatische Cholera im Russland in Jahren 1830 und 1831* (Berln, 1831), opposite p. 390.

4   Markus, *Rapport,* p. 76.
5   Markus, *Rapport,* pp. 157–58.
6   "Otchety Ego Imperatorskomu Velichestvu...," *Voenno-meditsinskii zhurnal,* VIII, No. 2 (1831), 163–236. The treatments all showed a family resemblance: rubbing and massage, heat, warm bottles, etc., to warm the body; some bleeding; use of various drugs, both stimulants and depressants, internally. For other examples, see Auguste Gerardin et Paul Gaimard, *Du choléra-morbus en Russie, en Prusse et en Austriche pendant les ánnees 1831 et 1832* (Paris, 1832), *passim;* and *Official Report Made to*

Government by Drs. Russell and Barry on the Disease Called Cholera Spasmodica as Observed by them during their Mission to Russia in 1831 (London, 1832), *passim.* (Cited hereafter as, Russell and Barry, *Report.*)

7   *Traktat o poval'no-zarazitel'noi bolezni kholere, byvshei v Rossii v 1830 i 1831 godu* (Sanktpeterburg, 1831), pp. 306–07. (Cited heeafter as *Traktat.*)

8   See Pollitzer, "Cholera Studies: Symptomatology, Diagnosis, Prognosis, and Treatment," *Bulletin of the World Health Organization,* XVI (1957), 362.

9   For a bibliographical discussion of this material, see R. E. McGrew, "The First Russian Cholera Epidemic: Themes and Opportunities," *Bulletin of the History of Medicine,* XXXVI, No. 2 (1962), 220–42. Rossiiskii's bibliography lists only a small fraction of this material.

10 The Russian authors most regularly cited in contemporary European works were those who published in French or German, including Lichtenstaedt, Markus, Jaehnichen, and Loder. Some Russian materials were translated, but neither the *Traktat* nor Mudrov's essays were noted, and such names as Venediktov or Diad'kovskii do not appear in the western literature. Dr. Pollitzer, who has done the best and most comprehensive survey of the cholera, recognized Hermann's chemical experiments and the injection treatment which followed them, but neither his notes nor the text suggest familiarity with Russian language publications on cholera.

11 *Traktat,* p. 5.

12 *Traktat,* pp. 12–17.

13 *Traktat,* pp. 23–25.

14 *Traktat,* p. 32.

15 *Traktat,* pp. 34 ff.

16 See N. F. Kramchaninov, "A Note on the History of the Epidemiology of Cholera in Russia," Trans., C. R. Pringle, *Journal of Microbiology, Epidemiology and Immunology* (Russian), XXXI, No. 3 (1960), 539. See also below for the discussion of this idea.

17 *Traktat,* pp. 34 ff.

18 *Traktat,* pp. 51–55.

19 *Traktat,* pp. 46 ff.

20 *Traktat,* pp. 193–95, 206–09.

21 Mudrov, "Kratkoe nastavlenie o kholere," p. 286.

22 Mudrov, "Kratkoe nastavlenie o kholere," part 3. Cf. the sanitary

instructions for Nizhny-Novgorod, *Journal de St. Pétersbourg,* September 25/October 7, 1830.

23   Markus, *Rapport,* pp. 204–14. The statements quoted are on p. 213.

24   Loder in Lichtenstaedt, *Die asiatische Cholera,* pp. 12 ff, 206 ff. Lichtenstaedt's comments are inter-lineated on pp. 12–14.

25   Markus, *Rapport,* pp. 173–74.

26   *Ibid.*

27   *Ibid.*

28   See N. F. Kramchaninov, "A Note on the History of the Epidemiology of Cholera in Russia," and the same author's "History of Native Science: the Contribution of Russian Doctors to the Study of the Epidemiology of Cholera in the First Third of the Nineteenth Century," *Journal of Microbiology, Epidemiology and Immunology* [*Zhurnal mikrobiologii, epidemologii, immunobiologii*], XXX, No. 1 (Oct., 1959), 146–53.

29   See Chap. 2 above.

30   See "Otchety Ego Imperatorskomu Velichestvu...." See also Lichtenstaedt, *Die asiatische Cholera,* pp. 244 ff. Lichtenstaedt built an entire therapeutic theory on a symptomological approach.

31   Russell and Barry, *Report,* p. 23.

32   Russell and Barry, *Report,* pp. 23–24. Not all physicians shared enthusiasm for this method, and it was not the method recommended by the Medical Council (see below). Dr. Zdrekauer of the Hospital of the Imperial Court Stables tried the bismuth approach and found "that it has not answered the expectations raised by Dr. Leo of Warsaw as to its efficacy..." (*ibid.,* p. 102).

33   Russell and Barry, *Report,* p. 23.

34   Mudrov, "Kratkoe nastavlenie o kholere," p. 286.

35   Markus, *Rapport,* p. 79. Markus noted nastily that this view was especially popular with those who had never seen the cholera, but knew it only from printed reports. He cited M. B. Dreyfus of Strasbourg, who wrote at the end of 1831, for confirmation of the views described.

36   Mudrov, "Kratkoe nastavlenie o kholere," part 4.

37   Markus, *Rapport,* pp. 150–51.

38   *Traktat,* pp. 391–403, 408 ff.

39   Markus, *Rapport,* 101–03.

40   Markus, *Rapport,* pp. 102–03. Keir's ideas are set forth fully in his *A Treatise on Cholera, Containing the Author's Experience of the Epidemic Known by that Name as it Prevailed in the City of Moscow in Autumn 1830 and Winter, 1831* (Edinburgh, 1832).

41 Markus, *Rapport*, p. 107.

42 Markus, *Rapport*, p. 133.

43 Markus, *Rapport*, pp. 150–51.

44 Markus, *Rapport*, p. 152.

45 Markus, *Rapport*, 151–52.

46 Markus, *Rapport*, p. 153. Jaehnichen, *Réflexions sur le choléra-morbus* (Moscou, 1831), pp. 63 ff. See also M. le docteur Jähnichen, "Mémoire sur le choléra-morbus qui règne en Russie," *Gazette médicale de Paris*, I–II (March 5, 1831), 85–88; Dr. Jaehnichen, "Die Cholera in Moskau mit kritischen Bemerkungen zu einem Aufsatz von Herrn Leibmedicus Dr. V. Loder über diese Epidemie," *Wissenschaftlichen Annalen der gesammten Heilkunde*, XIX (1831), 385–450.

47 Markus, *Rapport*, pp. 105–06.

48 Markus, *Rapport*, p. 153. On the infusion treatment, see Pollitzer, "Cholera Studies: Symptomatology, Diagnosis, Prognosis and Treatment," pp. 393–94.

49 Markus, *Rapport*, p. 153.

50 Lichtenstaedt, "Meine Erfahrungen über die asiatische Cholera während ihrer Herrschaft zu St. Petersburg," *Die asiatische Cholera*, pp. 244 ff. Sir James Wylie used a comparable approach. See: "Otchety Ego Imperatorskomu Velichestvu . . . ."

51 See Dr. P. Charukovskii, "Nabliudeniia i zamechaniia o kholere . . . ," *Voenno-meditsinskii zhurnal*, VIII, No. 2 (1831), 237–82, 283–323.

52 *Traktat*, pp. 315–17.

53 *Traktat*, pp. 317, 319–20, 323–28.

54 *Traktat*, pp. 306–07.

55 Russell and Barry, *Report*, pp. 40–43.

56 Markus, *Rapport*, p. 44; Moreau de Jonnès, "Moyens curatifs et hygièniques opposés au choléra-morbus pestilentiel," *Revue des deux mondes*, Part 3 (1831), 149–70.

57 Pollitzer, "Cholera studies: Symptomatology, Diagnosis, Prognosis, and Treatment," p. 362; W. Griesinger, "Cholera," in R. Virchow, Ed., *Handbuch der speciellen Pathologie und Therapie*, Vol. II, part 2, p. 242; quoted in Pollitzer, *ibid.*

58 *Edinburgh Medical and Surgical Journal*, XXXVI (1831), 120. It is also interesting that, although there were disagreements, European observers in Russian cholera centers all reported Russian methods and ideas as evidence to be considered seriously. The major criticisms related to administrative and police matters, not medical practice as such.

59 See *Journal de St. Pétersbourg*, June 23/July 5, 1831.

60   See Le docteur Ambrose Tardieu, *Du choléra epidemique: lecons professés à la faculté de médicine de Paris* (Paris, 1849). Tardieu devoted the first part of his lectures to an etymological and historical discussion of cholera (pp. 1–7) and then took up a description of the disease. He deemed that cholera was contagious (pp. 139–48), and concerning cholera's cause he wrote that, "We have no choice but to bow before the mystery of these pestilential diseases whose primary origin and essential principle are probably beyond reason" (p. 148). He strongly suggested certain preventive and protective measures (pp. 188–216), including isolation and sequestration, maintenance of cleanliness and a healthful atmosphere, the provision of public assistance, and the presentation of instructions for the people. He was especially strong (pp. 189–91) in stressing municipal responsibility for maintaining cleanliness and combatting local conditions which bred disease. Tardieu's lectures may be compared in content with Dr. E. Burguières, *Études sur le choléra-morbus observé à Smyrne, sa marche, ses causes et son traitement. Rapport adressé à M. le ministre du commerce* (Paris, 1849). It is interesting that Markus' *Rapport* was abridged and reprinted in 1847 for wider circulation. See *Notices sur le choléra en Russie publiées par le ministère de l'interieur* (St. Petersburg, 1847). It should be remembered that Tardieu's lectures, cited above, summarized a vast cholera literature which appeared between 1832 and 1847.

BIBLIOGRAPHY

The following list brings together the works which were consulted in preparing this study. The classifications used are arbitrary, and certain items could be listed in more than one class. Articles from such publications as the *Zhurnal ministerstva vnutrennikh del* have been listed individually, but the *Polnoe sobranie zakonov rossiiskoi imperii (PSZ)* has been given only a general citation since a listing of the particular memoranda, decrees, etc., would unecessarily extend the bibliography. The large technical medical bibliography dealing with cholera in the late nineteenth and twentieth centuries has not been listed since this study has been concerned with describing medical thought and practice during the first cholera epidemic and evaluating it in terms of its methodology and its relationship to contemporary medical science.

PRIMARY SOURCE MATERIAL

OFFICIAL AND SEMI-OFFICIAL PUBLICATIONS

"Cholera-morbus." *Voenno-meditsinskii zhurnal*, Chast' I, No. 3 (1823), pp. 379–435.
"Kratkoe nastavlenie k raspoznaniu priznakov kholery, predokhraneniiu ot onoi, i k pervonachal'nomu eia lecheniiu." *Zhurnal ministerstva vnutrennikh del*, Chast' III (1831), pp. 149–60.
"Kratkaia vedomost: o deistvii bolezni kholery v Orenburgskoi gubernii v 1829 i 1830 godakh." *Pribavlenie k Zhurnalu ministerstva vnutrennikh del*, No. 4 (1830), pp. 79–81.
"Kratkiia zamechaniia o chume." *Zhurnal ministerstva vnutrennikh del*, Chast' I (1829), pp. 159–84, 400–25, 607–26.
Lichtenstaedt, Jeremias. *Die asiatische Cholera in Russland in den Jahren 1829 und 1830.* Berlin, 1831.

Lichtenstaedt, Jeremias. *Die asiatische Cholera im Russland in Jahren 1830 und 1831.* Berlin, 1831.

"Lettre de la commission médicale envoyée en Russie, pour observer le choléra-morbus; addressé à M. le Ministre du Commerce et des Travaux Publics, et lue à l'Académie de Médicine." *Gazette Médicale de Paris,* Vols. I–II (Dec. 24, 1831), 436–39.

Markus, F. C. M. *Notices sur le choléra en Russie.* St. Pétersbourg, 1847.

————. *Rapport sur le choléra-morbus de Moscow.* Moscou, 1832.

"Nastavlenie: prostomu narodu, predokhraniat' sebia ot kholery i kak lechit' zanemogshikh seiu bolezniu v mestakh, gde net ni lekarei, ni aptek." *Zhurnal ministerstva vnutrennikh del,* Chast' II (1831), pp. 161–82.

"Nastavlenie o lechenii bolezni nazyvaemoi kholera (Cholera Morbus), sostavlennoi Meditsinskim Sovetom." *Voenno-meditsinskii zhurnal,* Chast' III, No. 2 (1824), pp. 177–93.

"Nastavlenie o lechenii bolezni, nazyvaemoi kholera (Cholera Morbus), sostavlennoe Meditsinskim Sovetom." *Zhurnal ministerstva vnutrennikh del,* Chast' I (1829), pp. 385–99.

"Note officielle du Ministère des Affaires étrangères du gouvernement national de Pologne, au cabinet de Berlin." *Les affaires polonaises.* Paris, 1831.

"O deistvii khloristoi sody i khloristoi izvesti vo vrachebnom otnoshenii." Pribavlenie k I knizhke. *Zhurnal ministerstva vnutrennikh del,* Chast' II (1830), pp. 66–85.

"O delakh meditsinskago departamenta." *Zhurnal ministerstva vnutrennikh del,* Chast' III (1831), pp. 160–92.

"O kholere." *Voenno-meditsinskii zhurnal,* Chast' II, No. 2 (1832), pp. 183–207.

"O kholere: rasprostranenie onoi v rossiiskikh provintsiakh po Kaspiiskomu moriu do Astrakhani." *Voenno-meditsinskii zhurnal,* Chast' III, No. 2 (1824), pp. 159–76.

"O poiavlenii i rasprostranenii kholery." *Zhurnal ministerstva vnutrennikh del,* Chast' I (1829), pp. 643–47.

"O sostoianii atmosfery v gorode Orenburge vo vremia svirepstvovaniia v onom kholery." Pribavlenie k IV knizhke. *Zhurnal ministerstva vnutrennikh del,* Chast' II (1830), pp. 76–78.

"Ob otkryvsheisia v g. Astrakhani kholere (Cholera Morbus)." *Voenno-meditsinskii zhurnal,* Chast' II, No. 1 (1823), pp. 75–83.

Observations sur le choléra-morbus, recueillies et publiées par l'ambassade de France en Russie. Paris, 1831.

Official Reports Made to Government by Drs. Russell and Barry on the Disease Called Cholera Spasmodica as Observed by them during their Mission to Russia in 1831. Published by Authority of the Lords

of His Majesty's Most Honorable Privy Council. London, 1832.
"Ofitsial'nyia izvestiia s 1-go Avgusta po 1-e Oktobria 1831 goda."
Voenno-meditsinskii zhurnal, Chast' VIII, No. 2 (1831), pp. 324–32.

"Opisanie khoda poval'noi bolezni, nazyvaemoi kholeroiu, otkryvsheisia
1829 goda, s nastupleniem oseni, v gorode Orenburge i Orenburgs-
kom uezde, s izlozheniem sposoba lecheniia." Pribavlenie k I knizkhe.
Zhurnal ministerstva vnutrennikh del, Chast' II (1830), pp. 1–27.

"Opisanie kholery, v pervykh chislakh sentiabria 1829 goda izvivsheisia
v Orenburge." Sostavlennoe Shtab-lekarem Sokolovym, Pribavlenie
k IV knizhke. *Zhurnal ministerstva vnutrennikh del,* Chast' II
(1830), pp. 1–75.

"Otchety Ego Imperatorskomu Velichestvu o sredstvakh, upotreblen-
nykh protiv kholery v voennykh gospitaliakh v S. Peterburge, s
prakticheskimi zamechaniiami o svoistvakh sei bolezni." *Voenno-
meditsinskii zhurnal,* Chast' VIII, No. 2 (1831), pp. 163–236.

*Papers Relative to the Disease Called Cholera Spasmodica in India now
Prevailing in the North of Europe.* Printed by Authority of His
Majesty's Most Honorable Privy Council. London, 1831.

Polnoe sobranie zakonov rossiiskoi imperii. 240 vols., Sanktpeterburg,
1830–1916. Especially Series I and II.

"Shtat imperatorskoi Mediko-khirurgicheskoi Akademii...." *Zhurnal
ministerstva vnutrennikh del,* Chast' V (1831), pp. 100–52.

*Sobranie aktov i nabliudenii, otnosiashchikhsia k kholere byvshei v
kontse 1829 g. v Orenburge.* Sanktpeterburg, 1830.

*Svod zakonov rossiiskoi imperii poveleniem gosudaria imperatora
Nikolaia Pavlovicha sostavlennyi.* Izdanie vtoroe. Sanktpeterburg,
1833.

*Traktat o poval'no-zarazitel'noi bolezni kholere, byvshei v Rossii v 1830
i 1831 godu.* Sanktpeterburg, 1831.

"Tsirkuliarnoe predpisanie upravliashchago miniserstvom vnutrennikh
del grazhdanskim gubernatoram ot 21 genvaria 1831 goda, ob
ostanovlenii prodachi prosrochennykh v prikazakh obshchestvennago
prizreniia zalogov po sluchaiu bolezni kholery." *Zhurnal ministerstva
vnutrennikh del,* Chast' III (1831), pp. 77–82.

"Ukaz pravitel'stvuiushchago senata ot 9 sentiabria 1830 goda, ob
uchrezhdenii tsentral'noi kommissii dlia presecheniia bolezni kholery."
Pribavlenie k IV khizhke. *Zhurnal ministerstva vnutrennikh del,*
Chast' II (1830), pp. 82–107.

"Ukaz pravitel'stvuiushchago senata ot 12 sentiabria 1830 goda, o
priniataii karantinnykh protivu kholery." Pribavlenie k IV knizhke.
Zhurnal ministerstva vnutrennikh del, Chast' II (1830), pp. 108–13.

"Ukaz pravitel'stvuiushchago senata ot genvaria 1831 goda, o tom,
chtoby v tekh guberniiakh, gde sushchestvuet kholera, dvorianskie

vybory otsrochit, do prekrashcheniia eia." *Zhurnal ministerstva vnutrennikh del,* Chast' III (1831), p. 73.

"Ukaz pravitel'stvuiushchago senata ot 7 fevralia 1831 goda, o vmenenii dvorianam i drugim litsam v sluzhbu vremeni provedennago po predokhranitel'nym meram ot kholery." *Zhurnal ministerstva vnutrennikh del,* Chast' III (1831), pp. 74–76.

"Vysochaishe utverzhdennoe 21 noiabria 1830 goda mnenie gosudarstvennago soveta, ob uchrezhdennii po gorodam sborov za upotreblenie obshchestvennykh vesov i mer v pol'zu gorodskikh dokhodov." *Zhurnal ministerstva vnutrennikh del,* Chast' III (1831), pp. 83 ff.

"Zakliuchenie meditsinskago soveta." Pribavlenie k IV knizhke. *Zhurnal ministerstva vnutrennikh del,* Chast' II (1830), pp. 82–86.

OTHER CONTEMPORARY MEDICAL MATERIALS

"Amtliche Nachrichten der Doktoren Spausta, Olexik und Zhuber über die Cholera in Russland." *Medicinische Jahrbücher des kaiserlichen königlichen österreichischen Staates,* neue Folge, Band II (1832), 299–312.

Anderson, William Steuart, M.D. "An Account of Cholera Morbus Epidemic in India in 1817 and 1818." *Edinburgh Medical and Surgical Journal,* XV (1819), 354–72.

"Asiatic Cholera, The." *Fraser's Magazine,* Part 4 (1831), 613–25.

"Bemerkungen über die epidemische Cholera. Aus einem Sendschrieben des Dr. v. Reider and C. F. v. Gräfe." *Journal der Chirurgie und Augen-Heilkunde,* Band XV, Teil 2 (1831), 326–28.

"Beobachtungen über die Cholera im Moscau; nach B. Zombkoff's Monographie im Auszuge mitgetheilt vom Dr. E. Gräfe." *Journal der Chirurgie und Augen-Heilkunde,* Band XV, Teil 4 (1831), 648–69.

Blumenthal, Dr. H. "Flüchtiger Schaltenriss der sogenannten *Cholera Indica,* wie sie im Jahre 1830 in der östlichen Hälfte des Europäischen Russlands epidemisch herrschte." *Magazin für die gesammte Heilkunde mit besonderer Rücksicht auf das Militair-Sanitäts-Wesen im königlich preussischen Staate,* Band XXXIII (1831), pp. 554–81.

Broussais, F. J. V. *Le choléra-morbus épidémique observé et traité selon la méthode physiologique.* Seconde Édition, Paris, 1832.

Buek, H. W. *Die bisherige Verbreitung der jetzt besonders in Russland herrschenden Cholera, erläutert durch eine Karte und eine dieselbe erklärende kurze Geschichte dieser Epidemie.* Hamburg, 1831.

Charukovskii, P. "Nabliudeniia i zamechaniia o kholere svirepstvo vavshei 1. S. Peterburge 1831 goda." *Voenno-meditsinskii zhurnal,* Chast' VIII (1831), pp. 237–82, 283–323.

"Cholera." *North American Review,* XXXV (1832), 92–118.

"Cholera, The." *Quarterly Review,* XLVI (1831–32), 170–212.

"Critical Analysis: on Epidemic Cholera." *Edinburgh Medical and Surgical Journal,* XXXVI (1831), 402–16.

"Critical Analysis of Dr. J. R. Lichtenstaedt, *Die asiatische Cholera in Russland.*" *Edinburgh Medical and Surgical Journal,* XXXVI (July, 1831), 118–45.

Edmondston, A., M.D. *A brief Inquiry into the Nature and Causes of the Cholera which has Prevailed and at Present Prevails, in the Russian Armies.* Edinburgh, 1831.

Embden, Dr. von. "An Historical Sketch of Medicine in the Russian Empire, from the Earliest Period to the Present Time." *Edinburgh Medical and Surgical Journal,* XIII (1817), 455–65.

"Epidemic Cholera." *London Medico-Chirurgical Review,* XVI (1832), 163–224, 266–83.

Gerardin, Auguste, et Paul Gaimard. *Du choléra-morbus en Russie, en Prusse et en Autriche pendant les ánnees 1831 et 1832.* Paris, 1832.

"Gesammelte Nachrichten in Beziehung auf die jetzt in Russland herrschende Epidemie." *Journal der Chirurgie und Augen-Heilkunde,* Band 15, Teil 4 (1831), 669–90.

Hawkins, Francis Bisset. *History of the Epidemic Spasmodic Cholera of Russia; including a copious account of the disease which has prevailed in India, and which has travelled under that name, from Asia into Europe.* London, 1831.

Herrmann, C. T. "Des progrès de la population en Russie par gouvernements. . . ." *Mémoires de l'académie impériale des sciences de St. Pétersbourg,* Series V, VIII (2 parts), 352 ff.

————. "Recherches statistiques sur les mariages, les naissances et les décès des habitants de St. Pétersbourg depuis 1808–1832." *Mémoires de l'académie impériale des sciences de St. Pétersbourg,* Series VI, III, 547 ff.

————. "Recherches sur le nombre des suicides et des homicides commis en Russie pendant les années 1819 et 1820." *Mémoires de l'académie impériale des sciences de St. Pétersbourg,* Series VI, I, 3–20.

————. "Recherches sur le nombre des suicides et des homicides commis en Russie pendant les années 1821 et 1822." *Mémoires de l'académie impériale des sciences de St. Pétersbourg,* Series VI, II, 257 ff.

————. "Recherches sur le nombre des suicides et des homicides commis en Russie pendant les années 1821 à 1824." *Mémoires de l'académie impériale des sciences de St. Pétersbourg,* Series VI, III, 558 ff.

Herrmann, C. T. "Réflexions sur l'état de la statistique en Russie et sur la nature de statistique en général." *Nova Acta Academiae Scientarum Imperialis Petropolitanae,* XV, 123 ff.

Hinze, Dr. Frederick. *Der Rathgeber der Cholera: Anweisung des Verhaltens während der Epidemie und bei Erkrankungsfällen entworfen nach Beobachtungen und Erfahrungen aus den Epidemien von 1831 und 1848 in Russland.* Lübeck, 1848.

Jähnichen, Dr. "Die Cholera in Moscau mit kritischen Bemerkungen zu einem Aufsatz vom Herrn Leibmedicus Dr. v. Loder über diese Epidemie." *Wissenschaftliche Annalen der gesammten Heilkunde,* XIX (1831), 385–450.

———. "Mémoire sur le choléra-morbus qui règne en Russie." *Gazette médicale de Paris,* Vols. I–II (1830–31), 85–88.

———. *Réflexions sur le choléra-morbus.* Moscow, 1831.

Jonnés, Moreau de. "Moyens curatifs et hygiéniques opposés au choléra-morbus pestilentiel." *Revue des deux mondes,* Part 3 (1831), pp. 149–70.

———. *Rapport au conseil supérieure de santé sur l'eruption du choléra pestilentiel in Russie pendant l'été et l'automne de 1830.* Paris, 1830.

Keir, James, M.D. *A treatise on Cholera, Containing the Author's Experience of the Epidemic Known by that Name as it Prevailed in the City of Moscow in Autumn 1830, and Winter, 1831.* Edinburgh, 1831.

Kinnis, John, M.D. "Observations on Cholera Morbus and other Diseases, which prevailed epidemically among the Soldiers of the 56th Regiment, stationed at Port Louis, Mauritius." *Edinburgh Medical and Surgical Journal,* XVII (1821), 1–29.

Krebel, Dr. R. "Choléra in Russland, in den Jahren 1829, 1830, 1831, 1846, 1847." *Medicinische Zeitung Russlands,* No. 39 (Sept., 1847), pp. 305–8.

Lanyer, M. "Du choléra-morbus en Russie." *Annales de la Médicine Physiologique,* XVIII (1830), 654–69.

Lefevre, George William, M.D. *Observations on the Nature and Treatment of the Cholera Morbus now prevailing epidemically in St. Petersburg.* London, 1831.

Lichtenstaedt, J. R. *Meine Erfahrungen über die asiatische Cholera während ihrer Herrschaft zu St. Petersburg im Sommer 1831.* Berlin, 1831.

————. *Mittheilungen über die Cholera-Epidemie zu St. Petersburg im Sommer 1831.* St. Petersburg, 1831[?].

Lloyd, Dr. William. "Case of the Epidemic Cholera Treated Successfully." *Edinburgh Medical and Surgical Journal,* XVII (1821), 527–29.

Mayer, Dr. Karl, von. *Skizze einiger Erfahrungen und Bemerkungen uber die Cholera-Epidemie zu St. Petersburg.* St Petersburg, 1832.

"Morgenländische Breckruhr in Sud: Russland, Die." *Hamburgisches Magazin der ausländischen Literatur der gesammten Heilkunde und Arbeiten des ärtzlichen Vereins zu Hamburg,* XIX (1830), 373–75.

Mudrov, M. Ya. "Kratkoe nastavlenie o kholere i sposob, kak predokhraniat' sebia ot onoi, kak izlechivat' ee i kak ostanavlivat' rasprostranenie onoi." In A. G. Gukasian, *M. Ya. Mudrov.* Moskva, 1949, pp. 284–94.

"O kholere: iz sochineniia Angliiskago khirurga Serla (Searle), nabliudavshago siu bolezn v ost-indii." *Voenno-meditsinskii zhurnal,* Chast' VIII, No. 1 (1831), pp. 33–52.

"Observations on Cholera, in a Letter from Harry Leake Gibbs, M.D., First Surgeon of the Naval Hospital, St. Petersburgh." *Edinburgh Medical and Surgical Journal,* XXXVI (1831), 395–98.

Ockel, Dr. "Observations on the Cholera as it was Experienced at St. Petersburgh in the course of last year." *London Medical Gazette,* IX (1831–32), 792–95.

"Official Correspondence on Mr. Henderson's Method of Treating the Indian Cholera." *Edinburgh Medical and Surgical Journal,* XXVI (July–Oct., 1826), 41–46.

Rehman, Dr. J. "Extension of the Cholera in the Russian Provinces about the Caspian Sea, as far as Astrakhan." *Edinburgh Medical and Surgical Journal,* XXIII (Jan.–April, 1825), 432–35.

————. "Progress of the Cholera Morbus from India to the Mediterranean and Caspian Seas." *Edinburgh Medical and Surgical Journal,* XXIII (Jan.–April, 1825), 222–24.

Reinfeldt, Dr. Ernst. "Notizen über die asiatische Cholera an einigen Orten des Russischen Reichs im Sommer 1831." *Archiv für medizinische Erfahrungen,* I (1832), 514–49.

"Report on the Epidemic Cholera of Asia." *Edinburgh Medical and Surgical Journal,* XXIV (July–Oct., 1825), 180–212.

"Reports on the Epidemic Cholera." *Edinburgh Medical and Surgical Journal,* XVI (1820), 458–70.

"Review of James Annesley, Esq., *Sketches of the most Prevalent Diseases of India."* *Edinburgh Medical and Surgical Journal,* XXV (Jan.–April, 1826), 168–87.

Supplement to the Edinburgh Medical and Surgical Journal Containing Official Reports and Analyses of other Recent Publications on Malignant Cholera, February, 1832. Edinburgh, 1832.

Telfair, C., Esq. "Account of the Epidemic Cholera as it Occurred at Mauritius...." Edinburgh Medical and Surgical Journal, XVII (1821), 517–26.

"Ueber die Cholera im Königreich Polens; aus einem Sendschreiben des Dr. Scipion Pinel an C. F. Gräfe." Journal der Chirurgie und Augenheilkunde, Band 15, Teil 4 (1831), 691–95.

"Vorlaufige Nachricht des Dr. Zhuber über die Cholera Morbus in Russland." Medicinische Jahrbücher des kaiserlichen königlichen österreichischen Staates, neue Folge, Band I (1831[?]), 132–38.

Wolff, Dr. H. S. "Erfahrungen und Bemerkunge über die Cholera in Petersburg ihren Charakter und beste Behandlung." Journal der Praktischen Heilkunde, LXXIII (1831), 82–100.

MEMOIRES, LETTERS, AND OTHER EYE-WITNESS ACCOUNTS

Arkhiv Kniazia Vorontsova. 40 vols., Moskva, 1870–95. Especially vols. 37, 38, 39.

"Bumagi grafa Arseniia Andreevicha Zakrevskago." Sbornik imperatorskago russkago istoricheskago obshchestva, CXXVIII. 1891.

Erinnerungen von Alexander Lwowitsch Seeland aus der polnischen Revolution von 1830–1831, Bibliothek russischer Denkwürdigkeiten. Herausgegeben Dr. Th. Schiemann. Band II, Stuttgart, 1894.

Figner, A. V. "Vospominanie o grafe A. A. Zakrevskom." Istoricheskii vestnik, XX (1885), 665–71.

"Gr. A. Kh. Benkendorf o Rossii v 1827–1830, gg." Krasnyi arkhiv, XXXVIII (1930), 135–37.

"Gr. A. Kh. Benkendorf o Rossii v 1831–1832, gg." Krasnyi arkhiv, XLVI (1931), 135–37.

Granville, A. B. St. Petersburgh: a Journal of Travels to and from that Capital; through Flanders, the Rhenish Provinces, Prussia, Russia, Poland, Silesia, Saxony, the Federated States of Germany, and France. 2 vols., London, 1828.

Hoven, I. R. Von-der-. "Bunt na Sennoi ploshchadi v S.-Peterburge." Russkaia starina, XLVII (1885), 61–68.

————. "Kholera v S.-Peterburge v 1831 g." Russkaia starina, XLIV (1884), 391–98, 401–16.

"Imperator Nikolai I v 1830–1831 gg." Soobshchil' N. Shil'der. Russkaia starina, LXXXVIII (1896), 65–69.

"Iz pis'ma V. A. Zhukovskago k printsesse Luize Prusskoi." Russkii arkhiv, 1866, pp. 339–43.

"Kholera v Moskve (1830): iz pisem Kristina k grafine S. A. Bobrinskoi." *Russkii arkhiv,* Chast' III (1884), 131–51.

"A. S. Khomiakov i gr. A. A. Zakrevskii." *Russkaia starina,* XXVI (1879), 537–38.

"Kratkoe biograficheskoe vospominanie o grafe A. A. Zakrevskom." *Russkii arkhiv* (1865), pp. 371–80.

"Lettres de Ferdinand Christine á une dame de sa connaissance." *Russkii arkhiv,* Chast' III (1884), pp. 117–64.

Nikitenko, A. V. *Dnevnik.* 3 vols., Moskva-Leningrad, 1955.

"Perepiska Imperatora Nikolaia Pavlovicha s Velikim Kniazem Tsesarevichem Konstantinom Pavlovichem." *Sbornik imperatorskago russkago istoricheskago obshchestva,* CXXXII (1911).

"Piece remise par S. M. l'Empereur Nicholas le 24 janvier 1826." *Lettres et papiers du Chancelier Comte de Nesselrode,* 11 vols., Paris, (1908[?]), VI, 275–89.

Pirogow, N. I. *Lebensfragen: Tagebuch eines alten Arztes, Bibliothek russischer Denkwurdigkeiten.* Herausgegeben Dr. Th. Schiemann. Band III, Stuttgart, 1894.

Pushkin, A. S. *Polnoe sobranie sochinenii v desiati tomakh; Pisma.* Moscow-Leningrad, 1949, T.X.

———. *Sochineniia.* Moscow, 1949.

Seriakov, L. A. "Moia trudovaia zhizn." *Russkaia starina,* XIV (1875), 161–84.

Vospominaniia A. I. Del'viga, Polveka Russkoi Zhizni. 2 vols., Moskva-Leningrad, 1930.

"Vospominaniia Andreia Mikhailovicha Fadeeva." *Russkii arkhiv,* 1891, pp. 385 ff.

"Vospominanie davnoproshedskago." (V. Kokorev), *Russkii arkhiv,* 1885, 263–73.

"Vospominaniia doktora I. I. Evropeusa: bunt Novgorodskikh voennykh poselian 1831 g." *Russkaia starina,* VI (1872), 547 ff.

"Vospominaniia doktora I. I. Evropeusa: sluzhba v voennykh poseleniiakh i graf Arakcheev: 1820–1826." *Russkaia starina,* VI (1872), 225 ff.

"Vospominaniia G. I. Filipsona." *Russkii arkhiv,* 1883, 73–200.

"Vospominaniia M. F. Kamenskoi." *Istoricheskii vestnik,* CVII (1894), 35–52.

"Vospominaniia O. A. Przhetslavskago." *Russkaia starina,* XI (1874), 665–98.

"Vospominanie o Konstantine Sergeeviche Aksakove." *Russkii arkhiv,* 1885, 371–415.

Zmeev, L. F. "Mnenie Imperatora Nikolaia Pavlovicha o kholere." *Russkii arkhiv,* X (1888), p. 295.

Zschokke, Dr. Theodore. *Moskau und Petersburg beim Ausbruck der Cholera morbus mit Bemerkungen über die bisher gemachten Erfahrungen von dieser Krankheit.* Aarau, 1832.

NEWSPAPERS

Journal de St. Pétersbourg, politique et littéraire, 1829–1831.
Russkii invalid ili voennyia vedemosti, 1829, 1831.

REFERENCE WORKS

Bazunov, Aleksandr Fedorovich. *Sistematicheskii katalog russkim knigam prodaiushchimsia v knizhnom magazine* (1825–1869). Sanktpeterburg, 1869.
Bol'shaia meditsinskaia entsiklopediia. Glavnyi redaktor N. A. Smashko. 34 TT., Moskva, 1936.
Bol'shaia sovetskaia entsiklopediia. Izd. vtoroe. 51 TT., Moskva, 1949–58.
Brokhauz, F. A., and I. A. Efron., *Entsiklopedicheskii slovar',* 41 TT., Sanktpeterburg, 1890–1904.
Evgenii, Mitropolit. *Slovar' russkikh svetskikh pisatelei.* TT. I, II, Moskva, 1845.
Gennadi, Grigorii. *Spravochnyi slovar' o russkikh pisateliakh i uchenykh umershikh v XVIII i XIX stoletiakh i spisok russkikh knig s 1725 po 1825.* T. I., Berlin, 1876.
Geografichesko-statisticheskii slovar' rossiiskoi imperii. 5 TT., Sanktpeterburg, 1863–85.
Meditsinskii referativnyi zhurnal. Razdel chetverty. Moskva, 1957 ff.
Pervoe pribavlenie k rospisi rossiiskim knigam dlia chteniia iz biblioteki Aleksandra Smirdina. Sanktpeterburg, 1829.
Rospis' rossiiskim knignam dlia chteniia iz biblioteki Aleksandra Smirdina. Sanktpeterburg, 1828.
Rossiiskii, D. M. *Istoriia otchestvennoi meditsiny i zdravookhraneniia: bibliografiia.* Moskva, 1956.
Rovinskii, D. A. *Podrobnyi slovar' russkikh gravirovannykh portretov.* 2 TT., Sanktpeterburg, 1889.
Russkii biograficheskii slovar'. 25 TT., Sanktpeterburg, 1896–1918.
Statisticheskoe izobrazhenie gorodov i posadov rossiiskoi imperii po 1825 god. Sanktpeterburg, 1829.
Volf, M. O. *Sorokoletie rosskoi literatury: 1830–1870: Katalog russkago otdeleniia knizhnago magazina.* Sanktpeterburg, 1872.

ADDITIONAL SECONDARY SOURCES:

BOOKS AND ARTICLES

GENERAL HISTORIES, MONOGRAPHS, BIOGRAPHIES

Arkhangel'skii, G. I. *Kholernyia epidemii Evropeiskoi Rossii v 50-tiletni period 1823–1872 gg.* Sanktpeterburg, 1874.

Arsenev, Konstanti. *Statisticheskie ocherki Rossii.* Sanktpeterburg, 1848.

Barikine, W., et H. Cazaneuve. *Le Foyer endemique de choléra de Rostov-sur-le-Don.* Geneva, 1925.

Brückner, Alexander. *Die Aerzte in Russland bis jum Jahre 1800.* St. Petersburg, 1887.

Bulgarin, Thaddäus. *Russland in historischer, statistischer, geographischer, und literarischer Beziehung.* B. I., Riga und Leipzig, 1839.

Burguieres, Dr. E. *Études sur le choléra-morbus observé á Smyrne, sa marche, ses causes et son traitement.* Paris, 1849.

Chevalier, Louis. *Classes laborieuses et classes dangereuses à Paris pendant la première moitié du XIXe siècle.* Paris, 1958.

———. *Le choléra: la première épidémie du XIXe siècle.* La Roche-sur-Yon, 1958.

Druzhinin, N. M. *Gosudarstvennye krestiane i reforma P. D. Kiseleva.* 2 TT., Moskva-Leningrad, 1946.

Evstafev, P. P. *Vosstanie novgorodskikh voennykh poselian.* Moskva, 1934.

Geling, Karl. *Opyt grazhdanskoi meditsinskoi politsii.* Vilna, 1842.

Grimm, A. Th., von. *Alexandra Feodorowna Kaiserin von Russland.* 2 vols., Leipzig, 1866.

Grunwald, Constantine de. *La vie de Nicolas Ier.* Paris, 1946.

Gukasian, A. G. *M. Ya. Mudrov.* Moskva, 1949.

Hardynski, Józef. *History of the Late Polish Revolution, and the Events of the Campaign.* [n.p., n.d.].

Heine, Maximilian. *Medicinisches-Historisches aus Russland.* St. Petersburg, 1851.

Hirsch, Dr. August. *Handbook of Geographical and Historical Pathology.* Tr., Charles Creighton, M.D. Vol. I, London, 1883.

Istoriia Moskvy: period razlozheniia krepostnogo stroia. Moskva, 1954.

Kunz, Hermann. *Die polnisch-russische Krieg von 1831.* Berlin, 1890.

Kuprianov, Nikolai. *Istoriia meditsiny v Rossii v tsartsvovanie Petra Velikago.* Sanktpeterburg, 1872.

Lacroix, Paul. *Historie de la vie et du règne de Nicolas Ier.* T. 5, Paris, 1868.

175 let pervago Moskovskago gosudarstvennago meditsinskago instituta. Moskva-Leningrad, 1940.

Mazour, A. G. *The First Russian Revolution: The Decembrist Movement.* Berkeley, Calif., 1937.

Menshutkin, Boris N. *Russia's Lomonosov.* Tr. Jeannette Eyre Thul and Edward J. Webster under the direction of W. Chapin Huntington. Princeton, 1952.

Miakotine, M. "Nicholas Ier, l'avènement et les idées de Nicolas Ier" in Miliukov, Paul, Charles Seignobos, L. Eisenmann, et al. *Histoire de Russie.* 3 TT., Paris, 1932. II, 717–29.

Moskovskii Universitet za 200 let: Kratkii istoricheskii ocherk. Moskva, 1955.

Ocherki po istorii statistiki SSSR. Akademiia Nauk SSSR: Institute Ekonomiki, Moskva, 1957.

Pavlovskii, L. *Kholernye gody v Rossii.* Sanktpeterburg, 1893.

Polievktov, M. *Nikolai I.* Sanktpeterburg, 1914.

Possart, P. A. R. F. *Das Kaiserthum Russlands.* 2 T., Stuttgart, 1840–41.

Presniakov, A. E. *Apogei samoderzhaviia.* Leningrad, 1925.

Puzvrewsky, Alexander. *Der Polnisch-russische Krieg 1831.* 3 vols., Wien, 1892.

Pypin, A. N. *Obshchestvennoe dvizhenie v Rossii pri Aleksandre I.* Sanktpeterburg, 1918.

Reden, Friedrich Wilhelm von. *Das Kaiserreich Russland: Statistisch-geschichtliche Darstellung seiner Kultur-Verhältnisse, nämmentlich in landwirtschaftlicher gewerblicher kommerzieller Beziehung.* Berlin, Posen, Bromberg, 1843.

Riasanovsky, N. V. *Nicholas I and Official Nationality in Russia.* Berkeley, Calif., 1959.

Richter, Wilhelm Michael von. *Geschichte der Medicin in Russland.* 3 vols., Moscow, 1813–17.

Rogger, Hans. *National Consciousness in Eighteenth Century Russia.* Cambridge, Mass., 1960.

Rosen. George. *A History of Public Health.* New York, 1958.

Rossiiskii, D. M. *200 let meditsinskago fakulteta Moskovskago gosudarstvennago universiteta i Moskovskago ordena Lenina meditsinskago instituta.* Moskva, 1955.

Shcherbatov, Général-Prince. *Le Feld-Maréchal Prince Paskévitsch, sa vie politique et militaire.* 4 TT., St. Pétersbourg, 1893.

Shcherbinin, M. P. *Biografiia general-fel'dmarshala kniaza Mikhaila Semenovicha Vorontsova.* Sanktpeterburg, 1858.
Schiemann, Theodor. *Geschichte Russlands unter Kaiser Nikolaus I.* 4 vols., Berlin, 1904–19.
Schnitzler, J. H. *Moscou: tableau statistique, géographique, topographique et historique et la ville et du gouvernement de ce non.* Saint-Pétersbourg et Paris, 1834.
Shil'der, N. K. *Imperator Nikolai I: ego zhizn' i tsarstvovanie.* 2 TT., Sanktpeterburg, 1903.
Smitt, Friedrich von. *Geschichte des polnischen Aufstandes und Krieges in den Jahren 1830 und 1831.* Berlin, 1848.
Spazier, Richard Otto. *Geschichte des Aufständes des polnische Volkes in den Jahren 1830 und 1831.* Altenburg, 1832.
Tardieu, Le docteur Ambrose. *Du choléra épidémique: leçons professées à la faculté de médicine de Paris.* Paris, 1849.
Vucinich, Alexander. *Science in Russian Culture: A History to 1860.* Stanford, Calif., 1963.
Wendt, Edmond Charles, et al. *A Treatise on Asiatic Cholera.* New York, 1885.
Zablotskii-Desiatovskii, A. P. *Graf P. D. Kiselev i ego vremia.* 2 TT., Sanktpeterburg, 1882.

ARTICLES

Arkhsharumov, D. D. "Kholera v Malo-rossii v 1830–1831." *Russkaia starina,* XLVII (1885), 209–22.
Brockington, C. Fraser. "The Cholera: 1831." *The Medical Officer,* XCVI (Aug., 1956), 75.
Brückner, Alexander. "Die Pest in Moskau 1771." *Russiche Revue,* XXVI (1886), 202–19.
———. "Zur Geschichte der Medicin in Russland." *Russische Revue,* XXVI (1886), 202–19.
Chave, S. P. W. "Henry Whitehead and the Cholera in Broad Street." *Medical History,* II, No. 2 (April, 1958), 92–108.
Dolgorukii, A. "Novgorodskie dvorianie i voennye poseliane." *Russkaia starina,* VIII (1873), 411–14.
Dubasov, I. "Kholernyi bunt v Tambove, 1830 g." *Russkaia starina,* XIV (1875), 742–47.
Freour, P., P. Coudray, M. Serisé et M. Jaubertie. "L'épidémie de choléra à Bordeaux en 1832." *Journal de médicine de Bourdeaux,* No. 6 (Juin, 1958), pp. 545–49.
Hans, Nicholas. "Russian Students at Leyden in the Eighteenth

Century." *Slavonic and East European Review,* XXXV (1957), 551–62.

Hutchinson, C. A. "The Asiatic Cholera Epidemic of 1833 in Mexico.: *Bulletin of the History of Medicine,* XXIII (1958), 1–23, 152–63.

"John Snow and the Cholera Epidemic of 1854." *St. Thomas Hospital Gazette,* LII (1954), 137–44.

"Kholera v 1830–1831 godakh v Kurskoi gubernii." *Istoricheskii vestnik,* XXV (1886), 132–46.

Kramchaninov, N. F. "History of Native Science: the Contribution of Russian Doctors to the Study of the Epidemiology of Cholera in the first third of the Nineteenth Century." *Journal of Microbiology, Epidemiology, and Immunobiology,* XXX, No. 1 (1959), 146–53. (Tr. from the Russian.)

————. "K istorii bor'by s kholeroi v Rossii v 1829–1830 gg." *Sovetskoe zdravookhranenie,* IV (1956), 46–49.

————. "A Note on the History of the Epidemiology of Cholera in Russia." *Journal of Microbiology, Epidemiology, and Immunobiology,* XXXI No. 3. (Tr. from the Russian.)

Kuleska, St. E. "Pervaya kholera v Bel'skom uezde, Smolenskoi gubernii v 1830." *Russkaia starina,* XXVI (1879), 538–40.

Lakhtin, M. Ja. "Kurzer Abriss über die Gerchichte der Medizin in Russland." *Janus* (Leiden), VII (1902), 635–36.

Mazour, A. G. "Le comte Alekseji Andreevič Arakčeev." *Le monde slave* (Juin, 1936), pp. 365–90.

McGrew, R. E. "The First Cholera Epidemic and Social History." *Bulletin of the History of Medicine,* XXXIV, No. 1 (1960), 61–73.

————. "The First Russian Cholera Epidemic: Themes and Opportunities." *Bulletin of the History of Medicine,* XXXVI, No. 3 (1962), 220–44.

Nikitin, A. F. "Origins of Russian Medicine." *Soviet Medicine,* XXI (9), (1957), 129–34. (Tr. from the Russian.)

Olzscha, Reiner. "Die Epidemiologie und Epidemiographie der Cholera in Russland." *Zeitschrift für Hygiene und Infektionkrankheiten,* CXXI (1939), 1–26.

Pollitzer, R., M.D. "Cholera Studies: Bacteriology." *Bulletin of the World Health Organization,* XII (1955), 777–865.

————. "Cholera Studies: Bacteriophage Investigations." *BWHO,* XIII (1955), 1–25.

————. "Cholera Studies: Clinical Pathology." *BWHO,* XVI (1957), 123–99.

————. "Cholera Studies: Epidemiology." *BWHO,* XVI (1957), 783–857.

————. "Cholera Studies: History of the Disease." *BWHO,* X (1954), 421–61.

————. "Cholera Studies: Pathology." *BWHO,* XII (1955), 1075–1199.

————. "Cholera Studies: Prevention and Control." *BWHO,* XVI (1957), 67–162.

————. "Cholera Studies: Symptomatology, Diagnosis, Prognosis, and Treatment." *BWHO,* XVI (1957), 295–430.

Pollitzer, R., M.D., and W. Burrows. "Cholera Studies: Problems in Immunology." *BWHO,* XII (1955), 944–1107.

Pollitzer, R., M.D., and S. Swarope. "Cholera Studies: World Incidence." *BWHO,* XII (1955), 311–58.

Puparev, A. G. "Kholernyi mesiats v S.-Peterburge, iiun 1831 g." *Russkaia starina,* XLVII (1885), 69–86.

Rodzevich, G. I. "Materialy dlia istorii meditsiny v Rossii: Ocherk pervoi epidemii kholery v Nizhnem-Novgorode v 1830 godu." *Russkaia meditsina,* XVII (1892), 327–30, 445–48, 494–96, 567–69.

Rosenberg, Charles E. "The Cholera Epidemic of 1832 in New York City." *Bulletin of the History of Medicine,* XXXIII (1959), 37–49.

Ukke, Dr. "Epidemii i nashi meditsinskie poryadki." *Vestnik Evropy* (June, 1882), pp. 826–82.

Vol'fson, I. Ya. "Ocherk meditsiny i zdravookhraneniia v Rossi v pervyiu polovinu XIX veka." *Sovetskaia vrachebnaia gazeta,* No. 6 (1934), pp. 451–64.

Yakunin, Iv. "Kholera v Tambove." *Vestnik Evropy,* No. 9 (1875), pp. 204–23.

DISSERTATIONS

McGrew R. E., "Nicolas I and the Genesis of Russian Officialdom." (Ph.D., Univ. of Minn., 1955).

INDEX

Epidemiology: in underdeveloped societies, 6, 7, 10; means of communication, 7; and sanitation, 7; means for control, 9–10; spread of cholera in
Asia to 1823, 18–19; epidemic patterns in Russia, 54–55, 98–99; in
Moscow, 85, 88–97
Erasmus, I. F.: medical faculty, University of Moscow, 37
Etiology: *vibrio cholerae,* 7; Koch, 8; early germ theories, 8–9; contradictory English views, 22; role of diet, 22; environmental theory, 22;
ignorance of cause of cholera, 22; environmental theory at Orenburg,
43–44; climatic theories rejected, 43–44; synthesis of predisposition and
"contagious principle," 44–45; Russian theories, 133–44

Frank, Johann Peter, Doctor: and Imperial Medico-Chirurgical Academy,
35

Golitsyn, D. M., Prince, Governor-General of Moscow: 153; first cholera
decrees of, 76–77; failures of in first phase of epidemic, 79; and Moscow
Cholera Council, 79–81; moderated regulations, 81; as Council head,
127
Gorianinov, P. F.: etiology of cholera, 139
Granville, Augustus Bozzi: assesses Russian medicine, 29–31

Haymarket riots: described, 110–14
Henle, F. G. J.: germ theory of infectious diseases of, 8
Hermann, Hans Rudolph: on blood changes in cholera patients, 145

Il'in, David: and Tambov cholera rebellion, 69
Imperial Medico-Chirurgical Academy: under Sir James Wylie, 30; history
of, 34–35; and Frank, 35; summary of graduates, 35; curriculum of,
35–36
Ivan III, the Great (1462–1505): medicine and westernization, 25–26

Jaehnichen, Doctor, Medical Supervisor of First Administrative District,
Moscow: and Hermann, 145; on decomposition of blood in cholera cases,
145–46; on therapy, 146; on vascular injection, 146–47; work compared
with Latta and O'Shaughnessy, 146–47

Kankrin, Igor, Count, Minister of Finance: 57; non-medical factors in
quarantine policy, 48
Kerstens, Johann Christian: medical faculty, Moscow University, 37
Kiselev, P. D., Count: 57; fear of cholera, 11; and population removal as
anti-cholera measure, 54; and cholera in Moldavia and Wallachia, 99
Koch, Robert: isolation of *comma bacillus,* 8, 9
Korabel'naia: 50–51
Kursk: conditions in before cholera epidemic, 73–74; public resistance in to
anti-cholera measures, 73–74; medical facilities of, 74; officials and
population, 74. *See also:* Count A. A. Zakrevskii

Langer, William L.: new approaches in historical method, 3
Lavrov, Ivan Pavlovich, Senator: administers Astrakhan during cholera epidemic, 53, 58
Leo, Doctor (of Warsaw): and the bismuth treatment, 140–41
Lichtenstaedt, Jeremias, Doctor: 137; affirms cholera contagiousness, 8; attacks Loder and anti-contagionists, 137; and syncretic therapy, 147–48
Loder, K. I., Doctor: spokesman for non-contagionists, 137; and cholera classification, 143
Lomonosov, Mikhail V.: Moscow University and medical education, 36

Malakhov, N. N.: and early germ theory of cholera, 139
Markus, F. C. M., Doctor, Secretary, Moscow Cholera Council: effectiveness of cholera treatment of, 131; anti-contagion argument of, 136–37; sees cholera as a disease of the heart, 143–44
Medical administration: and social questions, 5–6; in Russia, 15; Imperial Medical College, 33; medical administration in eighteenth century, 39; public health functions, 39; role of police, 39; organization in nineteenth century, 55–56; importance of Ministry of Interior, 55–56; role of ministries, 56; medical administration in crises, 56; medical administration as microcosm of Russian administration, 125–27
Medical education: history before eighteenth century, 26; and Peter the Great, 26–27; emphasis on practical training, 27; deficiencies of, 33; development of medical schools, 33–38; primacy of Petersburg and Moscow, 34; University of Moscow, 36–38
Medical facilities: described, 38–39
Medical profession: foreign domination of in eighteenth century, 27–28; expansion of native Russian medical personnel, 27–28, 37; quantitative deficiencies of, 28–29, 31; quality of, 29–30, 130–39, 150–52; contacts of with Europe, 30–31; medical publication, 30–32; societies, 32; empirical tradition of, 32; development of scientific tradition of, 37–38; historical significance of, 129–30; class character of, 130; performance during epidemic, 130–32; importance of Russian cholera theories, 132–33; validity of Russian theories, 139; and European medical science, 151–52; and social change, 156; and cultural history, 157
Methode excitante: cholera treatment, 144–45
Military colonies: peasant resentment of, 18; background of, 117; conditions in, 119–20; opposition to, 120; and cholera riots, 120–21; as punishments for rioters, 121
Mironov, I. S., Governor-General, Tambov: quarantine policy of, 68; reports of on Tambov riots, 72
Moscow: cholera approaches, 75; public hysteria in, 75–77; city quarantined, 78; quarantine regulations, 78–79; early cholera incidence and mortality, 81–82; Nicholas I visits, 82–84; significance of cholera in, 84–85; sociology of cholera in, 85; population statistics in cholera reports, 88; cultural character of, 88–90; administrative divisions of, 90; cholera incidence and mortality in, 90–92; sanitary conditions in, 92; and water supply, 92; cholera incidence by population groups, 92–96;

St. Petersburg: cholera arrives, 108; and Cholera Commission, 108–09; Haymarket riots, 111–12; reform of cholera regulations, 114–15; antagonism against officials, 115–16; demographic character, 122–24; compared with Moscow, 123; medical facilities, 124; and urban problems, 124–25

St. Petersburg Cholera Commission: compared with Moscow, 108–09; role of police, 109; attitude toward public, 109–11

Saratov: cholera outbreak, 55, 72–73; cholera incidence and mortality, 72–73; under Zakrevskii, 73

Sevastopol: quarantine riots, 50–51

Snow, John: transmission of cholera in water, 8–9

Social reactions: fear of cholera, 10–11; stable societies and epidemics, 11–12; public attitude toward anti-cholera measures in England and Russia, 15–16; cholera ignored until 1830, 41; attitude of Orenburg toward cholera, 46; Sevastopol riots, 50–51; behavior at Astrakhan and Tiflis, 53; dangers in stringent sanitary measures, 53–54; unrest in Volga, 67–69, 72–74; terror and social unrest, 67; effect of suspense in Tambov, 69; Tambov rebellion, 69, 72; hysteria in Moscow, 75–76; spirit of public service, 77–78; reception of Nicholas I, 82; social stability in Moscow, 96–97; poison hysteria, 106–07, 110–11, 116–17, 120–21; popular scapegoats, 106–07, 110, 116, 155; social reactions and epidemic intensity, 113–14; fear of revolution, 115; rebellions and revolutionary orientation, 116, 122, 154; military colonies, 117, 120; spread of rebellions, 121; urban problem in St. Petersburg, 122–25; riots and peasant revolutionary tradition, 154; riots and peasant reform, 155–56

Social reform: "localism" and reform, 8; cholera and reform in England, France, Russia, 13–15

Sociology of cholera: class character, 7; in Moscow, 85, 92–97

Staraia Russa: *See* Military colonies

Stolypin, Lieutenant-General, Acting Governor-General of Sevastopol: and Sevastopol riots, 50–51; killed, 51

Symptoms of cholera: early recognition important, 21–22; described, 21, 42

Tambov: cholera riots in 1830, 68–69, 72

Tiflis: first cholera attack on, 1823, 23; 1830 outbreak, 53; free movement of population, 53

Treatment: efficacy in Russia, 11, 131; early optimism, 20; English method, 21–22; Leo bismuth treatment, 140–41; *cura antiphlogistica* (English treatment), 142; stimulation, 144–45; vascular injection, 146–47; syncretic therapies, 147–49

University of Moscow: development of medical program of, 36–38; medical faculty in 1806, 37

Venediktov, Professor: 137; *contagium specificum* and environment, 135–36

Date Due